Chap 4
art 29, 30, 38
Prob. 206, 211, 217
art 31, 32
# 245, 249, 254

Chap 4 art 37
# 374, 376

# PART
# II
___
## Dynamics

## MECHANICS

By J. L. Meriam

MECHANICS—Second Edition

*Part I · Statics*
*Part II · Dynamics*

# PART
# II

Dynamics

# MECHANICS

*Second Edition*

## J. L. MERIAM

PROFESSOR OF ENGINEERING MECHANICS
UNIVERSITY OF CALIFORNIA

NEW YORK · JOHN WILEY & SONS, INC.
London

# PREFACE

## To the Student

Engineering analysis depends heavily on the principles of mechanics, and for this reason it is essential that the student of engineering be well grounded in this basic subject. The emphasis in this book is on engineering or applied mechanics, and it has been designed as a text for the basic mechanics courses in the normal engineering curriculum.

The representation of real situations by mathematical and graphical symbols constitutes an ideal descriptive model which approximates but never quite equals the actual situation. A useful understanding of mechanics requires a dual process of repeated transition of thought between the physical situation and its symbolic representation. The development of ability to make this transition of thought freely is one of the major aims of this book.

Mechanics is based on surprisingly few fundamental principles. Particular emphasis is placed on these principles and their application, and much secondary detail has been reduced or eliminated. Care has been taken not to sacrifice the rigor of the development, and attempt has been made to present the principles in clear and concise terms. The student will find that firm progress can be made only by an understanding of the physical and mathematical principles jointly and not by mere memorization of formulas with mechanical substitution of values therein.

Success in analysis depends to a surprisingly large degree on a well-disciplined method of attack from hypothesis to conclusion where a straight path of rigorous application of principles has been followed. The student is urged to develop ability to represent his work in a clear, logical, and neat manner.  The basic training in mechanics is a most excellent place for early development of this disciplined approach which is so necessary in most of engineering work which follows.

As in all subjects the student learns more when his interest is stimulated.  The author hopes that the reader will find interest and stimulation in many of the real and practical situations included in the problems.  Arrangement of problems is generally in the order of increasing difficulty, and the most difficult ones are starred.

J. L. MERIAM

*January, 1959*

# PREFACE

## To the Instructor

The natural learning process begins with simple situations and progresses to more complicated ones. Thus in mechanics most students are best initiated by exposure to simplified problems where irrelevant factors have been minimized. Problems presented in this way are already partially analyzed. A full and useful appreciation of mechanics does not come, however, until the analysis of real situations and actual working conditions is made. Here the student must be taught to define the problem by first isolating the pertinent factors and discarding the irrelevant ones. Principles are then applied and conclusions drawn. It is only when the principles of mechanics are applied to *practical* problems involving real situations that the full significance of mechanics can be seen. There has been a trend in the treatment of mechanics to avoid real problems of a practical and interesting nature in favor of the ideal symbolic problems which are stripped of reality, practical value, and interest. Such presentation places in jeopardy one of the most fundamental objectives of instruction in mechanics, namely, to develop ability in problem formulation where the connection between actuality and symbolic representation is required. The most difficult and at the same time the most interesting phase of engineering design lies in the formulation of problems.

It is true that many practical problems involve too many complicating factors for early exposure to the student. However, there is a wealth of problems which describe real, practical, and interesting situations that are not overly complex and which can enrich the experience and develop the ability of the student of mechanics far more than is possible with the overly idealized problems.

It is the purpose of this book to present a large selection of problems which illustrate wide application to the various fields of engineering and which will lead the student from the idealized and symbolic representation to the more practical, real, and interesting engineering situation. The author feels strongly that reality brought into the illustrations is of great help to the student in making the transfer of thought from the physical to the mathematical description. Consequently the book has been profusely illustrated, and effort has been made to produce reality and clarity. The problems in each set represent a considerable range of difficulty and are presented generally in order of increasing difficulty. Those problems which are considered the most difficult are starred. All problems have been worked and checked and are believed to be free of error. Computations have been made with the slide rule so that some disagreement in the third figures may be expected. Answers to approximately two thirds of the problems are given.

The wide response accorded the first edition of *Mechanics* by its users lends strong support to the desirability of providing students with as many practical and interesting engineering situations as possible. The many helpful comments received from both teachers and students have been studied carefully and have influenced a number of the changes made in the second edition. Over forty per cent of the problems have been replaced by new ones, although many problems which proved to be particularly instructive in the first edition have been retained. As in the first edition, the problems in the second edition are almost entirely original. The author has, however, obtained ideas for problems from many published sources.

In the second edition greater distinction is made between absolute and relative motion analysis in the chapter on kinematics. In this same chapter a new derivation of the Coriolis acceleration equation is presented which enables a direct geometric representation of the acceleration components.

Greater emphasis is placed on the formulation of problems in particle kinetics by means of the differential equation of motion, and several examples of numerical integration of the equation written as a finite difference equation are given in the problem work.

The chapter on force, mass, and acceleration is divided into two parts, particle kinetics and rigid-body kinetics. This change should help the student understand rigid-body problems by first providing him with experience in particle analysis.

In the treatment of work and energy a new section on virtual work is included which provides a powerful method of attack on certain types of problems and is a stepping stone to more advanced theory.

Throughout the second edition increased effort has been made, largely through the appropriate selection of problems, to draw attention to the advantages of analysis of complete systems. Although the study of engineering dynamics is based upon particle dynamics, its most important use comes in the analysis of the many types of particle systems encountered in engineering problems.

In the second edition a new section on review problems is added as Appendix A. The problems cover a wide range of topics but are arranged without regard for topic or method of solution. A new section on vector methods is added as Appendix B in which the dot and cross product and the derivative of vectors are developed with application to mechanics. This vector notation may be used as an alternate to that employed in the text if desired.

Somewhat more material is presented in *Part II* of *Mechanics* than can be covered in the average introductory course. This fact allows some latitude for selection of topics by the instructor and is further intended to indicate to the student that there is more to the subject than can be presented in a single course or book.

Special acknowledgment is given to Dr. A. L. Hale not only for his major contribution during the preparation of the first edition, but also for his critical review of all new problems which are included in the second edition. The valuable suggestions of Dr. K. E. Barnhart have also proved helpful in preparing the second edition as well as the first edition and are duly acknowledged along with those of other colleagues. The author is also deeply grateful for the large number of helpful comments and suggestions received from many users of the book.

J. L. MERIAM

*Berkeley, California*
*January, 1959*

# CONTENTS

# Contents

## APPENDIX D.  USEFUL TABLES

## INDEX

# MECHANICS

# PRINCIPLES OF DYNAMICS

**1. Introduction.** Mechanics has been defined as that physical science which deals with the state of rest or motion of bodies under the action of forces. Engineering had its origin in the development of this science and today depends on the continuing interpretation of mechanics probably more than on any other subject. The student of engineering will find that a thorough understanding of mechanics will provide one of his most reliable and widely used tools for analysis. Mechanics is logically divided into *statics* which deals with the equilibrium of bodies and *dynamics* which deals with the motion of bodies. *Part I* of *Mechanics* is devoted to statics, and *Part II* is a comprehensive introduction to dynamics. Dynamics, in turn, has two aspects, first, *kinematics*, which is a study of motion itself without reference to the forces which cause the motion, and, second, *kinetics*, which relates the action of forces on bodies to their resulting motions.

Compared with statics, dynamics is a relatively new subject. Galileo (1564–1642) is credited with the first substantial contribution to dynamics. He refused to accept the long-established philosophies of Aristotle which held, for instance, that heavy bodies fall more rapidly than light bodies. Galileo was handicapped by the lack of accurate means for measuring time, and the further development of dynamics awaited the invention of the pendulum clock by Huygens in 1657. Newton (1642–1727), guided by Galileo's work, was able to make an accurate formulation of the laws of motion and hence to put dynamics

1

on a sound basis. In terms of engineering application dynamics is an even more recent science. Only since machines have operated with high speeds and appreciable accelerations has it been necessary to make calculations based on the principles of dynamics rather than on the principles of statics.

The principles of dynamics are basic to the analysis of moving structures, to fixed structures subject to shock loads, and to practically all types of machinery such as engines, ships, wheeled vehicles, aircraft, rockets, etc. The student whose interests lead him into one or more of these and many other fields will find a constant need for applying his basic knowledge of dynamics.

The vast majority of dynamics problems in engineering may be solved by treating the moving bodies in question as perfectly rigid. The assumption of rigidity means that any relative motions between parts of a body are small compared with the motion of the body as a whole. This book is a study of rigid-body dynamics. The dynamics of nonrigid bodies is a much more difficult subject and one about which a great deal has yet to be learned. The transmission of shock waves in structures and machines subject to impact loading, for example, is an important problem in nonrigid-body dynamics.

**2. Basic Concepts.** There are certain definitions and concepts which are basic to the study of dynamics, and they should be understood at the outset.

*Space* is a region extending in all directions. Position in space is determined relative to some reference system by linear and angular measurements. The basic frame of reference for the laws of Newtonian mechanics is the *primary inertial system* or *astronomical frame of reference* which is an imaginary set of rectangular axes attached to the mean position of the so-called fixed stars. Measurements show that relative to this reference system the laws of Newtonian mechanics are valid as long as any velocities involved are negligible compared with the speed of light.* Measurements made with respect to this reference are said to be absolute, and this reference system is considered to be "fixed" in space. A reference frame attached to the surface of the earth has a somewhat complicated motion in the primary system, and a correction to the basic equations of mechanics must be applied for measurements made relative to the earth's reference frame. In the calculation of trajectories for high-altitude rocket and space flight, for

---

* For velocities of the same order as the speed of light, 186,000 mi./sec., the theory of relativity must be applied. See Art. 25 for a brief discussion of this theory and a numerical example of its effect.

example, the absolute motion of the earth becomes an important parameter. For most engineering problems, however, the corrections are extremely small and may be neglected. On this basis, then, the fundamental laws of mechanics may be applied directly for measurements made relative to the earth, and for most problems the word *absolute* may be used in a practical sense to refer to such measurements.

*Time* is a measure of the succession of events and is considered an absolute quantity in Newtonian mechanics. The unit of time is the second, which is a convenient fraction of the period of the earth's rotation.

*Force* is the action of one body on another. A force tends to move a body in the direction of its action upon it.

*Matter* is substance which occupies space.

*Inertia* is the property of matter causing a resistance to change in motion.

*Mass* is the quantitative measure of inertia.

A *body* is matter bounded by a closed surface.

A *particle* is a body of negligible dimensions. In some cases a body of finite size may be treated as a particle, or at other times the particle may be a differential element.

A *rigid body* is one which exhibits no relative deformation between its parts. This is an ideal hypothesis since all real bodies will change shape to a certain extent when subjected to forces. When such changes are small, the body may be termed rigid without appreciable error.

A *scalar* quantity is one with which a magnitude only is associated. Examples of scalars are time, volume, density, speed, energy, and mass.

A *vector* quantity is one with which a direction as well as a magnitude is associated. Examples of vectors are displacement, velocity, acceleration, force, moment, and momentum.

It is assumed at this point that the reader is familiar with the properties of vectors. It is necessary that he understand thoroughly the principle of transmissibility for force vectors, the difference between free, sliding, and fixed vectors, the addition and subtraction of vectors, and the resolution of vectors. A discussion of the properties of vectors may be found in Art. 3, Chapter 1, of *Mechanics, Part I, Statics,* for those who need to review these topics.

The notation used in *Dynamics* for vectors is illustrated by the vector equation $V = V_1 \nleftrightarrow V_2$ which refers to the vector sum $V$ of the two vectors $V_1$ and $V_2$. The $\nleftrightarrow$ sign is used to denote vector addition, and a $\rightarrow$ sign denotes vector subtraction.

An alternate system of notation where boldface type is used for vectors and lightface type for scalars is preferred by some. Thus the equation $V = V_1 + V_2$ means the same as the previous expression. The symbol $V$ stands for the magnitude of $V$. One difficulty with this system is the need for an additional identifying mark on the letters when the symbols are written by hand. The dot and cross product notation for preserving the vector aspects of multiplication and differentiation of vectors may also be used. This notation is particularly useful in formulating relationships in three dimensions. Any advantage it may have for two-dimensional problems is debatable. For those who wish to use this vector notation, a condensed development of the necessary vector algebra and calculus is included as Appendix B.

**3. Newton's Laws.** Sir Isaac Newton was the first to state correctly the basic laws governing the motion of a particle and to demonstrate their validity.* Slightly reworded, these laws are as follows:

*Law I.* A particle remains at rest or continues to move in a straight line with a uniform velocity if there is no unbalanced force acting on it.

*Law II.* The acceleration of a particle is proportional to the resultant force acting on it and is in the direction of this force. †

*Law III.* The forces of action and reaction between contacting bodies are equal in magnitude, opposite in direction, and collinear.

The correctness of these laws has been verified by innumerable accurate physical measurements. The first two laws hold for measurements made in an absolute frame of reference but are subject to slight correction when the motion is measured relative to a reference system having acceleration, such as the earth's surface.

Newton's second law forms the basis for most of the analysis in mechanics. As applied to a particle of mass $m$ it may be stated as

$$F = ma, \tag{1}$$

where $F$ is the resultant force acting on the particle and $a$ is the resulting acceleration. This equation is a *vector* equation since the direction of $F$ must be equal to the direction of $a$ in addition to the equality in magnitudes of $F$ and $ma$. Newton's first law is a consequence of the second since there is no acceleration when the force is zero, and the particle either is at rest or moves with a constant velocity. The

---

* Newton's original formulations may be found in the translation of his *Principia* (1687) revised by F. Cajori, University of California Press, 1934.

† To some it is preferable to interpret Newton's second law as meaning that the resultant force acting on a particle is proportional to the time rate of change of momentum of the particle and that this change is in the direction of the force. Both formulations are equally correct.

first law adds nothing new to the description of motion but is included since it was a part of Newton's classical statements.

The third law is basic to our understanding of force. It states that forces always occur in pairs of equal and opposite forces. Thus the downward force exerted on the desk by the pencil is accompanied by an upward force of equal magnitude exerted on the pencil by the desk. This principle holds for all forces, variable or constant, regardless of their source and holds at every instant of time during which the forces are applied. Lack of careful attention to this basic law is the cause of frequent error by the beginner. In analyzing bodies under the action of forces it is absolutely necessary to be clear as to which of the pair of forces is being considered. It is first of all necessary to *isolate* the body under consideration and then to consider only the one force of the pair which acts *on* the body in question.

In addition to formulating the laws of motion for a particle Newton was also responsible for stating the law which governs the mutual attraction between bodies. This *law of gravitation* is expressed by the equation

$$F = \gamma \frac{m_1 m_2}{r^2}, \tag{2}$$

where　$F$ = the mutual force of attraction between two particles,
　　　$\gamma$ = a universal constant known as the constant of gravitation,
　$m_1, m_2$ = the masses of the two particles,
　　　$r$ = the distance between the centers of the particles.

The mutual forces $F$ obey the law of action and reaction since they are equal and opposite and are directed along the line joining the centers of the particles. Experiment yields the value $\gamma = 6.67 \times 10^{-8}$ cm.$^3$/(gm. sec.$^2$) for the gravitational constant. Gravitational forces exist between every pair of bodies. On the surface of the earth the only gravitational force of appreciable magnitude is the force due to the earth's attraction. Thus each of two iron spheres 4 in. in diameter is attracted to the earth with a force of 8.90 lb. which is called its *weight*. On the other hand the force of mutual attraction between them if they are just touching is 0.0000000234 lb. This force is clearly negligible compared with the earth's attraction of 8.90 lb., and consequently the gravitational attraction of the earth is the only gravitational force of any magnitude which need be considered for experiments conducted on the earth's surface.

The *weight* of a body is the gravitational force of attraction exerted on the body by the earth and depends on the position of the body relative to the earth. An object weighing 10 lb. at the earth's surface will weigh 9.99500 lb. at an altitude of 1 mi., 9.803 lb. at an altitude of 40 mi., and 2.50 lb. at an altitude of 4000 mi. or a height approximately equal to the radius of the earth. It is at once apparent that the variation in the weight of high-altitude rockets must be accounted for.

Every object which is allowed to fall in a vacuum at a given position on the earth's surface will have the same acceleration $g$ as can be seen by combining Eqs. 1 and 2 and cancelling the term representing the mass of the falling object. This combination gives

$$g = \frac{\gamma m_0}{r^2},$$

where $m_0$ is the mass of the earth and $r$ is the radius of the earth.* The mass $m_0$ and mean radius $r$ of the earth have been found by experiment to be $5.98 \times 10^{27}$ gm. and $6.38 \times 10^8$ cm., respectively. These values, together with the value for $\gamma$ already cited, when substituted into the expression for $g$ give

$$g = 980 \text{ cm./sec.}^2 \quad \text{or} \quad g = 32.2 \text{ ft./sec.}^2$$

The absolute acceleration of gravity as determined from the gravitational law is the acceleration which would be measured from a set of reference axes with origin at the center of the earth but not rotating with the earth. It is also the acceleration which would be measured on the surface of a nonrotating earth. Because of the fact that the earth rotates, the acceleration of a freely falling body as measured from a position attached to the earth's surface is slightly less than the absolute value. At the equator the measured or relative value is $32.09 \text{ ft./sec.}^2$, whereas the absolute value is $32.20 \text{ ft./sec.}^2$ At the poles the measured and absolute values are the same and equal $32.26 \text{ ft./sec.}^2$

Accurate values of the acceleration of gravity as measured relative to the earth's surface account for the fact that the earth is a rotating oblate spheroid with flattening at the poles. These values are given by the International Gravity Formula

$$g = 978.049(1 + 0.0052884 \sin^2 \phi - 0.0000059 \sin^2 2\phi)$$

where $\phi$ is the latitude and $g$ is expressed in centimeters per second squared. The constants account for the deviation of the earth's shape from that of a sphere and also for the effect of the earth's ro-

---

* It can be proved that the earth may be considered a particle with its entire mass concentrated at its center.

tation. The proximity of large land masses and the variations in the density of the earth's crust also influence the local value of $g$ to a small but detectable amount. In almost all engineering problems where measurements are made on the surface of the earth the difference between the absolute and relative values of the gravitational acceleration and the effect of local variations are neglected, and 32.2 ft./sec.$^2$ is used for the sea level value of $g$. The variation of $g$ with altitude is easily determined by the gravitational law. If $g_0$ represents the absolute acceleration of gravity at sea level, the absolute value at an altitude $h$ is

$$g = g_0 \frac{r^2}{(r + h)^2}$$

where $r$ is the radius of the earth.

The mass $m$ of a body may be calculated from the results of the simple gravitational experiment. If the gravitational force of attraction or true weight of a body is $W$, then, since the body will fall with an absolute acceleration $g$ in a vacuum, Eq. 1 gives

$$W = mg \qquad \text{or} \qquad m = \frac{W}{g}. \tag{3}$$

The apparent weight of a body as determined by a spring balance, calibrated to read the correct force and attached to the surface of the earth, will be slightly less than its true weight. The difference is due to the rotation of the earth. The ratio of the apparent weight to the apparent or relative acceleration of gravity still gives the correct value of mass. The apparent weight and the relative acceleration of gravity are, of course, the quantities which are measured in experiments conducted on the surface of the earth.

**4. Units.** There are a number of systems of units used in relating force, mass, and acceleration. Four of these systems are defined in the table on the following page.

Engineers use a gravitational system in which length, force, and time are considered fundamental quantities and the units of mass are derived. Physicists use an absolute system in which length, mass, and time are considered fundamental and the units of force are derived. Either system, of course, may be used with the same results. The engineer prefers to use force as a fundamental quantity because most of his experiments involve direct measurement of force. The British or FPS gravitational system is the one used in this book. The engineer has not adopted a unit for mass which is universally used although *slug* and less often *g-pound* are seen occasionally in the literature. One

SYSTEMS OF UNITS

| Type of System (fundamental quantities) | Gravitational (length, force, time) | | Absolute (length, mass, time) | |
|---|---|---|---|---|
| Name of System | British or FPS | MKS | British or FPS | CGS |
| length  $L$ | foot (ft.) | meter (m.) | foot (ft.) | centimeter (cm.) |
| force   $F$ | pound (lb.) | kilogram (kg.) | poundal (pdl.) | dyne |
| time    $T$ | second (sec.) | second (sec.) | second (sec.) | second (sec.) |
| mass   $M$ | lb. ft. $^{-1}$ sec.$^2$ | kg. m. $^{-1}$ sec.$^2$ | pound (lb.) | gram (gr.) |
| System in use by | Engineers in English-speaking countries | Engineers in non-English-speaking countries | Physicists (occasionally) | Physicists everywhere |

slug (or $g$-pound) is the mass of a body which weighs 32.2 lb. at the earth's surface.

It is frequently necessary to convert a quantity from one set of units to another. During the process of conversion it is essential that the dimensions of the quantity remain unchanged. In order to convert a velocity of 30 mi./hr., for example, to the equivalent number of centimeters per second it is first necessary to know that

$$5280 \text{ ft. are contained in 1 mi.,}$$
$$30.48 \text{ cm. }``\quad\quad`` \quad`` \text{ 1 ft.,}$$
$$3600 \text{ sec. }``\quad\quad`` \quad`` \text{ 1 hr.}$$

The conversion is then

$$\left(30\,\frac{\text{mi.}}{\text{hr.}}\right)\left(5280\,\frac{\text{ft.}}{\text{mi.}}\right)\left(30.48\,\frac{\text{cm.}}{\text{ft.}}\right)\left(\frac{1}{3600}\,\frac{\text{hr.}}{\text{sec.}}\right) = 1340\,\frac{\text{cm.}}{\text{sec.}}$$

The units mi., hr., and ft. cancel, leaving cm./sec.

It is quite customary to write expressions stating equivalents in units such as

$$5280 \text{ ft.} = 1 \text{ mi.,}$$

or

$$30 \text{ mi./hr.} = 1340 \text{ cm./sec.}$$

The meaning of these equivalents is clear, but it is important to note that these expressions are *not* algebraic equations. Here the equal sign does not mean mathematical equality since 5280 $\neq$ 1 and ft. $\neq$ mi. The equal sign when used in this way actually means "are contained in."

**5. Dimensions.** A given dimension such as length can be expressed in a number of different units such as feet, centimeters, or miles. Thus the word *dimension* is distinguished from the word *unit*. Physical relations must always be dimensionally homogeneous, that is, the dimensions of each term in an equation must be the same. It is customary to use the symbols $L$, $F$, $T$, and $M$, to stand for length, force, time, and mass, respectively. In the engineer's or gravitational system mass is derived. From Eq. 1 mass has the dimensions of force divided by acceleration or

$$M = \frac{F}{L/T^2} = FL^{-1}T^2.$$

One important use of the theory of dimensions is found in checking the dimensional correctness of some derived physical relation. In deriving the expression for the velocity $v$ of a body of mass $m$ which is moved from rest a horizontal distance $x$ by a force $F$ the following equation results:

$$Fx = \tfrac{1}{2}mv^2,$$

where the $\frac{1}{2}$ is a dimensionless coefficient resulting from integration. This equation is dimensionally correct since substitution of $L$, $F$, and $T$ gives

$$[FL] = [FL^{-1}T^2][LT^{-1}]^2 = [FL].$$

Dimensional homogeneity is a necessary condition for correctness, but it is not sufficient since the correctness of dimensionless coefficients cannot be checked in this way.

A second important use for dimensional theory is in the prediction of full-scale performance from the results of experiments on models. There are many problems, such as the flow resistance of ships and airplanes and the behavior of loaded structures of complex shape, where a mathematical solution is not feasible by reason of the great complexity involved. The form of the relation which describes a physical problem certainly does not depend on the size of the units employed, and therefore a physical relation should describe equally well the behavior of a model or its prototype. A full discussion of this use of dimensional analysis is beyond the scope of this book,* and only one simple example of the procedure followed is given here.

Let it be desired to determine the expression for the period $\tau$ of vibration for a simple pendulum consisting of a small mass $m$ suspended by a cord of length $l$. Guided by observation, it will be assumed that the period is a function of the length $l$, the acceleration of gravity $g$, and the mass $m$. Next, it is assumed that this functional relationship is given by the products of these quantities raised to unknown powers $\alpha$, $\beta$, $\gamma$, or

$$\tau = kl^\alpha g^\beta m^\gamma,$$

where $k$ is a dimensionless constant to account for the units used. Expressing this relation in dimensional symbols gives

$$[T] = [L]^\alpha [LT^{-2}]^\beta [FL^{-1}T^2]^\gamma,$$

$$= [L^{\alpha+\beta-\gamma}][T^{-2\beta+2\gamma}][F^\gamma].$$

In order that the equation be dimensionally homogeneous it is necessary for the exponents of each of the three fundamental dimensions to be identical on each side of the equation. Equating the exponents of $T$, $L$, and $F$ in that order gives

$$1 = -2\beta + 2\gamma,$$

$$0 = \alpha + \beta - \gamma,$$

$$0 = \gamma.$$

The solutions are clearly $\gamma = 0$, $\beta = -\frac{1}{2}$, $\alpha = \frac{1}{2}$, and the assumed relation becomes

$$\tau = kl^{1/2}g^{-1/2} = k\sqrt{l/g}.$$

Dimensional considerations disclose that the period does not depend on the mass $m$. One carefully executed experiment for small amplitudes of vibration will give measurements for $\tau$ and $l$. Substitution of these measured values along with the known value of $g$ will give $k = 6.283$. Therefore the equation

$$\tau = 6.283\sqrt{l/g}$$

may be used to describe the period for *any* similar pendulum of a different size as long as a consistent set of units is used. In the case of the simple pendulum direct solution will disclose the fact that $k = 2\pi$ for small amplitudes.

* See *Dimensional Analysis* by P. W. Bridgman, Yale University Press, 1932.

**6. Description of Physical Problems.** The science of mechanics is based on certain physical laws and utilizes mathematics freely in the description of physical situations. Mathematics establishes the relationships between the various quantities involved and enables the prediction of effects to be made from these relations. The student must recognize that a dual thought process is necessary. He must think in terms of the physical situation, and he must also think in terms of the corresponding mathematical description. Analysis of every problem will require the repeated transition of thought between the physical and the mathematical. Without question one of the greatest difficulties that students have with mechanics is the inability to make this transition freely by interconnecting these two thought processes. The student should make a strong effort to connect each physical thought with its corresponding mathematical expression. He should recognize that the mathematical formulation of a physical problem represents an ideal limiting description or model which is approximated but never quite reached by the actual physical situation.

In the course of constructing the idealized mathematical model for any given engineering problem, certain approximations will always be involved. Some of these approximations may be mathematical, whereas others will be physical. For instance, it is often necessary to neglect small distances, angles, or forces and deal primarily with large distances, angles, or forces. A force which is actually distributed over a small area of the body upon which it acts may be considered as a concentrated force if the dimensions of the area involved are small compared with other pertinent dimensions. The retarding effect of bearing friction on the motion acquired by a machine as a result of applied forces or moments may often be neglected if the friction forces are small. However, these same friction forces cannot be neglected if the purpose of the inquiry is a determination of the drop in efficiency of the machine due to friction losses. Thus the degree of assumption involved depends upon what information is desired and the accuracy required. The student should be constantly aware of the various assumptions called for in the formulation of real problems in terms of a mathematical model. The ability to understand and make use of the appropriate assumptions in the course of the formulation and solution of engineering problems is, certainly, one of the most important characteristics of a successful engineer. One of the major aims of this book is to provide a maximum of opportunity to develop this ability through the portrayal of many practical problems.

Graphics is also an important means of description in mechanics and serves in three capacities. First, it enables the representation of a physical system to be made on paper by means of a sketch or diagram. This geometrical representation is vital to physical interpretation and aids greatly in visualizing the three-dimensional aspects of many problems. Second, graphics often affords a means of solving physical relations without the use of an algebraic solution. Graphical solutions not only provide practical means for obtaining results, but they also aid greatly in making the transition of thought between the physical situation and the mathematical expression because both are represented simultaneously. A third use of graphics is in the display of results on charts or graphs which become an invaluable aid to interpretation.

**7. Accuracy.** The number of significant figures shown in an answer should be no greater than that which corresponds to the least number of significant figures in the given data. Thus the cross-sectional area of a shaft whose diameter, 0.25 in., say, was measured to the nearest hundredth of an inch should be written as 0.049 in.$^2$ and not 0.0491 in.$^2$ as would be indicated when the numbers were multiplied out.

When calculations involve small differences in large quantities, greater accuracy must be achieved. Thus it is necessary to know the numbers 4.2503 and 4.2391 to an accuracy of five significant figures in order that their difference 0.0112 be expressed to three-figure accuracy. It is often difficult in somewhat lengthy computations to know at the outset the number of significant figures needed in the original data to insure a certain accuracy in the answer.

Slide-rule accuracy, usually three significant figures, is considered satisfactory for the majority of engineering calculations. The decimal point should be located by a rough longhand approximation which also serves as a check against large slide-rule error.

**8. Mathematical Limits and Approximations.** The essential purpose of applied mechanics is the mathematical description of engineering situations, and as such it is extremely necessary to understand and be able to apply certain limiting and approximating mathematical relations.

The *order* of differential quantities is the subject of frequent misunderstanding by students who are making application of the calculus for the first time. Higher-order differentials may always be neglected compared with lower-order differentials. As an example the element of volume $\Delta V$ of a right circular cone of altitude $h$ and base radius $r$ may be taken to be a circular slice a distance $x$ from the vertex and of thickness $\Delta x$. It can be verified that the exact expression for the volume of the element may be written as

$$\Delta V = \frac{\pi r^2}{h^2} \left[ x^2 \, \Delta x + x \, (\Delta x)^2 + \tfrac{1}{3} \, (\Delta x)^3 \right].$$

It should be recognized that, when passing to the limit in going from $\Delta V$ to $dV$ and from $\Delta x$ to $dx$, the terms in $(\Delta x)^2$ and $(\Delta x)^3$ drop out, leaving merely

$$dV = \frac{\pi r^2}{h^2} x^2 \, dx,$$

which is an exact expression.

In using trigonometric functions of differential quantities it is well to call attention to the following relations which are true in the mathematical limit:

$$\sin d\theta = \tan d\theta = d\theta,$$

$$\cos d\theta = 1.$$

The angle $d\theta$ is, of course, expressed in radian measure. When dealing with small but finite angles it is often convenient to replace the sine by the tangent or either function by the angle itself. These approximations, $\sin \theta = \theta$ and $\tan \theta = \theta$, amount to retaining only the first term in the series expansions for the sine and tangent. If a closer approximation is desired, the first two terms may be used which give $\sin \theta = \theta - \theta^3/6$ and $\tan \theta = \theta + \theta^3/3$. As an example of the first approximation, for an angle of 1 deg.,

$$\sin 1° = 0.0174524 \quad \text{and} \quad 1° \text{ is } 0.0174533 \text{ radian.}$$

The error in replacing the sine by the angle for 1 deg. is only 0.005 per cent. For 5 deg. the error is 0.13 per cent, and for 10 deg. the error is still only 0.51 per cent. Similarly, for small angles the cosine may be approximated by the first two terms in its series expansion which gives $\cos \theta = 1 - \theta^2/2$.

A few of the mathematical relations which are useful in mechanics are listed in Table D3, Appendix D.

**9. Method of Problem Solution.** An understanding of the method of attack on engineering problems is an essential aspect of their solution. This method involves a logical sequence of steps from hypothesis to conclusion and should include the following:

(*a*) given data,
(*b*) statement of results desired,
(*c*) necessary diagrams,

(d) statement of principles and basic equations which apply,

(e) application of principles and equations,

(f) answers or conclusions.

Presentation of information in this order represents a logical sequence, and all problem work should follow this general pattern. It is also important that the arrangement of work be neat and orderly. Careless solutions which cannot be easily read by others are of little or no value. It will be found that the discipline involved in adherence to good form will in itself be an invaluable aid to the development of the powers of analysis. Many problems which at first may seem difficult and complicated become clear and simple once they are begun with a logical and disciplined method of attack.

The science of mechanics is based on a surprisingly few fundamental concepts and involves mainly the application of these basic relations to a variety of situations. In this application the *method* of analysis is all-important. In solving a problem it is essential that the laws which apply be carefully fixed in mind and that these principles be applied literally and exactly. In applying the principles which define the requirements for forces acting on a body it is essential that the body in question be *isolated* from all other bodies so that complete and accurate account of all forces which act on this body may be taken. This *isolation* should exist mentally as well as be represented on paper. The drawing of such an isolated body with the representation of *all* external forces acting on it is called a *free-body diagram*. It has long been established that the *free-body diagram* method is the key to the successful application of the principles of mechanics. This is so because the *isolation* of a body is the tool by which *cause* and *effect* are clearly separated and by which attention on the literal application of a principle is accurately focused. The technique of drawing free-body diagrams is explained in Chapter 3 of *Mechanics, Part I, Statics.* Free-body diagrams serve exactly the same purpose in dynamics as they do in statics, and it is *absolutely essential* that they be understood thoroughly.

In applying physical laws to the solution of a problem numerical values of the quantities may be used directly in proceeding toward the solution. On the other hand algebraic symbols may be used to represent the quantities involved, and the answer left as a formula. In the first scheme the magnitude of all quantities expressed in their particular units is evident at each stage of the calculation. This is often an advantage when the practical significance of the magnitude of the terms is appraised. The second method, or symbolic solution, has several advantages over the numerical solution. In the first place the abbreviation achieved by the use of symbols aids in focusing attention on the interconnection between the physical situation and its related mathematical description. Second, a symbolic solution permits a dimensional check to be made at every step, whereas dimensional homogeneity may not be checked when numerical values are used. Furthermore a symbolic solution may be used repeatedly for obtaining answers to the same problem when different sets and sizes of units may be involved. Facility with both methods of solution is essential, and ample practice with each should be sought in the problem work.

# 2

# KINEMATICS

**10. Types of Motion.** The subject of kinematics deals with displacement, velocity, acceleration, and time and is often referred to as the "geometry of motion." The calculation of flight trajectories for aircraft and missiles and the design of cams, gears, and linkages to control or produce certain desired motions are examples of kinematical problems. Kinematics is a necessary introduction to kinetics since ability to describe motion is prerequisite to an understanding of the relations between force and motion.

Kinematics involves only two types of measurements or coordinates, linear and angular, to describe the position of points and lines. The determination of these coordinates and their time derivatives constitutes the problem of kinematics. The subject is developed by studying, first, the motion of points or particles and, second, the motion of rigid bodies. Particles move either on straight lines, which is called *rectilinear motion,* or on curved paths, which is called *curvilinear motion.* The curved path may be two or three dimensional.

Most of the motions of rigid bodies encountered in engineering work can be represented as occurring in a single plane, and such motion is termed *plane motion.* The connecting rod of a stationary reciprocating engine, for example, may be represented as moving in .a plane normal to the axis of the crankshaft. Although not as numerous as two-dimensional problems, there are many important applications which require analysis in three dimensions. The motions of a spinning projectile, a precessing gyroscope, a maneuvering aircraft, and the coupling in a rotating universal joint are examples of three-dimensional motion. The treatment of rigid-body motion in this chapter is restricted, for the most part, to plane motion where only two space coordinates are needed.

The motion of particles and rigid bodies is studied both by using coordinates measured from fixed axes and by using coordinates measured from moving axes. The first approach is known as an *absolute-motion* analysis, and the second approach is a *relative-motion* analysis. Part 1 of the chapter is devoted to the study of absolute motion which is prerequisite to the study of relative motion in Part 2 of the chapter.

## PART 1.  ABSOLUTE MOTION

**11. Rectilinear Motion of a Particle.**   Consider the motion of a point or particle $P$, Fig. 1, along the $s$-direction.  The position of $P$ at any time $t$ is described by its distance $s$ measured from some convenient fixed origin $O$.  If $P$ moves to $P'$ during time $\Delta t$, the change in its position coordinate $\Delta s$ is called the *linear displacement* of $P$ during that interval.   Displacement can be positive or negative, depending on the choice of the positive sense for measurement.   The *average velocity* of the point during this interval is $v_{\text{av.}} = \Delta s/\Delta t$.   The *instantaneous velocity* $v$ of the point at any position on its path is the instantaneous time rate of change of displacement or

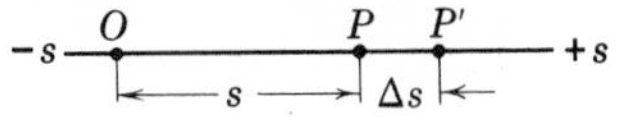

Fig. 1

$$v = \lim_{\Delta t \to 0} \frac{\Delta s}{\Delta t} \quad \text{or} \quad v = \frac{ds}{dt}. \tag{4}$$

If the difference between the instantaneous velocities of the point at $P$ and $P'$ is $\Delta v$, the *average acceleration* during the corresponding time interval $\Delta t$ is $a_{\text{av.}} = \Delta v/\Delta t$ and will be plus or minus, depending on whether the velocity is increasing or decreasing.  The instantaneous acceleration $a$ of the point at any position on its path is the instantaneous time rate of change of velocity

$$a = \frac{dv}{dt} \quad \text{or} \quad a = \frac{d^2s}{dt^2}. \tag{5}$$

By eliminating the time $dt$ between Eq. 4 and the first of Eqs. 5 a differential relation between displacement, velocity, and acceleration results which is

$$v \, dv = a \, ds. \tag{6}$$

The three relations expressed by Eqs. 4, 5, and 6 are the differential equations for the linear motion of a point.

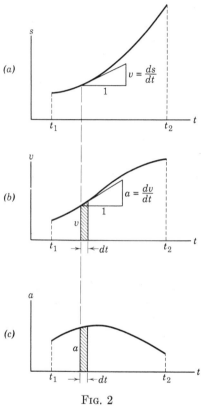

In the solution of many problems it is convenient to represent the relations between the several quantities graphically. Figure 2a represents any given relation between $s$ and $t$. The slope $ds/dt$ of the curve at any time gives the velocity $v$. Thus the velocity may be determined at all points on the curve and plotted against the time as in Fig. 2b. Similarly, the slope $dv/dt$ of the $v$–$t$ curve at any instant gives the acceleration at that instant, and an $a$–$t$ curve can therefore be plotted as in Fig. 2c.

The area under the $v$–$t$ curve during the time $dt$ is $v \, dt$, which equals $ds$, the displacement of the particle during that interval. It follows that the net displacement during the interval $t_1$ to $t_2$ is the area under the $v$–$t$ curve between these two limits. This statement is expressed by the integral of Eq. 4,

Fig. 2

$$\int_{s_1}^{s_2} ds = \int_{t_1}^{t_2} v \, dt, \qquad \text{or} \qquad s_2 - s_1 = \int_{t_1}^{t_2} v \, dt.$$

The graphical expression of displacement from the velocity-time curve is extremely useful in many problems.

The area under the $a$–$t$ curve during the time $dt$ is $a \, dt$, which equals $dv$, the change in velocity of the particle during that interval. It follows that the net or algebraic difference between the velocities at times $t_1$ and $t_2$ is the area under the $a$–$t$ curve between these two limits.

The integral of Eq. 5 expresses this statement and can be written as

$$\int_{v_1}^{v_2} dv = \int_{t_1}^{t_2} a \, dt, \quad \text{or} \quad v_2 - v_1 = \int_{t_1}^{t_2} a \, dt.$$

Two additional graphical relations should be mentioned. When the acceleration is plotted against the displacement as in Fig. 3a, an element of area under the curve is $a \, ds$, which equals $v \, dv$. Integrating this equation between the velocity $v_1$ corresponding to $s_1$ and the velocity $v_2$ corresponding to $s_2$ gives

$$\int_{v_1}^{v_2} v \, dv = \int_{s_1}^{s_2} a \, ds,$$

or

$$\tfrac{1}{2}(v_2{}^2 - v_1{}^2) = (\text{area under } a\text{–}s \text{ curve}).$$

The acceleration may be determined graphically from a plot of $v$ against $s$ as shown in Fig. 3b. At any point such as $A$ the normal $AB$ to the curve is drawn. The segment $CB$ will represent the acceleration, as can be seen from the fact that the two triangles shown are similar and that $a/v = dv/ds$ from Eq. 6. It is necessary that the velocity and displacement axes have the same numerical scale so that the acceleration read on the displacement scale in feet, say, will represent the actual acceleration in the units, feet per second squared.

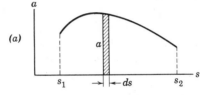

(a)

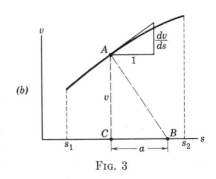

(b)

FIG. 3

Many of the problems commonly encountered involve motion with *constant* acceleration. Under this condition the three differential relations can be integrated directly. If it is agreed that $s = 0$ when $t = 0$ and that the velocity at $t = 0$ is $v_0$, the first of Eqs. 5 may be integrated to obtain

$$\int_{v_0}^{v} dv = a \int_{0}^{t} dt \quad \text{or} \quad v = v_0 + at. \tag{7}$$

Hence the velocity $v$ at any time $t$ equals the initial velocity $v_0$ plus the increment in velocity $at$ due to the acceleration. Substituting this value of velocity as a function of the time into Eq. 4 and integrating yields

$$\int_0^s ds = \int_0^t (v_0 + at)\, dt \qquad \text{or} \qquad s = v_0 t + \tfrac{1}{2}at^2. \tag{8}$$

A third relation is obtained from Eq. 6, which may be integrated as it stands since the acceleration is constant. Thus

$$\int_{v_0}^v v\, dv = a\int_0^s ds \qquad \text{or} \qquad v^2 = v_0{}^2 + 2as. \tag{9}$$

Equations 7, 8, and 9 may, or course, be used *only where the acceleration is constant*. A very common error is the attempt to apply them to problems where the acceleration is not constant.

It should be noted that for constant acceleration the plot of $s$ as a function of $t$, corresponding to Fig. 2$a$, gives a parabola as seen from Eq. 8. The plot of $v$ versus $t$, corresponding to Fig. 2$b$, gives a straight line whose slope is the constant acceleration $a$. Third, the $a$–$t$ curve is a horizontal line of constant acceleration.

In the case of bodies falling near the surface of the earth under the influence of gravity the acceleration is constant if air resistance is neglected and may be taken to be $g = 32.2$ ft./sec.$^2$ directed down. If the positive direction for all measurements is taken to be upward, the acceleration is $-g$, and Eqs. 7, 8, and 9 become

$$v = v_0 - gt,$$

$$h = v_0 t - \tfrac{1}{2}gt^2,$$

$$v^2 = v_0{}^2 - 2gh,$$

where $h$ is the vertical displacement above the datum plane at which $t = 0$.

Choice of the positive direction for the terms in Eqs. 7, 8, and 9 must be understood. If the sign of $s$, $v$, or $a$ turns out negative upon computation, this means that the quantity is directed in the sense opposite to that taken for positive $s$. If Eq. 8 is solved for $t$, there will be two solutions. Only one of the solutions may have practical meaning, and this one will be obvious in most instances from the requirements of the problem. It should be noted that $s$ represents the net displacement. Thus, if a particle moves a positive distance $d_1$ along a straight line, reverses its direction, and returns a distance $d_2$, the calculated displacement will be $s = d_1 - d_2$.

### SAMPLE PROBLEMS

**1.** The displacement of a particle which moves along a straight line is given by $s = 4t^3 + 3t^2 - 6$, where $s$ is in feet and $t$ is in seconds. Determine (a) the time it takes the particle to acquire a velocity of 6 ft./sec. from rest, (b) the acceleration of the particle when the velocity is 6 ft./sec., and (c) the displacement of the particle during the fifth second.

*Solution.* The velocity and acceleration are obtained by successive differentiation with respect to the time. Thus

$$\left[ v = \frac{ds}{dt} \right] \qquad\qquad v = 12t^2 + 6t,$$

$$\left[ a = \frac{dv}{dt} \right] \qquad\qquad a = 24t + 6.$$

Substituting $v = 6$ ft./sec. into the expression for velocity gives $6 = 12t^2 + 6t$, from which $t = \frac{1}{2}$ sec. or $t = -1$ sec. The negative answer describes a solution before the measurement of time had begun and so is of no interest. Therefore the positive root is the desired answer, and

$$t = \tfrac{1}{2} \text{ sec.} \qquad\qquad Ans.$$

The acceleration at $t = \frac{1}{2}$ sec. is

$$a = 24 \times \tfrac{1}{2} + 6 = 18 \text{ ft./sec.}^2 \qquad\qquad Ans.$$

The displacement when $t = 5$ sec. is $s_5 = 4 \times 5^3 + 3 \times 5^2 - 6 = 569$ ft., whereas that when $t = 4$ sec. is $s_4 = 4 \times 4^3 + 3 \times 4^2 - 6 = 298$ ft. Thus the net displacement during the fifth second of motion is

$$s = 569 - 298 = 271 \text{ ft.} \qquad\qquad Ans.$$

This result is identical with that obtained by evaluating the area under the $v$–$t$ curve for the interval 4 to 5 sec. This area is

$$\Delta s = \int_4^5 v \, dt = \int_4^5 (12t^2 + 6t) \, dt = 271 \text{ ft.}$$

**2.** A point starts from the origin with an initial velocity in the $x$-direction and moves for 6 sec. with a constant acceleration of $a_x = -15$ ft./sec.$^2$ If at this time the velocity is 30 ft./sec. in the negative $x$-direction, determine (a) the initial velocity $v_0$ at the origin, (b) the net displacement of the particle, and (c) the total distance covered by the particle.

*Solution.* The final velocity, the time, and the acceleration are known so that the initial velocity can be computed from Eq. 7, which applies to this case of constant acceleration. Thus

$$[v = v_0 + at] \qquad -30 = v_0 - 15 \times 6, \qquad v_0 = 60 \text{ ft./sec.} \qquad Ans.$$

The net displacement for constant acceleration is given by Eq. 8.  Hence

$$[s = v_0 t + \tfrac{1}{2}at^2] \qquad\qquad s = 60 \times 6 - \tfrac{1}{2} \times 15 \times 6^2 = 90 \text{ ft.} \qquad\qquad Ans.$$

Since the point reverses its direction on the $x$-axis, the total distance traveled will be that on the way out plus that on the way back.  (The difference in these

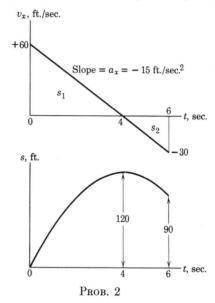

PROB. 2

two distances is the net displacement of 90 ft. just found.)  The point has a zero velocity for

$$[v = v_0 + at] \qquad\qquad 0 = 60 - 15t, \qquad t = 4 \text{ sec.}$$

Thus the two distances are

$$[s = v_0 t + \tfrac{1}{2}at^2] \qquad s_1 = 60 \times 4 - \tfrac{1}{2} \times 15 \times 4^2, \qquad s_1 = 120 \text{ ft.,}$$

$$s_2 = 0 \times 2 + \tfrac{1}{2} \times 15 \times 2^2, \qquad s_2 = \phantom{0}30 \text{ ft.,}$$

and the total distance traveled is

$$D = s_1 + s_2 = 150 \text{ ft.} \qquad\qquad Ans.$$

The variations of $v_x$ and $s$ with $t$ are shown in the figure.

**3.** The acceleration $a$ of a spring-mounted slider block is proportional to its displacement $s$ from the position of zero spring force and is directed opposite to the displacement.  The relation is written $a = -k^2 s$ where $k$ is a constant. (The constant $k$ is arbitrarily squared for later convenience in the form of the expressions.)  If the velocity of the block is $v_0$ when $s = 0$ and if the time $t$ is zero when $s = 0$, determine the displacement and velocity as functions of $t$.

*Solution I.* Since the acceleration is specified in terms of the displacement, the differential relation $v \, dv = a \, ds$ may be integrated. Thus,

$$\int v \, dv = \int -k^2 s \, ds + C_1, \text{ a constant,}$$

or

$$\frac{v^2}{2} = -\frac{k^2 s^2}{2} + C_1.$$

When $s = 0$, $v = v_0$, so that $C_1 = v_0^2/2$, and the velocity becomes

$$v = +\sqrt{v_0^2 - k^2 s^2}.$$

The plus sign of the radical is taken since $v$ is positive in the plus $s$-direction. This last expression may be integrated by substituting $v = ds/dt$. Thus

$$\int \frac{ds}{\sqrt{v_0^2 - k^2 s^2}} = \int dt + C_2, \text{ a constant,}$$

or

$$\frac{1}{k} \sin^{-1} \frac{ks}{v_0} = t + C_2.$$

With the requirements of $t = 0$ when $s = 0$, the constant of integration becomes $C_2 = 0$, and the expression may be solved for $s$ so that

$$s = \frac{v_0}{k} \sin kt. \qquad\qquad Ans.$$

The velocity is $v = ds/dt$ which gives

$$v = v_0 \cos kt. \qquad\qquad Ans.$$

It is noted that both $s$ and $v$ are periodic in the time. The period $\tau$ is the time to complete one entire oscillation during which the argument of the cosine increases by $2\pi$. Thus $k(t + \tau) = kt + 2\pi$, and $\tau = 2\pi/k$. The frequency $f$ of the motion is the number of oscillations or complete cycles per unit time and is $f = 1/\tau = k/2\pi$.

This motion is called *simple harmonic motion* and is characteristic of all oscillations where the restoring force, and hence the acceleration, is proportional to the displacement but opposite in sign.

*Solution II.* Since $a = d^2s/dt^2$, the given relation may be written at once as

$$\frac{d^2 s}{dt^2} = -k^2 s \qquad \text{or} \qquad \frac{d^2 s}{dt^2} + k^2 s = 0.$$

This is an ordinary linear differential equation of second order for which the solution is well known and is

$$s = A \sin Kt + B \cos Kt$$

where $A$, $B$, and $K$ are constants. Substitution of this expression into the differential equation shows that it satisfies the equation provided that $K = k$. The velocity is $v = ds/dt$ which becomes

$$v = Ak \cos kt - Bk \sin kt.$$

The boundary conditions $v = v_0$ when $t = 0$ require that $A = v_0/k$, and the conditions $s = 0$ when $t = 0$ give $B = 0$. Thus the solution is

$$s = \frac{v_0}{k} \sin kt \quad \text{and} \quad v = v_0 \cos kt. \qquad Ans.$$

## PROBLEMS

**4.** The shell in one type of bazooka rocket weapon has a muzzle velocity of 275 ft./sec. after a travel of 59 in. in the firing tube. Find the average acceleration during this period.      *Ans.* $a_{av.} = 7{,}690$ ft./sec.$^2$

**5.** Determine the time $t$ required for a rocket to reach an altitude of 2000 mi. in vertical flight if its upward acceleration is constant at $1.2g$. The rocket is fired from rest on the ground. What velocity $v$ would it have at this altitude?      *Ans.* $t = 12$ min. 19 sec., $v = 5.41$ mi./sec.

**6.** The muzzle velocity of a 30-caliber rifle bullet is about 2700 ft./sec. If air resistance is neglected, determine the maximum height $h$ to which the bullet could be fired.      *Ans.* $h = 21.4$ mi.

**7.** An object is thrown upward with an initial velocity $v$. Find the maximum altitude $h$ reached by the object and the total time $t$ required to return to its starting position. Neglect air resistance.      *Ans.* $h = v^2/2g,\ t = 2v/g$

**8.** The velocity of a particle which moves in a straight line is decreasing at the rate of 8 ft./sec. per foot of displacement at an instant when the velocity is 20 ft./sec. and the displacement is 14 ft. Determine the acceleration $a$ of the particle at this instant.

**9.** The average car can decelerate at the maximum rate of $0.8g$ on dry, clean, level pavement. Find the total emergency stopping distance $s$, measured from the point where the driver first sights the danger, for a car traveling at a speed of 60 mi./hr. The reaction time for a good driver is about $\frac{3}{4}$ sec. from the instant he sights the danger until he is actually applying the brakes.      *Ans.* $s = 216$ ft.

**10.** The velocity of a point moving with rectilinear translation is given by $v = 8 - 2t^2$, where $v$ is in feet per second and $t$ is in seconds. Determine the total distance $D$ traveled by the point and the net displacement $s$ both during the first 4 sec.

**11.** A rocket is launched from rest with an exhaust flow rate which gives it a constant vertical acceleration of magnitude $g$. A second rocket is launched 10 sec. later with a constant vertical acceleration of $2g$. Determine the altitude $h$ at which the second rocket overtakes the first.      *Ans.* $h = 18{,}760$ ft.

**12.** The displacement of a point which moves along a straight line is given by $s = 2t^3 + t^2 + 6$, where $s$ is in feet and $t$ is in seconds. Determine the displacement $\Delta s$ of the point during the time the velocity changes from 8 ft./sec. to 28 ft./sec., and find the acceleration $a$ when the velocity reaches 60 ft./sec.

**13.** An object is thrown vertically up over the top of a well 50 ft. deep. If the object strikes the bottom of the well 4 sec. later, determine the velocity $v$ with which the object hits the bottom, and find the height $h$ above the top of the well to which the object first rises.

$\textit{Ans.}\quad v = 76.9 \text{ ft./sec.}, \ h = 41.8 \text{ ft.}$

**14.** Work Sample Prob. 3 if the initial conditions are that the block is released from rest at $t = 0$ and then acquires a velocity $v_0$ as it passes the position for which $s = 0$.

**15.** A motorcycle which starts from rest reaches a speed of 90 mi./hr. with a constant acceleration and then immediately begins slowing to a stop with a constant deceleration. If the total distance traveled is 2000 ft., determine the elapsed time $t$. $\textit{Ans.}\quad t = 30.3 \text{ sec.}$

**16.** A train accelerates from rest at the rate of 6 ft./sec.² until it reaches its maximum permissible speed of 90 mi./hr. After running at this speed for a certain period, the train decelerates at the rate of 4 ft./sec.² until it comes to a stop. If the train has traveled a total distance of 3 mi., find the time $t$ required for the trip.

**17.** A car starts from rest and moves with a constant acceleration on a straight level road until it reaches a speed of 100 ft./sec. which is then maintained. If the car covers a distance of 25 ft. during the third second after starting, determine the total distance $s$ traveled 20 sec. after the start.

$\textit{Ans.}\quad s = 1500 \text{ ft.}$

**18.** A body moves in a straight line with a decreasing velocity whose square is linear with $s$ as shown. Find the time $t$ required for the body to travel the 100 ft. and the distance $\Delta s$ traveled during the last 2 sec. before coming to rest.

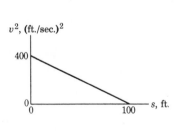

PROB. 18

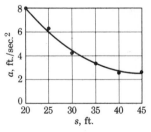

PROB. 19

**19.** Experimental measurements of the acceleration $a$ of an object which moves with a displacement $s$ in a straight line yield the plotted points shown. If the object has a velocity of 12 ft./sec. when $s = 20$ ft., determine the velocity of the object when $s = 45$ ft.

**20.** The following table gives the acceleration $a$ of the piston in terms of its position $x$ for the reciprocating engine shown. Plot the data and determine

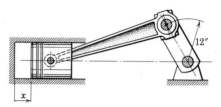

PROB. 20

the maximum velocity $v$ reached by the piston. At the ends of the stroke $da/dx = 0$.

| $x$, ft. | $a_x$, ft./sec.$^2$ | $x$, ft. | $a_x$, ft./sec.$^2$ |
|---|---|---|---|
| 0 | 1100 | 1.0 | $-120$ |
| 0.1 | 1050 | 1.2 | $-320$ |
| 0.2 | 925 | 1.4 | $-490$ |
| 0.4 | 650 | 1.6 | $-605$ |
| 0.6 | 385 | 1.8 | $-680$ |
| 0.8 | 120 | 2.0 | $-700$ |

*Ans.*   $v = 32.0$ ft./sec.

**21.** The following table of experimental data was obtained for the velocity of an object at various displacements along its straight-line path. Plot these data, draw a smooth curve through the points, and approximate the acceleration $a$ when $x = 20$ ft.

| $v$, in./sec. | $x$, ft. | $v$, in./sec. | $x$, ft. |
|---|---|---|---|
| 95 | 4 | 180 | 20 |
| 96 | 8 | 216 | 24 |
| 120 | 12 | 266 | 28 |
| 138 | 16 | 341 | 32 |

*Ans.*   $a = 12$ ft./sec.$^2$

**22.** The steel ball $A$ of diameter $D$ is attracted to the pole face $B$ of an electromagnet with a force which obeys the inverse-square law of attraction.

The acceleration of the ball along the fixed horizontal guide is, then, $a = K/(L - x)^2$ where $K$ is a measure of the strength of the field. If the ball is released from rest at $x = 0$, find the velocity $v$ with which it strikes the pole face.

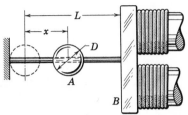

PROB. 22

**23.** A train which has a velocity of 60 mi./hr. applies its brakes as it reaches point $A$ and slows down with a constant deceleration. Its decreased velocity is observed to be 45 mi./hr. as it passes a point ½ mi. beyond $A$. A car moving at 30 mi./hr. passes point $B$ at the same time that the train reaches point $A$. In an effort to beat the train to the crossing, the driver "steps on the gas."

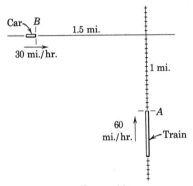

PROB. 23

Calculate the constant acceleration $a$ which the car must have in order to beat the train to the crossing by 5 sec., and find the velocity $v$ of the car as it reaches the crossing. (Experimental verification of the answer is not recommended.)

$$Ans. \quad a = 1.214 \text{ ft./sec.}^2, \quad v = 99.2 \text{ mi./hr.}$$

**24.** A particle starts from rest at time $t = 0$ and moves in a straight line. The unbalanced force acting on the particle decays with time and causes a corresponding decay of the acceleration given by $a = a_0 e^{-bt}$ where $b$ is a constant. Determine the maximum velocity $v_{max}$. which the particle can acquire, and find the displacement $s$ measured from the rest position at any time $t$.

$$Ans. \quad v_{max.} = \frac{a_0}{b}, \quad s = \frac{a_0}{b}\left[ t - \frac{1}{b}(1 - e^{-bt}) \right]$$

**25.** An object moves in a straight line with the accelerations shown. If the velocity is 4 ft./sec. in the positive $x$-direction when $t = 0$, draw the $v$–$t$ curve and determine the distance $s$ traveled by the object in the 8 sec.

PROB. 25

**26.** A train passes a control tower with a velocity $v_0$ and has a constant acceleration. At ½ mi. beyond the tower the velocity is 30 mi./hr., and at 1 mi. beyond the tower the velocity is 40 mi./hr. Find $v_0$.

$Ans.$   $v_0 = 14.1$ mi./hr.

**27.** The thrust for an experimental rocket sled produces an acceleration which varies with the time as shown. Calculate the distance $s$ traveled during the 40 sec. if the sled starts from rest at time $t = 0$.

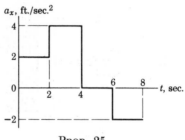

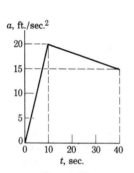

PROB. 27

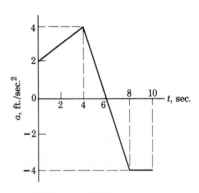

PROB. 28

**28.** A particle starts from rest and moves along a straight line with a variable acceleration as shown. Draw the $v$–$t$ curve for this motion and determine the displacement of the particle when $t = 10$ sec.          $Ans.$   $s = 96$ ft.

**29.** A particle moves in a straight line with constant acceleration. The displacement $s$ is measured from some position of the particle at which the time $t$ is not zero. When $t = 10$ sec., $s = 30$ ft., and when $t = 20$ sec., $s = 50$ ft.

Also the velocity $v$ is 1 ft./sec. when $t = 0$.  Find the acceleration $a$ and the distance $\Delta s$ traveled by the particle during the first 5 sec.

*Ans.*    $a = 0.0667$ ft./sec.$^2$, $\Delta s = 5.83$ ft.

**30.** The slider $A$ is brought to rest from a velocity of 30 ft./sec. by a nest of two coiled springs.  The first spring causes a deceleration which varies linearly with the spring compression.  The second spring increases the deceleration rate when the compression exceeds 6 in. as shown on the accompanying graph. Determine the maximum compression $x$ of the springs.    *Ans.*    $x = 0.828$ ft.

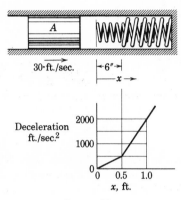

Prob. 30

**31.** A particle moves along a straight line with constant acceleration.  The displacement measured from a convenient position is $+4$ ft. at the time $t = 0$ and is zero when $t = 10$ sec.  Furthermore the velocity is zero when $t = 6$ sec. Determine the velocity $v$ when $t = 10$ sec.

**32.** A faucet leaks at the rate of four drops each second.  If air resistance is neglected, find the vertical separation $h$ between two consecutive drops after the lower one has fallen 20 ft.    *Ans.*    $h = 7.97$ ft.

**33.** In the test of an experimental rocket sled where the driving thrust and the frictional resistance are essentially constant, the acceleration $a$ in straight-line motion increases as the mass decreases.  This dependence is expressed by the relation $a = gT/(W - wt)$ where $g$, $T$, $W$, and $w$ are constants and where $t$ is the time measured from the initial rest position.  Determine the displacement $s$ as a function of $t$.

$$Ans. \quad s = \frac{gT}{w^2} \left[ wt + (W - wt) \log \frac{W - wt}{W} \right]$$

**34.** A particle which is constrained to move in a straight line is subjected to an accelerating force which increases with time and a retarding force which increases directly with the displacement.  The resulting acceleration is $a = Kt - k^2 x$ where $K$ and $k$ are positive constants and where both $x$ and $dx/dt$ are zero when $t = 0$.  Determine $x$ as a function of $t$.

$$Ans. \quad x = \frac{K}{k^3} (kt - \sin kt)$$

**35.** Determine the velocity $v$ and acceleration $a$ of the bucket as functions of $x$ if the velocity $v_B$ of the jeep is constant. When $x = 0$, ends $A$ and $B$ are coincident at $C$.

$$Ans. \quad v = \frac{xv_B}{\sqrt{H^2 + x^2}}, \quad a = \frac{H^2v_B^2}{\sqrt{(H^2 + x^2)^3}}$$

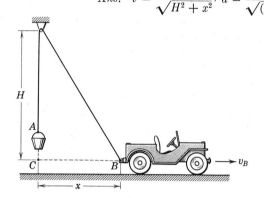

PROB. 35

**\*36.** The acceleration of atomic particles to large velocities in a drift-tube linear accelerator is accomplished by subjecting them to electrical forces due to an alternating radio-frequency voltage. The machine is designed so that a particle which is moving in the shielded tube 1 at a constant velocity $v_1$ enters the gap between tubes 1 and 2 at time $t_1$ and leaves the gap at time $t_2$. During

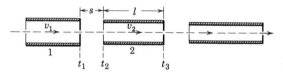

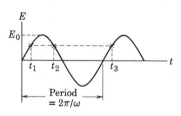

PROB. 36

this interval the particle is subjected to the time-varying force $eE = eE_0 \sin \omega t$ where $e$ is the charge on the particle, $E_0$ is the peak voltage gradient across the gap, and $\omega$ is the constant circular frequency. The acceleration during the interval is, then, $(e/m)E_0 \sin \omega t$ where $m$ is the mass of the particle (constant for low velocities). The particle travels with a new constant velocity through tube 2, which shields it from the negative electrical force while the field is reversed, and emerges into the next gap at time $t_3$. If $t_1$ is $\frac{1}{8}$ of the period as shown and $t_2$ and $t_3$ are as indicated, calculate the necessary length $l$ of tube 2 and the gap length $s$.

$$Ans. \quad l = \frac{3\pi}{2\omega} \left( v_1 + \frac{eE_0\sqrt{2}}{m\omega} \right),$$

$$s = \frac{\pi}{2\omega} \left( v_1 + \frac{eE_0}{m\omega\sqrt{2}} \right)$$

**\* 37.** The resistance to the motion of a projectile in air is approximately proportional to the square of its velocity $v$ for speeds not exceeding about 500 ft./sec. Thus the deceleration may be equated to $Kv^2$, where $K$ is taken to be a constant whose numerical value depends on the prevailing air conditions and the projectile shape, roughness, and mass. If a projectile which moves in a horizontal straight line is fired with an initial velocity $v_0$ (less than 500 ft./sec.), find the velocity $v$ and distance $s$ at a time $t$ after firing.

$$Ans. \quad v = \frac{v_0}{1 + Kv_0t}, \quad s = \frac{1}{K} \log (1 + Kv_0t)$$

**\* 38.** An object is dropped from rest at $t = 0$ from a high altitude. The acceleration at the start is $g$, but because of air resistance it decreases by the amount $cv^2$, where $c$ is a constant and $v$ is the downward velocity. Determine $v$ and the distance $h$ which the object falls as functions of the time $t$. What is the maximum velocity $v_{max}$. which the object can attain?

$$Ans. \quad v = \sqrt{\frac{g}{c}} \tanh \sqrt{gc}\, t, \quad h = \frac{1}{c} \log \cosh \sqrt{gc}\, t, \quad v_{max.} = \sqrt{\frac{g}{c}}$$

**\* 39.** A projectile moves in a straight line with a deceleration due to fluid resistance equal to $Kv^n$, where $K$ and $n$ are constants and $n$ is greater than unity. If the projectile is fired with an initial velocity $v_0$ at $t = 0$, determine the velocity $v$ and the distance $s$ as functions of the time $t$ after firing.

$$Ans. \quad v = [v_0^{1-n} + (n-1)Kt]^{\frac{1}{1-n}},$$

$$s = \frac{1}{(n-2)K} [v_0^{1-n} + (n-1)Kt]^{\frac{n-2}{n-1}} - \frac{v_0^{2-n}}{(n-2)K}$$

**\* 40.** The thrust on a certain rocket is programmed so that it increases linearly with the time $t$ after release of the rocket. For the initial period of its straight-line motion the resistance consists of a constant term and a term proportional to the velocity $v$. The expression for the acceleration is $a = Kt - kv - c$ where $K$, $k$, and $c$ are all positive constants. Determine the displacement $s$ from the initial rest position in terms of the time $t$. (*Hint:* The resulting differential equation is a nonhomogeneous linear equation.)

$$Ans. \quad s = \frac{Kt^2}{2k} + \frac{K + ck}{k^3} (1 - kt - e^{-kt})$$

## 12. Angular Motion of a Line.

The second coordinate or measurement used in kinematics is the angular position of a line. The angular position of line $AB$ in Fig. 4 is described by the angle $\theta$ measured from some convenient fixed reference axis. If the line moves to $A'B'$ so that its angular position changes from $\theta$ to $\theta + \Delta\theta$ during the time interval $\Delta t$, then the change $\Delta\theta$ in the angular coordinate is called the *angular displacement* of the line during that interval. The angular displacement is positive if the angular position $\theta$ increases, as in Fig. 4, and is negative if the angle $\theta$ decreases. The choice of reference axis and the positive sense of measurement, clockwise or counterclockwise, is arbitrary and is wholly a matter of convenience.

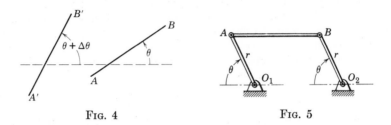

Fig. 4                           Fig. 5

The angular motion or rotation of a line depends only on its angular coordinate $\theta$. Thus the center line $AB$ of the link in Fig. 5, for example, has no angular motion during the rotation of the links $O_1A$ and $O_2B$ since there is no change in the angular coordinate of $AB$ with respect to a fixed reference axis such as $O_1O_2$. The lines $O_1A$ and $O_2B$, on the other hand, have angular motions as $\theta$ changes with time.

A point or particle can have no angular motion since the concept of rotation is associated with the angular motion of a line. In Fig. 5 point $A$ is said to revolve about $O_1$, but the angular motion is actually that of the line joining $A$ with $O_1$.

The *angular velocity* $\omega$ and *angular acceleration* $\alpha$ of a line are, respectively, the first and second time derivatives of its angular displacement $\theta$. These definitions give

$$\omega = \frac{d\theta}{dt},$$

$$\alpha = \frac{d^2\theta}{dt^2} = \frac{d\omega}{dt}, \qquad (10)$$

$$\omega \, d\omega = \alpha \, d\theta.$$

The third relation is obtained by eliminating $dt$ from the first two. In each of these relations the positive direction for $\omega$ and $\alpha$, clockwise or counterclockwise, is the same as that chosen for $\theta$. Equations 10 should be recognized as analogous to the definitions for the linear motion of a point expressed by Eqs. 4, 5, and 6. In fact all relations which were described for rectilinear translation in Art. 11 apply to the case of rotation if the linear quantities $s$, $v$, and $a$ are replaced by their respective equivalent angular quantities $\theta$, $\omega$, and $\alpha$.

Graphical representation of the relations between $\theta$, $\omega$, $\alpha$, and $t$ will be found useful for problems in rotation of lines. This representation is identical with that illustrated in Figs. 2 and 3 for rectilinear motion of a particle except for a change of symbols from linear to angular quantities. The reader should sketch these relations in symbolic form for the case of rotation.

For rotation with *constant* angular acceleration $\alpha$, Eqs. 10 may be integrated directly. The initial and final conditions which determine the limits of integration will be chosen in the same way as for rectilinear translation. Thus it will be assumed that $\theta = 0$ when $t = 0$ and that $\omega = \omega_0$ when $t = 0$. The integration is mathematically identical with that for rectilinear motion treated in Art. 11, and the results are

$$\omega = \omega_0 + \alpha t,$$

$$\theta = \omega_0 t + \tfrac{1}{2}\alpha t^2, \tag{11}$$

$$\omega^2 = \omega_0{}^2 + 2\alpha\theta.$$

The reader should perform the indicated integrations and compare these results with Eqs. 7, 8, and 9. For rotation with variable angular acceleration, Eqs. 11 *cannot* be used, and the differential relations, Eqs. 10, must be integrated and account of the variation in $\alpha$ taken.

Angular measurements may be expressed in degrees, revolutions, or radians. Inasmuch as the relation between arc length and angle occurs so frequently, the radian is the simplest unit to use. The need to change units from revolutions per minute to radians per second, for example, occurs frequently, and the student should be prepared to make this and similar changes readily.

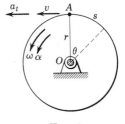

When a line rotates about a fixed point, such as the radial line $OA$ of the fixed-axis wheel of Fig. 6, the relation between the angular motion of the line and the linear motion of any point on

Fig. 6

the line is easily determined. During a rotation $\theta$ of the line the distance $s$ traveled by $A$ along the arc is the product of the constant radius $r$ and the subtended angle $\theta$ expressed in radians. This relation and its first and second time derivatives give the magnitude of the velocity $v$ and the tangential acceleration $a_t$ of point $A$. Thus

$$s = r\theta,$$

$$v = r\omega, \tag{12}$$

$$a_t = r\alpha$$

where $\omega = d\theta/dt$ is the angular velocity of the line and $\alpha = d\omega/dt = d^2\theta/dt^2$ is the angular acceleration of the line. The quantity $a_t = d|v|/dt = d^2s/dt^2$ represents the acceleration of point $A$ in the direction tangent to the circle. Point $A$ has a component of acceleration along $r$ which is discussed in Art. 14, and hence the subscript $t$ is used to distinguish the tangential component from the radial one. It should be noted that $\omega$ and $\alpha$ need not have the same sense of rotation. If a line has a clockwise angular velocity which decreases with time, for instance, its angular acceleration will be counterclockwise.

$\omega = \dfrac{d\theta}{dt} \qquad \alpha = \dfrac{d\omega}{dt}$

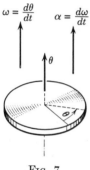

FIG. 7

Angular motion may be represented vectorially. The angular displacement $\theta$ of the disk in Fig. 7 may be represented by the vector $\theta$ with the aid of the right-hand rule to establish the positive sense. The angular velocity $\omega$ and angular acceleration $\alpha$ are also represented by vectors as shown. Rotation may be considered to be a sliding vector or a free vector depending on whether it is desired to designate the axis about which rotation takes place or not. As long as rotation is confined to a single plane, the rotation vectors $\theta$, $\omega$, and $\alpha$ will be parallel to each other. Thus nothing is gained by the vector description, and $\theta$, $\omega$, and $\alpha$ may be considered scalar quantities. The algebraic sign is sufficient to account for either sense of the vector.

The foregoing description applies only to rotation in a given plane. A more general treatment would describe rotation in space such as occurs with the blade of an airplane propeller during a turn of the airplane. Here there are components of the angular motion about three mutually perpendicular axes, and the change in the direction as well as the magnitude of the rotation vectors must be accounted for. This more general problem calls for representation by vectors and is treated briefly in the discussion of gyroscopic motion in Chapter 6. Most motions of structures and machines are plane motions although there are important exceptions such as missiles, aircraft, and gyros which call for a three-dimensional analysis.

## SAMPLE PROBLEMS

**41.** A flywheel which is turning freely at 1800 rev./min. clockwise is subjected to a constant counterclockwise torque which produces a uniform counterclockwise angular acceleration of 24 rad./sec.$^2$ Determine the angular velocity in revolutions per minute 10 sec. after the torque is applied. Also find the total number of revolutions (clockwise turns plus counterclockwise turns) through which the wheel rotates during this interval.

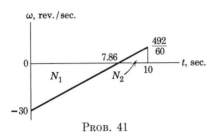

PROB. 41

*Solution.* Since the angular acceleration is constant, Eqs. 11 may be used. With the counterclockwise sense as positive the new angular velocity is

$$[\omega = \omega_0 + \alpha t] \qquad \omega = -\frac{1800 \times 2\pi}{60} + 24 \times 10 = 51.5 \text{ rad./sec.,}$$

or

$$\omega = \frac{51.5 \times 60}{2\pi} = 492 \text{ rev./min.} \qquad\qquad Ans.$$

If desired, the time could be expressed in minutes and the acceleration as $(24/2\pi)(60)^2$ rev./min.$^2$ The formula would then give the angular velocity directly in revolutions per minute.

A plot of the angular speed in revolutions per second against the time in seconds discloses the angular displacements which are represented by the area under the curve. The time at which the wheel reverses its motion is

$$[\omega = \omega_0 + \alpha t] \qquad 0 = -\frac{1800 \times 2\pi}{60} + 24t, \qquad t = 7.86 \text{ sec.}$$

From the areas on the diagram the total clockwise displacement is

$$N_1 = \tfrac{1}{2} \times 30 \times 7.86 = 117.9 \text{ rev.,}$$

and the counterclockwise displacement is

$$N_2 = \tfrac{1}{2} \times \tfrac{492}{60} \times (10 - 7.86) = 8.78 \text{ rev.}$$

Thus the total number of turns is

$$N = N_1 + N_2 = 126.7 \text{ rev.} \qquad\qquad Ans.$$

**42.** An aircraft tracking device is trained on an airplane $A$ flying horizontally with a constant velocity $v$ at an altitude $h$. Compute the angular velocity $\omega$ and the angular acceleration $\alpha$ of the line of sight $OA$ for any angle $\theta$.

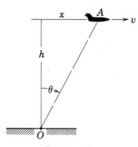

PROB. 42

*Solution.* The angular velocity and acceleration of the line of sight will be the first and second time derivatives, respectively, of its angular coordinate $\theta$. Thus an expression for $\theta$ must be obtained first and then differentiated. From the right triangle, $x = h \tan \theta$,

$$\left[ v = \frac{dx}{dt} \right] \qquad v = h \sec^2 \theta \frac{d\theta}{dt} = h\omega \sec^2 \theta.$$

Thus

$$\omega = \frac{v}{h} \cos^2 \theta. \qquad\qquad Ans.$$

The angular acceleration is

$$\left[ \alpha = \frac{d\omega}{dt} \right] \qquad \alpha = -2 \frac{v}{h} \cos \theta \sin \theta \frac{d\theta}{dt}$$

$$= -\frac{v^2}{h^2} \sin 2\theta \cos^2 \theta. \qquad\qquad Ans.$$

If the velocity $v$ were not constant, its derivative would have to be evaluated when differentiating both $x$ and $\omega$.

**PROBLEMS**

**43.** The angular velocity of a gear is controlled according to $\omega = 6 - 3t^2$, where $\omega$, in radians per second, is positive in the clockwise sense, and where $t$ is in seconds. Find the net angular displacement $\theta$ from the time $t = 0$ to $t = 3$ sec. *Ans.* $\theta = 9$ rad. counterclockwise

**44.** A braking torque causes a flywheel to slow down at the constant rate of 20 rev./min. during each second. If the wheel comes to rest from a speed of 1800 rev./min., find the number of revolutions $N$ made during this interval. *Ans.* $N = 1350$ rev.

**45.** The angular displacement of a wheel is given by $\theta = 2t^3 + 3t^2 + 2$, where $\theta$ is in radians, clockwise, and $t$ is in seconds. Find the angular displacement $\Delta\theta$ during the time $(t > 0)$ that the velocity is changing from 12 to 72 rad./sec., both clockwise.                    *Ans.* $\Delta\theta = 76$ rad.

**46.** Experimental data for a rotating control element reveal the relation between angular velocity $\omega$ and angular displacement $\theta$ shown. Determine the angular acceleration $\alpha$ of the element when $\theta = 5$ rad.

*Ans.* $\alpha = 4.3$ rad./sec.$^2$

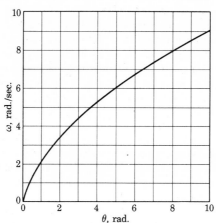

PROB. 46

**47.** In the hoisting rig shown the pinion $A$ reaches a speed of 900 rev./min. in 10 sec. from rest with constant acceleration. Determine the acceleration $a$ of the load $W$.

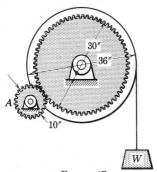

PROB. 47

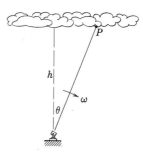

PROB. 48

**48.** A searchlight puts a spot of light $P$ on a horizontal layer of clouds at an altitude $h$. If the beam of light is revolved in a vertical plane at a constant angular velocity $\omega$, determine the linear acceleration $a$ of the spot for any angle $\theta$.                    *Ans.* $a = 2h\omega^2 \sec^2\theta \tan\theta$

**49.** A flywheel is rotating at a uniform clockwise speed of 2 rad./sec. when a variable torque is applied to it at time $t = 0$. As a result there is a clockwise angular acceleration $\alpha$ which increases in direct proportion to the angle $\theta$ through which the wheel turns from the instant $t = 0$. After 16 complete turns from this time the angular acceleration is 4 rad./sec.[2] Determine the angular velocity $\omega$ of the wheel at this instant.

**50.** The motion of a rotating element in a mechanism is controlled so that the rate of change of angular velocity $\omega$ with angular displacement $\theta$ is a constant $k$. If the angular velocity is $\omega_0$ when both $\theta$ and the time $t$ are zero, determine $\theta$, $\omega$, and the angular acceleration $\alpha$ as functions of $t$.

**51.** The frictional resistance to the rotation of a flywheel consists of a resistance due to air friction which varies as the square of the angular velocity and a constant bearing resistance. Thus the angular acceleration which the flywheel has while it is allowed to coast is $\alpha = -K - k\omega^2$ where $K$ and $k$ are constants. Calculate the time required for the flywheel to come to rest from an initial angular velocity $\omega_0$.

$$Ans. \quad t = \frac{1}{\sqrt{Kk}} \tan^{-1} \left( \omega_0 \sqrt{\frac{k}{K}} \right)$$

**52.** A gear, which turns with constant angular acceleration, has a displacement of 4 rad. when $t = 0$. After 10 sec. it has a displacement of zero, and, when $t = 4$ sec., the gear reverses the direction of its motion. Find the angular velocity $\omega$ when $t = 10$ sec.      *Ans.* $\omega = -2.4$ rad./sec.

**53.** The elements of a wheel-and-disk type mechanical integrator are shown in the figure. The integrator wheel $A$ turns about its fixed axis and is driven

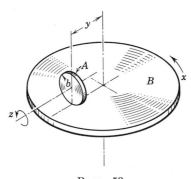

PROB. 53

by friction from disk $B$ without slippage tangent to its rim. The distance $y$ is a variable and can be controlled at will. Show that the angular displacement of the integrator wheel shaft is given by $z = (1/b) \int y \, dx$, where $x$ is the angular displacement of the disk.

**54.** For the wheel-and-disk integrator shown with Prob. 53 calculate the angular acceleration $\alpha_A$ of the wheel $A$ which results from moving $A$ away from the center of $B$ at a constant rate of $v = dy/dt$. The disk $B$ revolves at a speed $\omega_B$ which increases at the rate $\alpha_B = d\omega_B/dt$. It is assumed that there is no slipping between $A$ and $B$ in the direction tangent to $A$ at the contact point.

$$Ans. \quad \alpha_A = \frac{1}{b}(y\alpha_B + v\omega_B)$$

**55.** A cable is wound around a shaft against the face of a disk so that the cable forms a spiral as shown. If the radius of the coil at any instant is $r$ and is large compared with the cable diameter $D$, find the vertical acceleration $a$ of the load $L$ if the shaft is turning at a constant speed $\omega$.

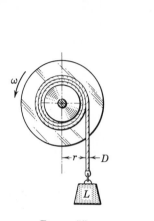

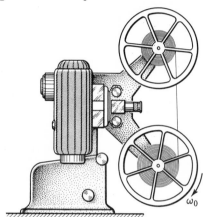

PROB. 55             PROB. 56

* **56.** In rewinding the film for the moving-picture projector shown, the lower reel is turned by the motor at a constant angular velocity $\omega_0$. At any instant when the radii of the driving and driven rolls of film are $r_0$ and $r$, respectively, find the angular acceleration $\alpha$ of the driven reel. The thickness of the film is $b$.

$$Ans. \quad \alpha = \frac{b\omega_0^2}{2\pi r}\left(1 + \frac{r_0^2}{r^2}\right)$$

* **57.** A searchlight with its beam fixed at a constant angle $\beta$ from the vertical revolves around its vertical axis with a constant angular velocity $\omega$. From a distance the beam appears to oscillate in a vertical plane through a total angle $2\beta$. Derive an expression for the angular velocity $\Omega$ of the projection of the beam on a vertical plane for any angle $\gamma$ between the vertical axis and the projection of the beam on the vertical plane. The angular velocity is $\Omega = d\gamma/dt$.

$$Ans. \quad \Omega = \omega \cos^2 \gamma \sqrt{\tan^2 \beta - \tan^2 \gamma}$$

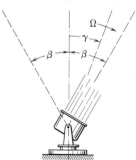

PROB. 57

\* **58.** An aircraft-tracking device employs two directional beams 1 and 2 emanating from two ground stations a distance $b$ apart. The angular coordinates and their time derivatives are fed into a computer which calculates the position and motion of the aircraft. For the simple case illustrated where the target is flying at a constant altitude $h$ in a vertical plane containing the two ground stations, determine the expressions for altitude $h$, velocity $v$, and acceleration $a$ of the aircraft in terms of the angular displacements of the tracking beams and the angular velocity $\omega_1$ and angular acceleration $\alpha_1$ of beam 1.

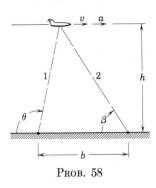

*Ans.* $h = \dfrac{b}{\operatorname{ctn}\beta - \operatorname{ctn}\theta}$,

$$v = \frac{b\omega_1 \csc^2\theta}{\operatorname{ctn}\beta - \operatorname{ctn}\theta},$$

$$a = \frac{b\csc^2\theta}{\operatorname{ctn}\beta - \operatorname{ctn}\theta}(\alpha_1 - 2\omega_1^2 \operatorname{ctn}\theta)$$

PROB. 58

**13. Curvilinear Motion of a Particle; $x$–$y$ Components.** The motion of a particle on a curved path is called curvilinear motion. Although the most general case involves a space curve where all three coordinates are needed, two-dimensional motion only will be discussed here. In Fig. 8 the motion of a particle along a plane curve in the $x$–$y$ plane is illustrated. The path may be described directly as $y = f(x)$ or else may be expressed parametrically in terms of the time $t$ as $y = f_1(t)$ and $x = f_2(t)$. At any time $t$ when the particle is at $A$ its location is specified by the *position vector s* measured from the origin of the coordinate system. As the particle moves to $A'$ its position vector becomes $s'$, and the change in its position vector is the displacement $\Delta s$ of the particle during this interval. This change in position is clearly independent of the choice of origin for the measurement of $s$. The position at $A$ and the displacement may be expressed by the vector equations

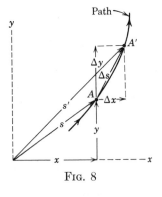

FIG. 8

$$s = x \mathbin{+\!\!+} y,$$

and

$$\Delta s = \Delta x \mathbin{+\!\!+} \Delta y.$$

The displacement of the particle between points $A$ and $A'$ is the vector $\Delta s$, whereas the *distance* traveled by the particle is the length of the path measured along the arc between $A$ and $A'$ and is a scalar quantity.

If the time to go from $A$ to $A'$ is $\Delta t$, the average velocity between these two points is

$$v_{\text{av.}} = \frac{\Delta s}{\Delta t} = \frac{\Delta x}{\Delta t} \nleftrightarrow \frac{\Delta y}{\Delta t},$$

and the instantaneous velocity at $A$ is the limit of this expression as $\Delta t$ approaches zero.  Thus

$$\frac{ds}{dt} = \frac{dx}{dt} \nleftrightarrow \frac{dy}{dt},$$

or

$$v = v_x \nleftrightarrow v_y. \tag{13}$$

The direction of the vector $v$ is along the tangent to the curve as shown in Fig. 9.  It is clear that

$$v^2 = v_x{}^2 + v_y{}^2 \qquad \text{and} \qquad \tan \theta = \frac{v_y}{v_x}.$$

The velocity of the particle is a vector quantity, whereas the *speed* of

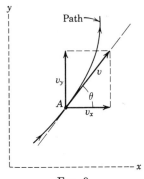

Fig. 9

the particle along the path is the magnitude of the velocity and hence is a scalar quantity.

The change in velocity between $A$ and $A'$ is the vector difference $\Delta v$, shown in Fig. 10, which may be represented by the equation

$$\Delta v = \Delta v_x \nleftrightarrow \Delta v_y.$$

The average acceleration between $A$ and $A'$ is

$$a_{\text{av.}} = \frac{\Delta v}{\Delta t} = \frac{\Delta v_x}{\Delta t} \nleftrightarrow \frac{\Delta v_y}{\Delta t},$$

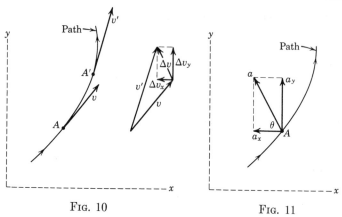

FIG. 10　　　　　　　　FIG. 11

and the instantaneous acceleration at $A$ is the limit of this expression as $\Delta t$ approaches zero.  Thus

$$\frac{dv}{dt} = \frac{dv_x}{dt} \nrightarrow \frac{dv_y}{dt},$$

or

$$a = a_x \nrightarrow a_y. \tag{14}$$

The components may also be expressed as $a_x = d^2x/dt^2$ and $a_y = d^2y/dt^2$.  The acceleration and its components are indicated in Fig. 11. The angle $\theta$ made by $a$ with the $x$-direction is

$$\tan \theta = \frac{a_y}{a_x}.$$

The acceleration is, in general, *not* along the tangent to the path since $(d^2y/dt^2)/(d^2x/dt^2)$ is not equal to $(dy/dt)/(dx/dt)$ except for motion along a straight line or at a point of inflection in a curved path.

From the foregoing discussion it should be recognized that plane curvilinear motion is merely the superposition of the coordinates of two simultaneous rectilinear motions in the $x$- and $y$-directions.

### SAMPLE PROBLEM

**59.** A projectile is fired with a muzzle velocity $u$ at an angle $\theta$ with the horizontal.  Neglect the effect of air resistance and determine the equations of the trajectory, the range $R$ on a horizontal plane, and the maximum altitude $h$ reached in flight.

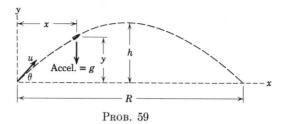

PROB. 59

*Solution.* With the neglect of air resistance the only force acting on the projectile is its weight, and hence the acceleration at all times is $g$ directed vertically down. Thus $a_x = 0$ and $a_y = -g$. The resulting motion, then, is a superposition of two rectilinear motions with constant acceleration. With zero acceleration in the $x$-direction the horizontal distance traveled equals the constant horizontal component of velocity multiplied by the time. Thus

$$[s = v_0 t] \qquad\qquad x = ut \cos \theta.$$

The $y$-coordinate of the projectile is given by Eq. 8 for constant acceleration and is

$$[s = v_0 t + \tfrac{1}{2} a t^2] \qquad\qquad y = ut \sin \theta - \tfrac{1}{2} g t^2.$$

These two expressions for $x$ and $y$ are the equations for the motion of the projectile in terms of the parameter $t$. The equation of the trajectory is obtained by eliminating $t$ between the expressions and is

$$y = x \tan \theta - \frac{gx^2}{2u^2 \cos^2 \theta}. \qquad\qquad Ans.$$

From the form of the equation the curve is seen to be a parabola with vertical axis as shown in the figure.

The range $R$ is obtained by equating to zero either of the two expressions for $y$. The second equation gives

$$0 = x \left( \tan \theta - \frac{gx}{2u^2 \cos^2 \theta} \right)$$

which has two solutions. The solution $x = 0$ is of no concern, but the other value is

$$x = R = \frac{2u^2 \sin \theta \cos \theta}{g} = \frac{u^2 \sin 2\theta}{g}. \qquad\qquad Ans.$$

The maximum range occurs for $\sin 2\theta = 1$ or $\theta = 45$ deg. and is

$$R_{max.} = \frac{u^2}{g}.$$

The time of flight for the range $R$ may be obtained by equating $y$ to zero in the second of the two parametric expressions. Thus

$$0 = t \left( u \sin \theta - \frac{1}{2} g t \right), \qquad \text{and} \qquad t = \frac{2u \sin \theta}{g}.$$

By symmetry the time of flight to the apex of the parabola is one half that for the complete journey. Substitution of this time into the expression for $y$ gives a maximum altitude of

$$h = y = \frac{u^2 \sin^2 \theta}{g} - \frac{g}{2}\left(\frac{u^2 \sin^2 \theta}{g^2}\right), \qquad h = \frac{u^2 \sin^2 \theta}{2g}. \qquad Ans.$$

Accurate calculations for trajectories must account for the effect of air resistance, which is appreciable at high velocities. Wind velocity and direction as well as the rotation and curvature of the earth may also become important.

### PROBLEMS

Except where indicated, neglect air resistance in the problems involving projectile motion.

**60.** Use the conditions and notation of Sample Prob. 59 to show that the range is $R = 4h \operatorname{ctn} \theta$ and that this relation is independent of the initial velocity $u$ and the acceleration of gravity.

**61.** The curvilinear motion of a particle is described by $x = 2t^3 - 3t$ and $y = 4t^2$, where $x$ and $y$ are in inches and $t$ is in seconds. Determine the velocity $v$ and acceleration $a$ of the particle when $t = 2$ sec.

$Ans.$   $v = 26.4$ in./sec., $a = 25.3$ in./sec.$^2$

**62.** A particle moves along the positive branch of the curve $x = 4y^2$ such that $y = t^3/3$, where $x$ and $y$ are measured in inches and $t$ is in seconds. Determine the velocity $v$ and acceleration $a$ of the particle when $t = \frac{1}{2}$ sec.

$Ans.$   $v = 0.263$ in./sec., $a = 1.301$ in./sec.$^2$

**63.** Find the target lead $L$ which a dive-bomber pilot must allow when releasing a bomb from an altitude $h = 2000$ ft. The flight angle is $\theta = 45$ deg., and the bomber is traveling 600 mi./hr. $\qquad Ans.$   $L = 133$ ft.

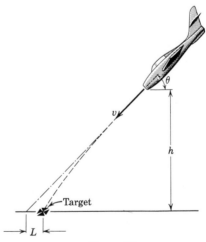

PROB. 63

**64.** A bomber flying horizontally with a velocity $v$ and at an altitude $h$ is to score a direct hit on a train moving with a constant velocity $v_0$ in the same direction and in the same vertical plane. Determine the expression for the correct angle $\theta$ between the line of sight to the target and the horizontal at the instant the bomb should be released.

$$Ans. \quad \theta = \operatorname{ctn}^{-1}\left\{\sqrt{\frac{2}{gh}}\,(v - v_0)\right\}$$

**65.** The $x$-coordinate of a particle which moves with curvilinear motion is $x = 40t + 4t^3$, where $x$ is in inches and $t$ is in seconds. When $t = 2$ sec., the total acceleration is 64 in./sec.$^2$ If the acceleration in the positive $y$-direction is constant and the particle starts from the origin with $v_y = 0$ at $t = 0$, determine the velocity $v$ of the particle when $t = 4$ sec.

$$Ans. \quad v = 287 \text{ in./sec.}$$

**66.** Electrons are emitted at $A$ with the velocity $u$ at an angle $\theta$ into a space between two charged plates. The electric field or voltage gradient between the plates is $E$ and is in a direction to repulse the electrons approaching the plate on the left. The electron acceleration in the direction of the field $E$ is $eE/m$ where $e$ is the electron charge and $m$ is its mass. Determine the strength $E$ of the field which will permit the electrons to cross one-half of the gap. Also find the distance $s$.

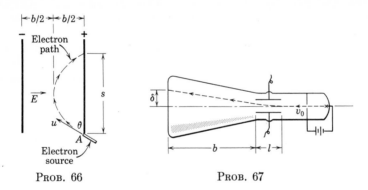

PROB. 66                    PROB. 67

**67.** In the cathode-ray tube electrons traveling horizontally with a velocity $v_0$ are deflected by an electric field $E$ due to the voltage gradient across the plates. The deflecting force causes an acceleration in the vertical direction on the sketch equal to $eE/m$ where $e$ is the electron charge and $m$ is its mass. Once clear of the plates the electrons travel in straight lines. Determine the deflection $\delta$ for the tube and plate dimensions shown.

$$Ans. \quad \delta = \frac{eEl}{mv_0^2}\left(\frac{l}{2} + b\right)$$

**68.** The following data were taken from a test firing of a rocket. The horizontal distance $x$ and the vertical distance $y$ are given in thousands of feet from the launching site along with the corresponding elapsed time $t$ of flight in seconds. Plot these data and determine (a) the velocity $v$ of the rocket at $t = 100$ sec. and (b) the final velocity $v_f$ when the rocket returns to earth at the same elevation as the launching site. Indicate the procedure for finding the acceleration of the rocket at any time.

| $t$ | $x$ | $y$ | $t$ | $x$ | $y$ |
|---|---|---|---|---|---|
| 0 | 0 | 0 | 225 | 173 | 519 |
| 25 | 1 | 19 | 250 | 194 | 508 |
| 50 | 10 | 68 | 275 | 215 | 480 |
| 75 | 28 | 160 | 300 | 236 | 435 |
| 100 | 53 | 280 | 325 | 258 | 369 |
| 125 | 79 | 374 | 350 | 278 | 280 |
| 150 | 105 | 441 | 375 | 300 | 170 |
| 175 | 130 | 488 | 400 | 320 | 57 |
| 200 | 152 | 515 | 413 | 332 | 0 |

*Ans.* (a) $v = 3200$ mi./hr.,
(b) $v_f = 3100$ mi./hr.

**69.** An object is released from rest at point $A$ a distance $h$ above a horizontal surface. Because of the earth's rotation it may be shown that the object has an eastward acceleration as measured from the ground which equals $2v_y\omega \cos \gamma$ where $v_y$ is the free-fall downward velocity at any instant, $\omega$ is the angular velocity of the earth, and $\gamma$ is the angle of north latitude. Determine the distance $\delta$ to the east of the vertical line through $A$ at which the object strikes the ground.

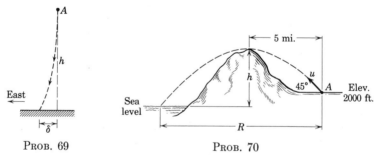

PROB. 69                    PROB. 70

**70.** A long-range rifle at $A$ is aimed at an angle of 45 deg. with the horizontal, and its shell is just able to clear the mountain peak at the top of its trajectory. Determine the muzzle velocity $u$, the height $h$ of the mountain above sea level, and the range $R$ to the sea.

*Ans.* $u = 1304$ ft./sec., $h = 15,200$ ft.,
$R = 18,200$ yd.

**71.** The muzzle velocity for a certain gun is 2000 ft./sec. The target and gun are on the same horizontal plane, and the range is 5000 yd. Find the two values of the angle $\theta$ made by the barrel with the horizontal for which a direct hit can be scored.

**72.** Find the initial velocity $u$ of a ball thrown down the slope as shown.

*Ans.* $u = 68.3$ ft./sec.

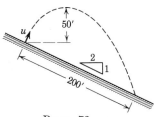

PROB. 72

* **73.** A projectile is fired horizontally with a velocity $v_0$. Air resistance causes a horizontal deceleration proportional to its horizontal velocity so that $a_x = -kv_x$. The vertical acceleration is $g$. Determine the equation of the trajectory and the angle $\theta$ between the tangent to the path and the horizontal at any time $t$ after firing.

*Ans.* $x = \dfrac{v_0}{k}(1 - e^{-k\sqrt{2y/g}}), \theta = \tan^{-1} \dfrac{gte^{kt}}{v_0}$

* **74.** Show that the acceleration of a point moving on the arc of the circle $x^2 + y^2 = r^2$ with a velocity of constant magnitude $v$ is equal to $v^2/r$ and is directed toward the center of the circle. Prove by considering the $x$- and $y$-components of acceleration.

* **75.** Find the range $R$ for a projectile fired onto the inclined plane shown. What is the maximum value of $R$ for a given muzzle velocity $u$?

*Ans.* $R = \dfrac{2u^2}{g} \dfrac{\cos\theta \sin(\theta - \alpha)}{\cos^2\alpha}, R_{max.} = \dfrac{u^2}{g(1 + \sin\alpha)}$

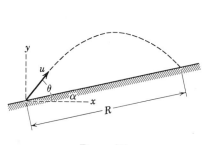

PROB. 75

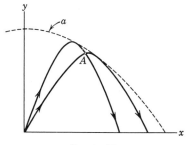

PROB. 76

* **76.** Find the equation of the envelope $a$ to the parabolic trajectories of an anti-aircraft gun which fires at any angle but has a constant muzzle velocity $u$. (*Hint:* Substitute $m = \tan\theta$ in the equation of the trajectory. The two roots $m_1$ and $m_2$ of this relation give the firing angles for the two trajectories shown

such that the shells pass through the same point $A$. Point $A$ approaches the curve $a$ when the two roots approach equality.)

$$Ans. \quad y = \frac{u^2}{2g} - \frac{gx^2}{2u^2}, \text{ a vertical parabola}$$

*77. An electron of charge $e$ and mass $m$ is emitted with a velocity $v_0$ in the $x$-direction into a uniform magnetic field of strength $B_z$ in the $z$-direction. As a result of its motion the forces on the electron at any time are proportional to the velocity components which are perpendicular to the forces and are $F_y = eB_zv_x$ and $F_x = -eB_zv_y$. The accelerations in the $x$- and $y$-directions are, consequently, $a_y = eB_zv_x/m$ and $a_x = -eB_zv_y/m$ where $v_x$ and $v_y$ are the components of the velocity of the electron in the respective coordinate directions. Specify the path followed by the electron.

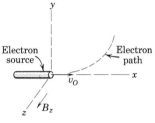

PROB. 77

$$Ans. \quad \text{A circle in the } x\text{-}y \text{ plane of radius } \frac{mv_0}{eB_z} \text{ with center at } \left(0, \frac{mv_0}{eB_z}\right)$$

**14. Curvilinear Motion of a Particle; $n$–$t$ Components.** The motion of a particle on a plane curve will now be described by coordinates which are along the normal $n$ and the tangent $t$ to the curve at the instantaneous position of the particle. Figure 12 shows any

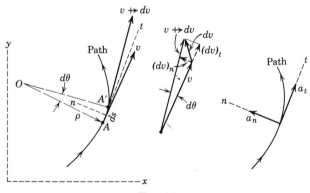

Fig. 12

curvilinear path of a particle in the $x$–$y$ plane. The linear displacement of the particle in going from $A$ to $A'$ in time $dt$ is along the tangent to the curve and has a magnitude $ds = \rho\, d\theta$ where $\rho$ is the radius of curvature to the path at the observed position of the particle. The instantaneous velocity of the particle has a magnitude $v = ds/dt$, called the _speed,_ and a direction tangent to the path.  Thus

$$v = \rho \frac{d\theta}{dt} \quad \text{or} \quad v = \rho\omega \tag{15}$$

where $\omega$ is the angular velocity of the radial line $AO$.

The acceleration of the particle is the time rate of change of its velocity.  For curvilinear motion the derivative must account for the change in both magnitude and direction of the velocity vector $v$.  In Fig. 12 the velocity of the particle at $A$ is $v$ and at $A'$ is $v \leftrightarrow dv$ a time $dt$ later.  The vector change $dv$ has two components, one $(dv)_t$ due to the change in the magnitude of $v$ and directed along the tangent $t$ to the path, and the other $(dv)_n$ due to the change in the direction of $v$ and directed along the normal $n$ to the path.  These components are given by the vector equation

$$dv = (dv)_n \leftrightarrow (dv)_t.$$

The acceleration $a$, then, has two components and is

$$\frac{dv}{dt} = \frac{(dv)_n}{dt} \leftrightarrow \frac{(dv)_t}{dt},$$

$$a = a_n \leftrightarrow a_t. \tag{16}$$

The normal acceleration component $a_n$ depends on $(dv)_n$ and is therefore due to the _change in direction_ of the velocity.  From the velocity diagram in Fig. 12 the vector $(dv)_n$ may be considered in the limit as a differential length of arc of radius $v$ with a subtended angle $d\theta$.  Thus $(dv)_n = v\,d\theta$, and the normal component of acceleration becomes

$$a_n = \frac{(dv)_n}{dt} = v\frac{d\theta}{dt}.$$

With the substitution $\omega = d\theta/dt = v/\rho$, the normal acceleration may be written in three different but equal forms

$$a_n = v\omega = \rho\omega^2 = v^2/\rho. \tag{17}$$

This result is extremely important and must be thoroughly understood.  It should be carefully noted that the direction of the normal component of acceleration is _always toward the center of curvature._

The tangential component of acceleration is obtained from $(dv)_t$, which is the change in the magnitude of the velocity.  Thus

$$a_t = \frac{(dv)_t}{dt} = \frac{d|v|}{dt} = \frac{d^2s}{dt^2}, \tag{18}$$

where $s$ here is the scalar distance measured along the curve. It may be observed from Eq. 18 that, as long as all measurements of the motion are made in a direction along the curve, the distance $s$, the speed $|v|$, and the tangential acceleration $a_t$ bear the same relationships as were discussed in Art. 11 and expressed in Eqs. 4, 5, and 6 for rectilinear translation. The tangential component of acceleration may also be expressed in terms of the radius of curvature $\rho$ and the angle $\theta$ by introducing $v = \rho(d\theta/dt)$. Thus

$$a_t = \frac{d|v|}{dt} = \frac{d}{dt}\left(\rho\,\frac{d\theta}{dt}\right) = \rho\,\frac{d^2\theta}{dt^2} + \frac{d\rho}{dt}\frac{d\theta}{dt} = \rho\alpha + \omega\,\frac{d\rho}{dt}$$

where $\alpha = d\omega/dt = d^2\theta/dt^2$ is the angular acceleration of the radial line $OA$. The second term in the expressions for $a_t$ will be zero when $d\rho/dt = 0$, which occurs when $\rho$ is constant, as for a circle or at points which represent a maximum or minimum radius of curvature.

The total or resultant acceleration is the vector sum of its two components as given by Eq. 16. In Fig. 13$a$ is shown a schematic repre-

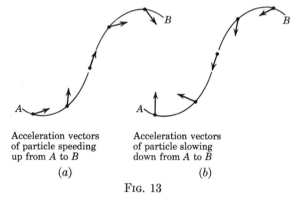

Acceleration vectors
of particle speeding
up from $A$ to $B$

$(a)$

Acceleration vectors
of particle slowing
down from $A$ to $B$

$(b)$

Fig. 13

sentation of the variation of the total acceleration vector $a$ for a particle moving with increasing speed along the curve from $A$ to $B$. In Fig. 13$b$ is represented the acceleration of the particle when its speed is decreasing in going from $A$ to $B$. In both cases the acceleration has a normal component directed toward the center of curvature.

### SAMPLE PROBLEM

**78.** A rocket has a total acceleration of 60 ft./sec.[2] in the direction shown at a certain point in its trajectory where its speed is 10,000 mi./hr. Calculate the radius of curvature $\rho$ of the path at this position. If $\rho$ is increasing at the rate

of 18 mi./sec. at the instant considered, calculate the instantaneous angular
acceleration $\alpha$ of the radius of curvature to the rocket.

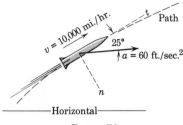

PROB. 78

*Solution.* The radius of curvature is determined from the normal acceleration which is $a_n = 60 \sin 25° = 25.4$ ft./sec.$^2$ Thus

$$\left[ a_n = \frac{v^2}{\rho} \right] \qquad \rho = \frac{(10,000 \times \frac{44}{30})^2}{25.4}$$

$$= 8.49 \times 10^6 \text{ ft.} \qquad \text{or} \qquad \rho = 1608 \text{ mi.} \qquad \textit{Ans.}$$

The angular acceleration of the radius of curvature depends on the tangential acceleration which is $a_t = 60 \cos 25° = 54.4$ ft./sec.$^2$ Thus

$$\left[ a_t = \frac{d}{dt}(\rho\omega) = \rho\alpha + \omega \frac{d\rho}{dt} \right]$$

$$54.4 = (8.49 \times 10^6)\alpha + \frac{10,000 \times \frac{44}{30}}{8.49 \times 10^6} \times (18 \times 5280)$$

$$\alpha = -12.93 \times 10^{-6} \text{ rad./sec.}^2 \qquad \textit{Ans.}$$

The minus sign shows that the angular acceleration is in the opposite sense to
the angular velocity of the radius of curvature.

## PROBLEMS

**79.** At the bottom of a loop an airplane has a normal acceleration of $4g$ and a
velocity of 500 mi./hr. Find the radius $\rho$ of the loop.  *Ans.* $\rho = 4170$ ft.

**80.** Consider the polar axis of the earth to be fixed in space and compute the
acceleration of an object attached to the surface of the earth at the equator.
The radius of the earth is 3960 mi.  *Ans.* $a_n = 0.111$ ft./sec.$^2$

**81.** A bullet is fired horizontally from a gun with a muzzle velocity of
2400 ft./sec. Calculate the radius of curvature $\rho$ of the path of the bullet as it
leaves the gun.  *Ans.* $\rho = 178,000$ ft.

**82.** The motion of the equilateral triangular plate is controlled by the
rollers which move in a circular guide of 18 in. radius. If the rollers are moving
up the guide with a velocity of 4 ft./sec. in the position shown and if this

velocity is increasing at the rate of 5 ft./sec. each second, determine the total acceleration $a$ of point $A$ at the instant described.

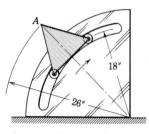

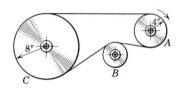

PROB. 82                                PROB. 83

**83.** A flexible belt connects the driving pulley $A$ with the driven pulley $C$ and passes over an idler pulley $B$. If $A$ is increasing its speed at the rate of 60 rev./min. each second, determine the magnitude of the total acceleration $a$ of a point on the rim of pulley $C$ at the instant when $A$ has reached a speed of 30 rev./min.

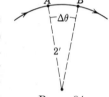

*Ans.*   $a = 2.66$ ft./sec.²

**84.** A particle moves with a constant speed of $v = 10$ ft./sec. on the circular path shown. During the movement from $A$ to $B$ the velocity undergoes a vector change. Divide this change by the time interval between the two points to obtain the average normal acceleration for (a) $\Delta\theta = 30$ deg., (b) $\Delta\theta = 15$ deg., and (c) $\Delta\theta = 5$ deg. Compare the results with the instantaneous normal acceleration.

PROB. 84

**85.** A point on the rim of a flywheel has a peripheral speed of 10 ft./sec. at an instant when this speed is increasing at the rate of 30 ft./sec. each second. If the total acceleration of the point at this condition is 50 ft./sec.², find the radius $r$ of the flywheel.                    *Ans.*   $r = 2.5$ ft.

**86.** A brake is applied to a flywheel 18 in. in diameter to bring it to rest with a constant deceleration. If the total acceleration of a point on the rim makes an angle of 1 deg. with the radial direction when the brake first begins to act, find the time $t$ required to bring the wheel to a stop from a peripheral speed of 30 ft./sec.

**87.** The rim speed of a flywheel 12 in. in diameter increases with constant acceleration from 20 ft./sec. to 40 ft./sec. during 10 rev. of the wheel. If the speed continues to increase at the same time rate, find the normal acceleration $a_n$ of a point on the rim after the wheel has turned through another 10 rev.

*Ans.*   $a_n = 5600$ ft./sec.²

**88.** A train enters a section of curved track at 60 mi./hr. and slows down with constant deceleration to 30 mi./hr. in 11 sec. while rounding the curve. An accelerometer, which is a delicate instrument for measuring acceleration, is mounted inside the train and records a horizontal acceleration of 5 ft./sec.²

when the train is 6 sec. past the beginning of the curve. Find the radius of curvature $\rho$ of the track for this position of the train.

**89.** The 30 in. diameter drum of the power winch is turning at a constant speed of 120 rev./min. while pulling the small car up the curved track. The curve has a shape defined by the parabola $y = x^2/40$ where $x$ and $y$ are in feet. Determine the acceleration $a$ of the car as it reaches an elevation 2 ft. below the top. The radius of curvature is given by $\rho = [1 + (dy/dx)^2]^{3/2}/(d^2y/dx^2)$. Neglect the dimensions of the car compared with those of the path.

*Ans.* $a = 9.38$ ft./sec.²

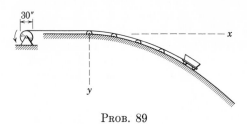

Prob. 89

**90.** A projectile is fired at an angle of 30 deg. above the horizontal with a muzzle velocity of 1500 ft./sec. Determine the radius of curvature $\rho$ of its path 10 sec. after firing. Neglect air resistance so that the weight of the projectile is the only force acting. Its acceleration is, consequently, $g$ down.

**91.** The slotted guide $A$ is moving to the right with a constant velocity. At the position shown the acceleration of the pin $P$ has a magnitude of 36 ft./sec.² Determine the velocity $v$ of $P$ along the circular slot at this position.

*Ans.* $v = 6$ ft./sec.

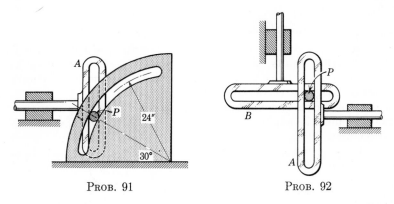

Prob. 91          Prob. 92

**92.** The pin $P$ moves along a curved path and is controlled by the motions of the slotted links $A$ and $B$. At the instant shown $A$ has a velocity of 12 ft./sec. and an acceleration of 10 ft./sec.², both to the right, while $B$ has a velocity of 16 ft./sec. and an acceleration of 5 ft./sec.², both vertically up. Find the radius of curvature $\rho$ of the path of $P$ at this position.

**93.** The rotation of the arm $OA$ is controlled by the slotted link. If the link has an acceleration of 20 ft./sec.² and a velocity of 2 ft./sec. both down at the instant when $\theta = 30$ deg., determine the corresponding angular acceleration $\alpha$ of $OA$.

         *Ans.*    $\alpha = 30.8$ rad./sec.² clockwise

**94.** The only vertical force on a rocket when flying horizontally at the top of its trajectory is its weight, and the vertical acceleration is, therefore, the acceleration of gravity at that particular altitude. Determine the radius of curvature $\rho$ of the path at the position of maximum altitude for the rocket whose trajectory is specified in the table. The altitude $h$ and horizontal coordinate $x$ are measured from the sea-level launching site and are given in terms of the time of flight. The radius of the earth is 3960 mi.

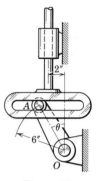

PROB. 93

| $t$ sec. | $x$ mi. | $h$ mi. | $t$ sec. | $x$ mi. | $h$ mi. |
|---|---|---|---|---|---|
| 0 | 0 | 0 | 140 | 14 | 109 |
| 20 | 0 | 2 | 160 | 26 | 116 |
| 40 | 0.5 | 7 | 180 | 45 | 117 |
| 60 | 1.5 | 15 | 200 | 69 | 114 |
| 80 | 2.5 | 30 | 220 | 90 | 111 |
| 100 | 4 | 58 | 240 | 105 | 106 |
| 120 | 7.5 | 93 | | | |

         *Ans.*    $\rho = 160$ mi. $(\pm 10\%)$

*95. A particle starts from rest at the origin and moves along the positive branch of the curve $y = 2x^{3/2}$ such that the distance $s$ in inches measured along the curve varies with the time $t$ in seconds according to $s = 2t^3$. Find the total acceleration $a$ of the particle when $t = 1$ sec. (Recall that the radius of curvature $\rho$ is given by $\rho = [1 + (dy/dx)^2]^{3/2}/(d^2y/dx^2)$.)

         *Ans.*    $a = 12.17$ in./sec.²

*96. The path of a fluid particle in the centrifugal pump with straight vanes shown is to be approximated by the spiral $r = r_0 e^{b\theta}$, where $b$ is a dimensionless constant. The angular position of both the fluid particle and the pump impeller is given by $\theta$, and the radial distance to

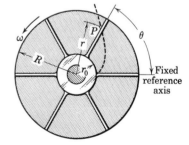

PROB. 96

the particle is specified by $r$.  If the pump turns with constant speed so that $d\theta/dt = K$, a constant, find the total acceleration of the fluid particle as it leaves the impeller by considering the acceleration components normal and tangent to the curve.  In polar coordinates the radius of curvature is

$$\rho = [r^2 + (dr/d\theta)^2]^{3/2}/[r^2 + 2\,(dr/d\theta)^2 - r\,(d^2r/d\theta^2)]$$

$$Ans.\quad a = K^2(1 + b^2)R$$

**15. Curvilinear Motion of a Particle; $r-\theta$ Components.**  Polar coordinates provide a third method for describing plane curvilinear motion.  The position of the particle at some point $A$ on its curved path, Fig. 14$a$, is specified by the coordinates $r$ and $\theta$.  During an

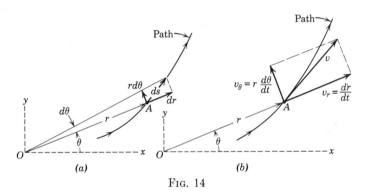

F$_{IG}$. 14

infinitesimal movement $ds$ along the path the coordinates change by $dr$ and $d\theta$, and the vector relation

$$ds = dr \nrightarrow r\,d\theta$$

may be seen from the figure.  The velocity of the particle is along the path and is obtained by dividing $ds$ by $dt$.  Thus

$$\frac{ds}{dt} = \frac{dr}{dt} \nrightarrow r\,\frac{d\theta}{dt},$$

or

$$v = v_r \nrightarrow v_\theta. \tag{19}$$

These velocity components are shown in Fig. 14$b$.

The acceleration is obtained by differentiating Eq. 19.  It is necessary to account for both the change in direction and the change in magnitude for each component of $v$ in determining its time derivative.  These changes are shown in Fig. 15$a$, where the motion of the particle from $A$ to $A'$ during time $dt$ is accompanied by the change in velocity from $v$ to $v'$.  Each of these velocity vectors is divided into its $r$- and

$\theta$-components as shown, and the changes in these components during motion are treated in the same manner as that developed in Art. 14 for the normal and tangential components of acceleration.

Consider first the change in the radial component $v_r$ of the velocity between $A$ and $A'$. The difference $dv_r$ between $v_r$ and $v_r'$ is shown in the vector sketch in Fig. 15$b$, where the scale has been increased for

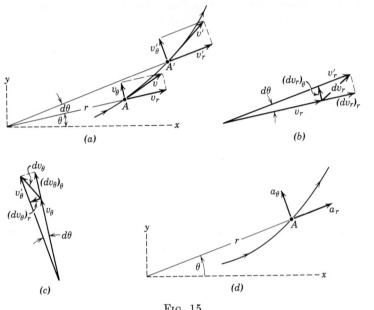

Fɪɢ. 15

clarity. This change $dv_r$ will have two components, a radial one $(dv_r)_r$ and a transverse one $(dv_r)_\theta$. The radial component is merely the increase in the magnitude of $v_r$, and the acceleration due to this change is

$$\frac{(dv_r)_r}{dt} = \frac{d|v_r|}{dt} = \frac{d^2r}{dt^2} \qquad \text{[plus } r\text{-direction]}.$$

From Fig. 15$b$ it is seen that the transverse component of the change in radial velocity may be expressed in the limit as the differential circular arc of radius $v_r$ with subtended angle $d\theta$. Hence $(dv_r)_\theta = v_r\, d\theta$, and the acceleration due to this change is

$$\frac{(dv_r)_\theta}{dt} = v_r\frac{d\theta}{dt} = \frac{dr}{dt}\frac{d\theta}{dt} \qquad \text{[plus } \theta\text{-direction]}.$$

The change $dv_\theta$ in the transverse velocity component is similarly treated and is shown in Fig. 15c.  Again it is clear from the diagram that this vector has components in both the θ- and _r_-directions.  The change in the θ-direction is the change in magnitude of $v_\theta$ or $(dv_\theta)_\theta =$

$$d\,|v_\theta| = d\left(r\,\frac{d\theta}{dt}\right).$$  The acceleration due to this change is

$$\frac{(dv_\theta)_\theta}{dt} = \frac{d\left(r\dfrac{d\theta}{dt}\right)}{dt} = r\,\frac{d^2\theta}{dt^2} + \frac{dr}{dt}\frac{d\theta}{dt} \qquad \text{[plus θ-direction].}$$

It should be noted that this portion of the acceleration is due to the change in magnitudes of both $r$ and $d\theta/dt$.

Finally the radial change $(dv_\theta)_r$ must be accounted for.  Figure 15c shows that, in the limit, $(dv_\theta)_r = v_\theta\,d\theta$.  The acceleration due to this change is then

$$\frac{(dv_\theta)_r}{dt} = v_\theta\,\frac{d\theta}{dt} = r\left(\frac{d\theta}{dt}\right)^2 \qquad \text{[minus _r_-direction].}$$

The components of acceleration just computed in each of the two directions may now be combined.  Thus the resultant _r_- and θ-components shown in Fig. 15d are

$$a_r = \frac{d^2r}{dt^2} - r\left(\frac{d\theta}{dt}\right)^2,$$

$$a_\theta = r\,\frac{d^2\theta}{dt^2} + 2\,\frac{dr}{dt}\frac{d\theta}{dt}. \tag{20}$$

The second component may be written in more compact form as

$$a_\theta = \frac{1}{r}\frac{d}{dt}\left(r^2\,\frac{d\theta}{dt}\right),$$

the equivalence of which is verified easily by differentiation.

When the radius $r$ is constant, the motion is circular, and the origin and center of curvature are coincident.  Equations 20 then reduce to the expressions obtained in Art. 14 for the case of circular motion, namely,

$$-a_r = a_n = r\left(\frac{d\theta}{dt}\right)^2 = \frac{v^2}{r},$$

$$a_\theta = a_t = r\,\frac{d^2\theta}{dt^2} = \frac{d^2s}{dt^2}.$$

Equations 20 for the acceleration components in polar coordinates may also be obtained by direct differentiation of the coordinate expressions $x = r \cos \theta$ and $y = r \sin \theta$ to get $a_x = d^2x/dt^2$ and $a_y = d^2y/dt^2$. Each of these rectangular components of acceleration may then be resolved into $r$- and $\theta$-components. Combination of the $r$-components and $\theta$-components yields $a_r$ and $a_\theta$ as given in Eqs. 20. It is recommended that the student carry out these operations. The vector approach presented in this article, however, has the distinct advantage of picturing the changes upon which the acceleration depends.

### SAMPLE PROBLEM

**97.** The slotted arm $OB$ carries a small pin $A$ of negligible diameter whose position in the slot is determined by the rotation of the arm about the fixed circular cam. If $OB$ rotates at a constant rate $d\theta/dt = K$ for a certain interval, find the total acceleration of $A$.

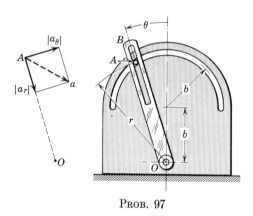

PROB. 97

*Solution.* The motion of $A$ may be expressed in polar coordinates $r$ and $\theta$. The equation of the circular cam surface relative to the pole $O$ is $r = 2b \cos \theta$. The velocity of $A$ along the arm is

$$\frac{dr}{dt} = -2b \sin \theta \frac{d\theta}{dt} = -2Kb \sin \theta.$$

The second time derivative of $r$ is only a part of the radial acceleration and is

$$\frac{d^2r}{dt^2} = -2Kb \cos \theta \frac{d\theta}{dt} = -2K^2b \cos \theta.$$

Substitution of these derivatives together with $d\theta/dt = K$ and $d^2\theta/dt^2 = 0$ into

Eqs. 20 gives

$$a_r = \frac{d^2r}{dt^2} - r\left(\frac{d\theta}{dt}\right)^2 = -4K^2b\cos\theta,$$

$$a_\theta = r\frac{d^2\theta}{dt^2} + 2\frac{dr}{dt}\frac{d\theta}{dt} = -4K^2b\sin\theta.$$

The total acceleration is

$$a = \sqrt{a_r{}^2 + a_\theta{}^2} = 4K^2b \qquad\qquad Ans.$$

and is in the direction shown.

### PROBLEMS

**98.** The arm $OB$ revolves in a horizontal plane at a constant clockwise rate of 100 rev./min. The velocity of the slider block $A$ outward along the arm has a constant magnitude of 12 in./sec. Find the acceleration $a$ of the block when it is 4 in. from $O$.   *Ans.* $a = 506$ in./sec.$^2$

**99.** The polar coordinates of a particle which moves on a plane curve are given by $r = 3t^3 + 2t$ and $\theta = 8t^2$ where $r$ is in feet, $\theta$ is in radians, and $t$ is in seconds. Determine the acceleration $a$ of the particle when $t = \frac{1}{2}$ sec.   *Ans.* $a = 120$ ft./sec.$^2$

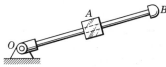

PROB. 98

**100.** A satellite $m$ moves in an elliptical orbit around the earth. There is no force on the satellite in the $\theta$-direction, so that $a_\theta = 0$. Prove Kepler's second law of planetary motion which says that the radial line $r$ sweeps through equal areas in equal times. The area $dA$ swept by the radial line during time $dt$ is shaded on the figure.

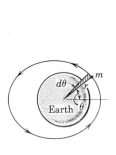

PROB. 100

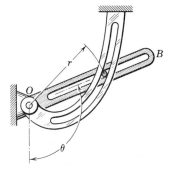

PROB. 101

**101.** The slotted arm $OB$ forces the small pin to move in the spiral guide defined by $r = k\theta$. If $OB$ rotates with a constant angular speed $d\theta/dt = K$, find the total acceleration of the pin in terms of its angular position $\theta$.

**102.** The fixed cam shown has a shape such that the center of the roller $A$ which follows the contour moves on the limaçon defined by $r = b - c \cos \theta$,

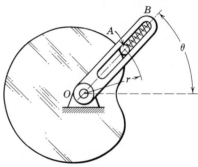

PROB. 102

where $b > c$. If the slotted arm $OB$ rotates at the angular rate $d\theta/dt = K$, a constant, determine the radial and transverse components of acceleration, $a_r$ and $a_\theta$, of the center of the roller for any value of $\theta$.

         *Ans.*    $a_r = K^2(2c \cos \theta - b)$, $a_\theta = 2K^2c \sin \theta$

**103.** If the slotted arm $OB$ in Prob. 102 remains fixed and the cam revolves at the constant angular rate of $d\theta/dt = K$, find the acceleration of the roller $A$.

**104.** By the method of this article solve for the fluid acceleration $a$ just before exit for the centrifugal pump of Prob. 96.

         *Ans.*    $a = K^2R(1 + b^2)$ at $r = R$

**105.** The tracking system for the missile shown yields the coordinates $r$ and $\theta$ in terms of the time $t$ as given in the table. Graph these data, and determine within the accuracy of the plots the velocity $v$ of the missile at its maximum altitude. Describe the procedure for obtaining the acceleration of the missile at any particular value of $t$.

| $t$ sec. | $r$ mi. | $\theta$ deg. |
|---|---|---|
| 0 | 0 | 40. |
| 10 | 6.4 | 39.7 |
| 20 | 11.4 | 38.0 |
| 25 | 13.3 | 36.6 |
| 30 | 14.8 | 34.5 |
| 35 | 15.8 | 31.2 |
| 40 | 16.3 | 26.0 |
| 45 | 16.7 | 16.8 |
| 50 | 16.8 | 0 |

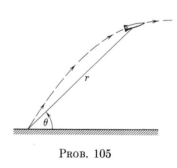

PROB. 105

         *Ans.*    $v = 950$ mi./hr.

**106.** The arm $OA$ rotates with a constant angular velocity $d\theta/dt = K$ for a certain interval of its limited motion. Determine the components of acceleration $a_r$ and $a_\theta$ for the guided pin $B$ in terms of $\theta$ by differentiating the expressions for the coordinates $r$ and $\theta$ of the pin.

*Ans.* $a_r = 2bK^2 \sec \theta \tan^2 \theta$, $a_\theta = 2bK^2 \sec \theta \tan \theta$

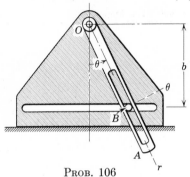

PROB. 106

*\*107.* If the arm $OB$ in Prob. 102 is revolving counterclockwise at the constant rate of 20 rev./min. and the cam is revolving clockwise at the constant rate of 40 rev./min., determine the acceleration of the center of the roller $A$ when the arm and cam are in the relative positions for which $\theta = 90$ deg. The dimensions of the curve are $b = 4$ in. and $c = 2$ in. (*Caution:* Redefine the coordinates as necessary after noting that the $\theta$ in the expression $r = b - c \cos \theta$ is not the absolute angle appearing in Eqs. 20.)

*Ans.* $a = 55.5$ in./sec.$^2$

*\*108.* The centrifugal pump with radial vanes shown with Prob. 96 rotates at the constant rate $d\theta/dt = K$. An element of the fluid being pumped will be considered here as a smooth particle $P$ which is introduced at the radius $r_0$ without radial velocity and which moves outward along the vane without friction. There is no force on the particle in the direction along the vane, so that it has zero acceleration in this direction. Under these conditions determine the equation of the path of the particle if the time $t$ is zero for $r = r_0$.

*Ans.* $r = r_0 \cosh \theta$

**16. Motion of Rigid Bodies.** The plane motion of a rigid body may be divided into several categories as represented in Fig. 16. *Translation* is defined as any motion in which every line in the body remains parallel to its original position at all times. *Rectilinear translation*, part $a$, is translation in which all points move in straight lines. *Curvilinear translation*, part $b$, is translation in which all points move on congruent curves. In curvilinear translation there is *no rotation of any line in the body.* It should be noted that in each case of translation the motion of the body is completely specified by the motion of any point in the body, since all points have the same motion.

*Rotation* about a fixed axis, part *c*, is the angular motion about the axis. It follows that all particles move in circular paths about the axis of rotation, and all lines in the body (including those that do not pass through the axis) rotate through the same angle in the same time.

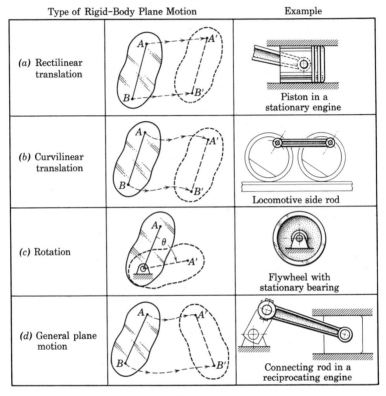

FIG. 16

*General plane motion* of a rigid body, part *d*, is a combination of translation and rotation.

In each of the examples cited all particles in the body move in parallel planes. The motion, however, is represented by its projection onto a single plane parallel to the motion called the *plane of motion*. This plane is usually considered as passing through the center of gravity of the body.

Consider now the plane motion of the body shown in Fig. 17. Lines 1 and 2 are any two lines fixed to the body in the plane of motion. Their angular positions are specified from any fixed reference line and are related by $\theta_2 = \theta_1 + \beta$ where $\beta$ is a constant angle if the body is rigid. Since $\beta$ does not change during an angular displacement of the body, two successive differentiations with time give $d\theta_2/dt = d\theta_1/dt$ and $d^2\theta_2/dt^2 = d^2\theta_1/dt^2$. Thus the two lines and hence _all lines in the body in the plane of motion have the same angular displacement in the same time and have the same angular velocity and angular acceleration at the same instant._ This conclusion does not hold for a nonrigid body if the change in $\beta$ with time is significant. In Fig. 18 is shown a finite displacement from position $A$ to position $A'$ of a rigid body having

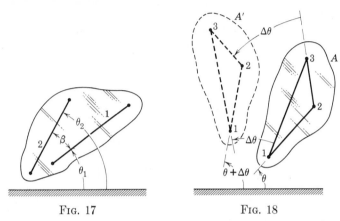

FIG. 17          FIG. 18

plane motion. Line 1–2 has an angular displacement $\Delta\theta$, and lines 2–3 and 1–3 also have the same angular displacement $\Delta\theta$. Thus the angular motion of a rigid body is completely specified by the angular motion of any line in the body in its plane of motion.

Velocity and acceleration, both linear and angular, in rigid-body motion may be determined by direct differentiation of the expressions for the linear and angular displacements. The displacement relations are determined from the geometry of the particular problem. The procedure is best illustrated by sample problems, two of which follow.

### SAMPLE PROBLEMS

**109.** A wheel of radius $r$ rolls to the left on a straight path without slipping. Determine the angular motion of the wheel in terms of the linear motion of its center.

*Solution.* The relation between the linear displacement of the center $O$ and the angular displacement of the wheel is obtained first. As the wheel rolls from position 1 to position 2 shown in the figure, the center $O$ has a displacement $s$. This distance equals the arc length $r\theta$ along the arc upon which the wheel rolls if there is no slipping.  Hence

$$s = r\theta, \qquad\qquad Ans.$$

and the first time derivative gives

$$v = r\omega \qquad\qquad Ans.$$

for the velocity of the center $O$ in terms of the rolling radius $r$ and the angular velocity $\omega$ of the wheel.  One more differentiation with time yields

$$a = r\alpha \qquad\qquad Ans.$$

which expresses the acceleration of $O$ in terms of the angular acceleration $\alpha$ of the wheel.  It is noted that these relations are identical with Eqs. 12.

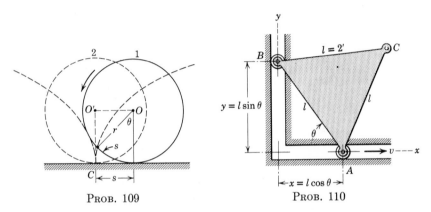

PROB. 109          PROB. 110

**110.** The equilateral triangular plate is guided by the corner rollers which move at right angles to each other.  If roller $A$ is given a constant velocity of 4 ft./sec. to the right during a short interval of its motion, determine the angular velocity and acceleration of the edge $BC$ and the linear velocity and acceleration of roller $B$ at the instant when $\theta = 30$ deg.

*Solution.*  The velocity of $A$ is the time rate of change of $x$, or

$$v_A = \frac{dx}{dt} = \frac{d}{dt}(l \cos \theta) = -l \sin \theta \frac{d\theta}{dt}.$$

The angular velocity of edge $BC$ is the same as that of $AB$ and is

$$\omega_{BC} = \omega_{AB} = \frac{d\theta}{dt} = -\frac{v_A}{l} \csc \theta,$$

and for $\theta = 30$ deg. and $l = 2$ ft.,

$$\omega_{BC} = -\tfrac{4}{2} \times 2 = -4 \text{ rad./sec.} \qquad\qquad Ans.$$

The minus sign indicates that the angular velocity is counterclockwise since $\theta$ is measured clockwise.

The angular acceleration is obtained by differentiation of $\omega_{BC}$. Thus

$$\alpha_{BC} = \alpha_{AB} = \frac{d^2\theta}{dt^2} = -\frac{v_A}{l}\frac{d}{dt}\csc\theta = +\frac{v_A}{l}\operatorname{ctn}\theta\csc\theta\frac{d\theta}{dt} = -\frac{v_A{}^2}{l^2}\operatorname{ctn}\theta\csc^2\theta.$$

For $\theta = 30$ deg. and $l = 2$ ft. this becomes

$$\alpha_{BC} = -\frac{4^2}{2^2}\sqrt{3}\times 2^2 = -27.7 \text{ rad./sec.}^2 \qquad Ans.$$

Again the negative sign indicates that $\alpha_{BC}$ is counterclockwise since $\theta$ and its derivatives are positive in a clockwise sense.

The linear motion of $B$ is obtained by differentiation of the dimension $y$. Thus

$$v_B = \frac{dy}{dt} = \frac{d}{dt}(l\sin\theta) = l\cos\theta\frac{d\theta}{dt} = -v_A\operatorname{ctn}\theta,$$

and for $\theta = 30$ deg. and $l = 2$ ft.,

$$v_B = -4\times\sqrt{3} = -6.93 \text{ ft./sec.} \qquad Ans.$$

The minus sign shows that the velocity of $B$ is actually down in the sense opposite to that for positive measurement of $y$ and its derivatives.

By differentiation the acceleration of $B$ is

$$a_B = \frac{d^2y}{dt^2} = -v_A\frac{d}{dt}\operatorname{ctn}\theta = +v_A\csc^2\theta\frac{d\theta}{dt} = -\frac{v_A{}^2}{l}\csc^3\theta.$$

For $\theta = 30$ deg. and $l = 2$ ft. this becomes

$$a_B = -\frac{4^2}{2}\times 2^3 = -64 \text{ ft./sec.}^2 \qquad Ans.$$

As before, the minus sign indicates that the acceleration is opposite to the positive direction for the measurement of $y$ and is therefore down.

### PROBLEMS

**111.** If $A$ has an upward displacement, velocity, or acceleration, $B$ has a corresponding downward motion. What is the ratio $n$ of the motion of $B$ to that of $A$?

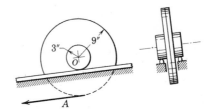

PROB. 111    PROB. 112

**112.** The wheel rolls up the incline on its hubs without slipping as the cable $A$ is pulled down the incline. If the cable has a velocity of 4 ft./sec. and an acceleration of 6 ft./sec.$^2$ down the incline at the instant considered, determine the velocity $v$ and acceleration $a$ of the center $O$ of the wheel.

              *Ans.*   $v_O = 2$ ft./sec., $a_O = 3$ ft./sec.$^2$ both up the incline

**113.** The spool rolls up the inner cable $A$ as the outer cable $B$ is pulled down. At the instant considered $B$ has a downward velocity of 10 ft./sec. which is decreasing at the rate of 4 ft./sec. each second. Determine the velocity $v$ and acceleration $a$ of the center $O$ at this instant.

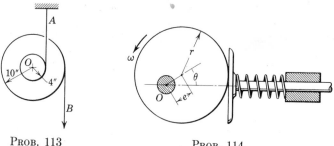

Prob. 113                        Prob. 114

**114.** The circular disk is mounted eccentrically and turns about the shaft at $O$ with a constant angular velocity $\omega$. Find the acceleration $a$, measured positive to the right, of the plunger for any angle $\theta$ of the circular cam.   *Ans.*   $a = -e\omega^2 \cos\theta$

**115.** The two slotted links are caused to rotate about their fixed bearings by the movement of the connecting pin in the vertical slot. If the pin has a constant upward velocity $v$, find the angular acceleration $\alpha$ of the links in terms of $\theta$.

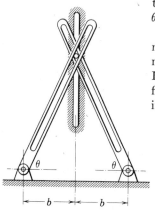

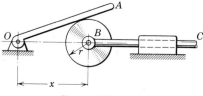

Prob. 115                       Prob. 116

**116.** The angular motion of the link $OA$ is produced by the horizontal movement of the link $BC$ in its guide. If $BC$ has a velocity $v$ to the left, determine the angular velocity $\omega$ of $OA$ in terms of the distance $x$.

          *Ans.*   $\omega = \dfrac{vr}{x\sqrt{x^2 - r^2}}$

**117.** The wheel rolls to the left without slipping, and its center $O$ has a constant velocity $v_O$. Determine the velocity $v$ and acceleration $a$ of point $A$ on the rim of the

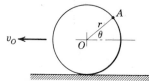

Prob. 117

wheel in terms of the angle $\theta$ measured counterclockwise from the horizontal.

**118.** Show that the expressions $v = r\omega$ and $a_t = r\alpha$ hold for the motion of the center $O$ of the wheel which rolls on the circular arc, where $\omega$ and $\alpha$ are the absolute angular velocity and acceleration, respectively, of the wheel.

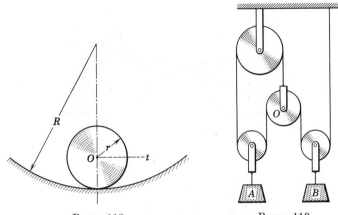

PROB. 118                          PROB. 119

**119.** If weight $A$ has an upward displacement $s_1$ and weight $B$ has a simultaneous downward displacement $s_2$, determine the corresponding displacement $s$ of the center $O$ of the middle pulley. Assume $s_1 > s_2$.

*Ans.* $s = 2(s_1 - s_2)$ up

**120.** A device to produce oscillation of the shaft at $A$ is shown in the figure. The eccentric circular cam turns with a constant clockwise angular velocity $\omega_0$.

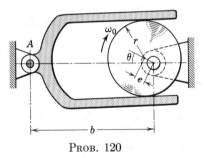

PROB. 120

Determine the angular velocity $\omega$ of the fork in terms of the cam angle $\theta$.

$$Ans. \quad \omega = \frac{b \cos \theta - e}{b^2 - 2be \cos \theta + e^2} e\omega_0$$

**\*121.** Determine the velocity $v$, measured positive to the right, of the piston $A$ in the reciprocating engine in terms of $r$, $l$, and $\theta$ if the engine speed is $\omega = d\theta/dt$.

$$Ans. \quad v = r\omega \left[ \sin \theta + \frac{r \sin 2\theta}{2l\sqrt{1 - \left(\frac{r}{l}\sin\theta\right)^2}} \right]$$

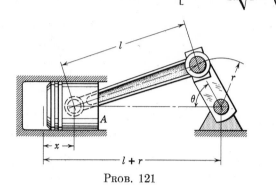

PROB. 121

## PART 2. RELATIVE MOTION

**17. Introduction.** In many problems the analysis of motion is simplified by using measurements which are made with respect to a moving coordinate system. These measurements together with the observed motion of the moving coordinate system permit the determination of the absolute motion of the body in question. This approach is known as a *relative-motion* analysis.

The motion of the moving coordinate system is specified with respect to a fixed coordinate system. Strictly speaking this fixed system in Newtonian mechanics is the primary inertial system which is assumed to have no motion in space. However, for most engineering problems a set of axes attached to the surface of the earth is taken as the fixed system, and measurements referred to this system are said to be "absolute." For problems such as rocket and earth-satellite flight, a set of axes with origin at the center of the earth is used for the fixed system.

The moving coordinate system in relative-motion analysis may either be translating or rotating, or it may have a combination of the two motions. In the following five articles attention is directed to the analysis of motion relative to a translating (nonrotating) coordinate system. The last article in the chapter is devoted to a discussion of motion relative to axes which have rotation.

Relative-motion analysis is particularly useful in the determination of many types of machine motions and lends itself readily to a graphical solution. The graphical approach is not only useful for obtaining numerical results, but it also aids greatly in visualizing the various motions and their component relationships.

**18. Relative Linear Displacement.** Consider the motions of any two points in a given plane. These points need not be connected, as would be the case if they were attached to a rigid body. In Fig. 19 the two points occupy positions $A$ and $B$ at time $t$. The location of the points measured in the fixed $x$–$y$ system is given by their position vectors $s_A$ and $s_B$. The vector position of point $A$ as measured from a nonrotating coordinate system $x_0$–$y_0$ attached to and moving with $B$ is the vector $s_{A/B}$ which is read "the position vector of $A$ with respect to $B$." The triangle $OBA$ is expressed by the vector equation

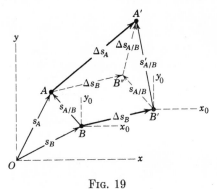

Fɪɢ. 19

$$s_A = s_B \nrightarrow s_{A/B}.$$

This equation states that the vector position of $A$ equals the vector position of $B$ plus (vectorially) the position of $A$ relative to $B$.

During time $\Delta t$ point $A$ undergoes a vector displacement $\Delta s_A$ in moving to $A'$, and $B$ has a displacement $\Delta s_B$ in moving to $B'$. The position of $A'$ with respect to the moving $x_0$–$y_0$ system is now $s'_{A/B}$. The change in the relative positions, $s'_{A/B} \rightarrow s_{A/B}$, is the relative displacement of $A$ with respect to $B$, or $\Delta s_{A/B}$. This vector change is seen from triangle $B'B''A'$. From triangle $AB''A'$ the relation between the displacements becomes

$$\Delta s_A = \Delta s_B \nrightarrow \Delta s_{A/B}. \tag{21}$$

This vector relation could have been written down immediately from the vector position equation in the same way that it may be said for the equality of two quantities $u = v$ that $\Delta u = \Delta v$. Equation 21 expresses the fact that the displacement of point $A$ equals the displacement of point $B$ plus (vectorially) the displacement of $A$ with respect to $B$. It is not difficult to imagine oneself attached to the moving coordinate system and observing the apparent or relative displacement $\Delta s_{A/B}$ of point $A$.

In the foregoing analysis the moving system was arbitrarily attached to point $B$. It may be attached to $A$ equally well in which case the motion of $B$ would be observed from a station moving with $A$. It is left to the student to construct the appropriate diagram and to show that the resulting relative displacement of $B$ with respect to $A$ is equal and opposite to the displacement of $A$ with respect to $B$. Thus $\Delta s_{A/B} = -\Delta s_{B/A}$, and the relative displacement equation may be written

$$\Delta s_B = \Delta s_A \;+\!\!\!\!+\; \Delta s_{B/A}.$$

When the two points are fixed to a *rigid* body having plane motion, an additional requirement holds. In Fig. 20$a$ the rigid body undergoes

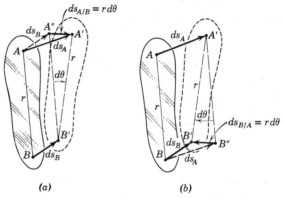

(a)                           (b)

Fig. 20

an infinitesimal movement from the full to the dotted position. Any two points on the body, such as $A$ and $B$, are a *fixed distance* $r$ apart and move to the new positions $A'$ and $B'$. The line $AB$ has a movement which may be considered as composed of two parts, first, a *translation* $ds_B$ to the position $B'A''$, and, second, a *rotation* $d\theta$ about $B'$ to the final position. The differential triangle $AA'A''$ is expressed by Eq. 21 in differential form. Thus

$$ds_A = ds_B \;+\!\!\!\!+\; ds_{A/B} \quad \text{where } ds_{A/B} = r\, d\theta.$$

The term $r\, d\theta$ is the displacement of $A$ relative to $B$ and is the arc movement due to the rotation about $B$. Consequently this relative component is *perpendicular* to $AB$.

The motion of line $AB$ may be considered equally well as the translation $ds_A$ plus a rotation $d\theta$ about $A$ as shown in Fig. 20$b$. In this case the relation

$$ds_B = ds_A \;+\!\!\!\!+\; ds_{B/A} \quad \text{where } ds_{B/A} = r\, d\theta$$

holds. The vector $ds_{B/A}$ is equal and opposite to $ds_{A/B}$, but both rotations are, of course, in the same clockwise sense.

It is important to recognize clearly the two components of plane motion of a rigid body, translation and rotation. It is necessary to see that the term $ds_{A/B}$ in the relative displacement equation is determined by considering point $B$ to be fixed and measuring the movement of $A$ due to the rotation about $B$.

**19. Relative Linear Velocity.** If the relative vector displacement relation, Eq. 21, is divided by the time interval $\Delta t$ during the displacement and if $\Delta t$ is allowed to approach zero, there results the relative velocity equation

$$v_A = v_B \mathbin{+\mkern-10mu+} v_{A/B}. \tag{22}$$

In words this equation states that the velocity of point $A$ equals the velocity of point $B$ plus (vectorially) the velocity of $A$ measured relative to $B$. It should be emphasized that this relative velocity $v_{A/B}$ is the measurement from a set of nonrotating axes which has the same velocity as does $B$. The directions of $v_A$ and $v_B$ coincide with the directions of the corresponding displacement increments $ds_A$ and $ds_B$ and are, consequently, tangent to the respective paths of the points. It is noted that Eq. 22 may be obtained by direct differentiation of the vector position relation $s_A = s_B \mathbin{+\mkern-10mu+} s_{A/B}$.

When the two points $A$ and $B$ are on a rigid body having general plane motion, the relative velocity term becomes

$$v_{A/B} = \frac{ds_{A/B}}{dt} = r\frac{d\theta}{dt} = r\omega. \tag{23}$$

It should be observed in this relation that the *relative* linear velocity $v_{A/B}$ is determined by the *absolute* angular velocity $\omega$. This relative velocity is the velocity which would be measured from a nonrotating station attached to point $B$, and, consequently, only the rotation of $A$ about $B$ is observed as though $B$ were fixed. The combination of translational velocity and relative rotational velocity is illustrated in Fig. 21. The vector representation of Eq. 22 for this motion is shown at the right side of the figure. It is necessary to recognize that the relative velocity term $v_{A/B}$ is *perpendicular* to the line $AB$. This is *always the case for a rigid body* where the length of the line does not change with time.

The velocity relations shown in Fig. 21 are based on rotation about $B$. The same results are achieved by considering the relative velocity of $B$ due to rotation about $A$. In this event the equation is

$$v_B = v_A \nrightarrow v_{B/A}.$$

The reader should draw the figure corresponding to that in Fig. 21 and verify that $v_{B/A} = -v_{A/B}$ and that the direction of the angular velocity is the same for either reference point.

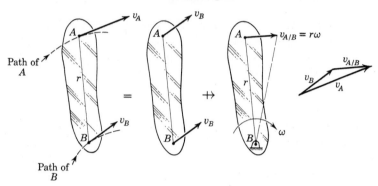

(Plane motion)   =   (Translation)   $\nrightarrow$   (Rotation)

Fig. 21

Equation 22 is a vector equation which is equivalent to the two scalar equations

$$(v_A)_x = (v_B)_x + (v_{A/B})_x,$$

$$(v_A)_y = (v_B)_y + (v_{A/B})_y.$$

Thus there are these six components to the vector equation with the three terms. The six components may also be considered as the magnitude and direction of each of the three vector terms in the vector equation. It becomes apparent that a single vector equation in two dimensions is sufficient for the solution of *two* unknown scalar quantities.

There are two general types of problems for which Eq. 22 may be applied. The first deals with the relative velocity of two points on the same rigid body and hence a fixed distance apart. The relative velocity is always perpendicular to the line joining the two points as shown in Fig. 21. In the second class of problems the points are not on the same rigid body, and the direction of their relative velocity is determined by other considerations such as the constraints which may guide the separate motions of the points. Both types of problems are illustrated in the sample problems which follow.

## SAMPLE PROBLEMS

**122.** A wheel of radius $r$ is rolling to the left on the straight path without slipping. If the velocity of the center $O$ is $v_O$ at the instant considered, determine the velocity of any point in the wheel.

*Solution.* The velocity of any point such as $A$ will be determined. Since the center $O$ is a point whose velocity is known, the velocity of $A$ will be referred to $O$ by the equation

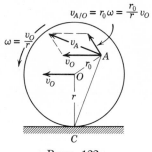

PROB. 122

$$v_A = v_O \mathbin{+\!\!\!\!+} v_{A/O}.$$

From Sample Prob. 109 the angular velocity of the wheel is $\omega = v_O/r$ since there is no slipping. The velocity of $A$ with respect to $O$ depends on the constant distance $r_0$ between the two points and the angular velocity of the line $AO$. This angular velocity is the same as the angular velocity of *every* line in the wheel in its plane of motion and is $\omega = v_O/r$. Thus by Eq. 23

$$v_{A/O} = r_0\omega = \frac{r_0}{r}v_O.$$

The direction of this term is perpendicular to the line $AO$ and is up and to the left as shown, since the rotation with respect to $O$ is counterclockwise. The vector addition of $v_O$ and $v_{A/O}$ is shown on the sketch and gives the velocity of $A$ in both magnitude and direction.

A second method for determining the velocity of $A$ is important to know. The point on the rim of the wheel in contact with the ground is $C$, and its path describes a cycloid, shown by the dotted lines in the figure for Sample Prob. 109. In the position shown $C$ has zero velocity, so that the use of this point for reference results in

$$v_A = v_{A/C}.$$

Since the relative velocity of two points on a rigid body is normal to the line joining the points, the velocity $v_A$ is normal to $AC$. Also the magnitude of the velocity of $A$ is

$$v_A = v_{A/C} = \overline{AC}\omega_{AC} = \overline{AC}\omega = \frac{\overline{AC}}{r}v.$$

The magnitude and direction of the velocity of any point on the wheel may be determined easily by using $C$ as the reference point. The magnitude of this velocity will vary linearly with the distance of the point from $C$. Instantaneously the wheel is pivoted about $C$, and the direction and magnitude of the velocities of all points may be determined as though the wheel were rotating about $C$ as a momentary fixed point.

**123.** The rotating slotted arm $OC$ causes the pivoted slider blocks to move in both slots. Determine the velocity of the pin $A$ at the instant shown for which $OC$ has a counterclockwise angular velocity of 4 rad./sec.

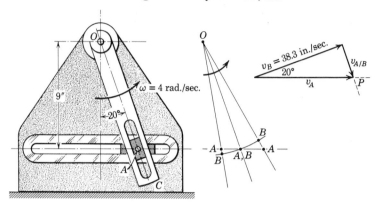

PROB. 123

*Solution.* A point $B$ considered to be on the arm $OC$ and coincident with $A$ for the position shown is chosen as a reference point for determining the velocity of $A$. The relative velocity equation is

$$v_A = v_B \nrightarrow v_{A/B}.$$

In this case, contrary to the preceding sample problem, the two points selected are *not* attached to the same rigid body. The velocity of $B$ is easily computed and is

$[v = r\omega]$                  $v_B = \dfrac{9}{\cos 20°} \times 4 = 38.3$ in./sec.

in a direction perpendicular to $OC$. The direction of the velocity of $A$ with respect to $B$ is along the arm $OC$. This direction may be seen from the diagram at the right side of the figure, where the positions of $A$ and $B$ are shown an instant before and an instant after coincidence. From a vantage point attached to $B$ it is seen that, as the arm $OC$ turns counterclockwise, point $A$ approaches $B$ from a direction along the arm and moves away from $B$ radially outward along the slot in $OC$. Thus $v_{A/B}$ is a vector parallel to $OC$ with a sense from $O$ to $C$.

At this point it should be noted that only two quantities remain unknown in the relative velocity equation, namely, the magnitude of $v_A$ and the magnitude of $v_{A/B}$. The velocity $v_B$ is completely known, and the direction of $v_A$ is, of course, along the horizontal slot. Thus the solution can now be made. The vector $v_B$ is laid off to scale as shown in the diagram, and the directions of $v_{A/B}$ and $v_A$ are drawn through the ends of $v_B$. The intersection occurs at point $P$, and the unknown magnitudes may be scaled from the figure. In the case of such a simple figure, the vector diagram may be used to determine the algebraic relations which govern the solution. Thus,

$$v_A = \frac{v_B}{\cos 20°} = \frac{38.3}{0.940} = 40.8 \text{ in./sec.}$$         *Ans.*

**124.** Determine the velocity of the piston and the angular velocity of the connecting rod of the reciprocating engine shown for the conditions of $\theta = 60$ deg., $r = 5$ in., $l = 14$ in., and for a clockwise crank speed of 1500 rev./min.

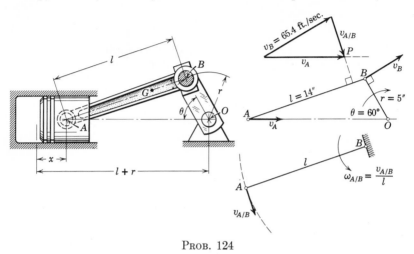

PROB. 124

*Solution.* Points $A$, $B$, and $O$ are first located in their proper positions for the given values as shown in the diagram to the right of the engine. The velocity of $B$ is easily found, so that $B$ is used as the reference point for determining the velocity of $A$. Thus

$$v_A = v_B \nrightarrow v_{A/B}.$$

The crank-pin velocity $v_B$ is

$[v = r\omega]$         $$v_B = \frac{5}{12} \times \frac{1500 \times 2\pi}{60} = 65.4 \text{ ft./sec.}$$

and is perpendicular to the crank $BO$ as shown. The direction of $v_A$ is, of course, along the cylinder axis, and the direction of $v_{A/B}$ must be perpendicular to the line $AB$, as explained in the present article for the case of two points on a rigid body. Thus the magnitudes of $v_A$ and $v_{A/B}$ are the only remaining unknowns, and the vector equation can therefore be solved for these two quantities.

The vector $v_B$ is first drawn to scale as shown. Next a line with the direction of $v_{A/B}$ is drawn through the head of $v_B$. This line is perpendicular to the rod $AB$. Finally, the known direction of $v_A$ is established through the tail of $v_B$, and the intersection $P$ gives the solution of the equation. Vectors $v_A$ and

$v_{A/B}$ are labeled with the proper sense such that $v_A$ equals the vector sum of $v_B$ and $v_{A/B}$. Their magnitudes are scaled off the diagram and are

$$v_{A/B} = 34.4 \text{ ft./sec.}, \qquad v_A = 67.3 \text{ ft./sec.} \qquad Ans.$$

The angular velocity of $AB$ is due to the rotation of $A$ about $B$ (or $B$ about $A$). Thus from a station on $B$ ($B$ considered as fixed) $A$ appears to rotate around $B$ with the tangential velocity $v_{A/B}$ as shown in the bottom view in the figure. Therefore the absolute angular velocity of the rod is

$$\left[ \omega = \frac{v}{r} \right] \quad \omega_{AB} = \frac{v_{A/B}}{l} = \frac{34.4}{14/12} = 29.5 \text{ rad./sec., counterclockwise.} \qquad Ans.$$

The problem may also be analyzed by considering the motion of $B$ relative to $A$. The student should sketch the solution by this procedure.

If an algebraic solution is desired, the trigonometry of the velocity triangle may be used to indicate the necessary relations. Thus the law of sines could be used to solve for $v_A$ or $v_{A/B}$ provided the angles of the velocity triangle were first obtained. The calculation of these angles, however, usually involves more work than that accompanying a graphical solution from which satisfactory accuracy can be obtained.

## PROBLEMS

125. If $v_A$ and $v_B$ are the instantaneous velocities of the respective ends of the rigid link, show that the angular velocity of the link is given by the expression $(v_A \sin \theta - v_B \sin \beta)/l$ and that $v_A \cos \theta = v_B \cos \beta$.

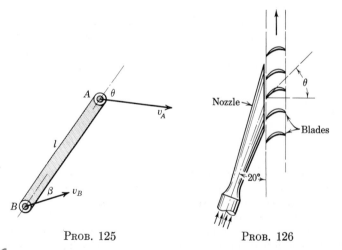

PROB. 125          PROB. 126

126. In the design of the blades for an impulse turbine it is essential that there be a minimum of turbulence when the operating fluid hits the blade. This problem is met by designing the blade entrance angle $\theta$ so that the fluid

from the nozzle enters at this angle relative to the blade.   Find the proper angle $\theta$ for a turbine designed to operate with a peripheral blade speed of 500 ft./sec., a nozzle angle of 20 deg., and a fluid velocity of 1000 ft./sec. at the nozzle exit.                              *Ans.*   $\theta = 52° 7'$

**127.** The motion of the slider $B$ is controlled by the rotation of the link $OA$ about $O$.   If the angular velocity of $OA$ is 2 rad./sec. clockwise when $x = 4$ in., determine the corresponding angular velocity $\omega_{AB}$ of link $AB$ and the velocity $v_B$ of $B$.              *Ans.*   $v_B = 12.4$ in./sec., $\omega_{AB} = 0.97$ rad./sec. clockwise

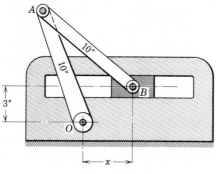

PROB. 127

**128.** The destroyer moves at 35 knots (1 knot = 1.152 mi./hr.) and fires a rocket at an angle which trails the line of sight to the target by the angle $\alpha$. The launching velocity is 300 ft./sec. relative to the ship and has an angle of elevation of 45 deg.   If the missile continues to move in the same vertical plane as that determined by its absolute velocity at launching, determine $\alpha$ for $\theta = 60$ deg.                              *Ans.*   $\alpha = 13° 57'$

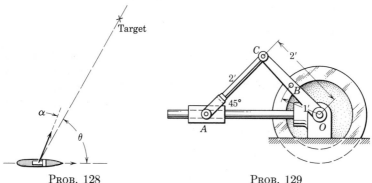

PROB. 128                              PROB. 129

**129.** The slider $A$ moves back and forth along the fixed rod because of an oscillation of the wheel.   Determine the angular velocity of the wheel and attached arm $OB$ if the slider $A$ has a velocity of 20 ft./sec. to the left in the position shown.

**130.** A passenger on a ship traveling north at 10 knots notices that the wind appears to come from the west. The ship increases its speed to 20 knots, and the wind appears to come from the northwest. Find the magnitude and direction of the actual wind velocity $v_W$. *Ans.* $v_W = 10\sqrt{2}$ knots from southwest

**131.** The wheel rolls on the bar without slipping. If the bar has a velocity of 4 ft./sec. to the right and the wheel has a counterclockwise angular velocity of 0.5 rad./sec., determine the velocity $v_O$ of the center $O$ of the wheel.

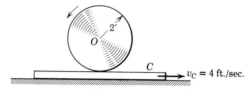

PROB. 131

**132.** The drum $D$ rotates clockwise with a velocity of 20 rev./min. and winds up the cable which is also wrapped around the disk. Determine the velocities of points $O$ and $A$ on the integral disk and gear unit for the position shown.
$Ans.$   $v_O = 0.699$ ft./sec., $v_A = 1.408$ ft./sec.

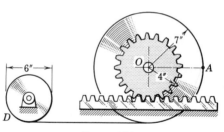

PROB. 132

**133.** The bar is guided by its two pins $A$ and $B$ which move in the fixed guides. If $A$ has a velocity of 30 ft./sec. to the right in the position shown, determine the corresponding velocity $v_C$ of end $C$ at this same instant.
$Ans.$   $v_C = 108$ ft./sec.

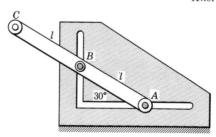

PROB. 133

**134.** Determine the velocity of $C$ for the position of the linkage shown. Link $OA$ is revolving clockwise with a velocity of 15 rad./sec.

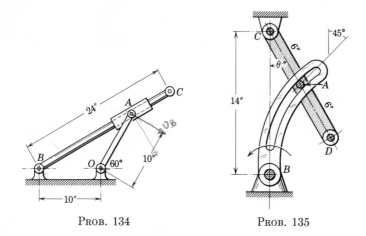

PROB. 134          PROB. 135

**135.** At the instant represented the slotted arm is revolving counterclockwise about $B$ with an angular velocity of 2 rad./sec. The pin $A$ is attached to arm $CD$. Determine the velocity of point $D$ at the instant represented when $\theta = 30$ deg.          *Ans.* $v_D = 129$ in./sec.

**136.** Pin $A$ of the link $OA$ slides freely in the slot of the circular disk. If the rod has a velocity of 0.5 ft./sec. to the right at the instant shown when the slot is in a 45 deg. position, determine the angular velocity $\omega$ of the wheel at this position. The disk rolls without slipping.

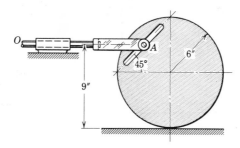

PROB. 136

**137.** Determine the angular velocity $\omega$ of the telescoping link $AB$ at the instant represented. The angular velocity of each of the driving links is indicated on the figure.          *Ans.* $\omega = 1.08$ rad./sec. counterclockwise

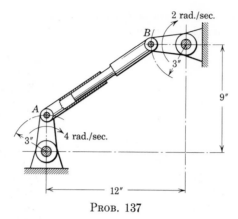

PROB. 137

**138.** The gear is rolling on the rack with a velocity of 10 rad./sec. counterclockwise at the instant represented when $AB$ is vertical. Determine the angular velocity of $AB$.

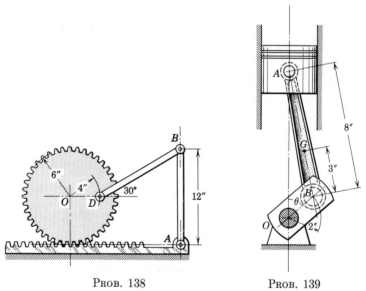

PROB. 138                           PROB. 139

**139.** The piston, connecting rod, and crankshaft of an automobile engine are shown in the figure. Determine the velocity $v_A$ of the piston and the angular velocity $\omega_{AB}$ of the connecting rod for a clockwise engine speed of 2700 rev./min. and a crank angle of $\theta = 30$ deg.

    *Ans.* $v_A = 28.7$ ft./sec., $\omega_{AB} = 61.7$ rad./sec. counterclockwise

**140.** Determine the velocity $v_A$ of the piston for the engine described in Prob. 139 when $OB$ and $OA$ are perpendicular. For this condition also determine the velocity of the center of gravity $G$ of the connecting rod.

   Ans.  $v_A = 48.6$ ft./sec., $v_G = 47.3$ ft./sec.

**141.** Work Prob. 139 for $\theta = 240$ deg., and also find the velocity of a point $M$ midway between $A$ and $B$.

**142.** The wheel shown is rolling counterclockwise and slipping at the same time. The center has a velocity of 10 ft./sec. to the left, and point $A$ has a total velocity of 20 ft./sec. in the position indicated. Determine the angular velocity $\omega$ of the wheel.    Ans.  $\omega = 8.68$ rad./sec.

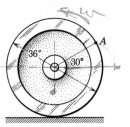

PROB. 142

**143.** Determine the velocity of the upper end $C$ of the oscillating arm of the quick-return mechanism for the position shown if the driving pinion is turning clockwise at 200 rev./min.

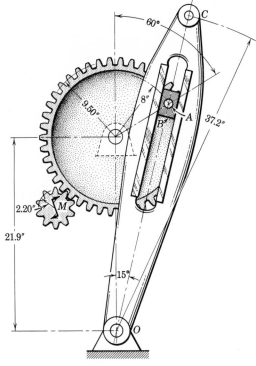

PROB. 143

**144.** The curved arm $OA$ is given an oscillatory motion through the action of the link $BC$ which is attached to the crank $CD$. If $CD$ revolves clockwise with a constant angular velocity of 120 rev./min., determine the velocity $v_A$ of point *A* as it reaches the position for which $\theta = 45$ deg.   Also find the angular velocity $\omega_{BC}$ of link *BC* at this instant.

Ans.   $v_A = 50.2$ in./sec., $\omega_{BC} = 1.11$ rad./sec. clockwise

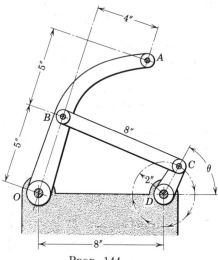

PROB. 144

**145.** In the linkage shown pin *A* has an upward velocity of 20 ft./sec. and pin *B* has a downward velocity of 30 ft./sec.   At the instant when $x = 6$ in. determine the velocity $v_C$ of point *C*.                Ans.   $v_C = 20$ ft./sec.

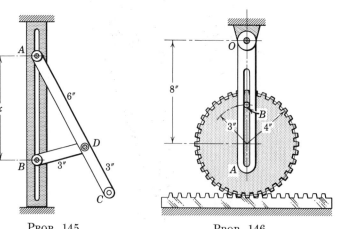

PROB. 145                      PROB. 146

**146.** The slotted arm *OA* oscillates about *O* and causes the gear to roll back and forth on the rack through the action of the pin *B* of the gear in the slot. If the arm has a clockwise angular velocity of 0.5 rad./sec. at the instant that the center of the gear has moved a distance of 2 in. to the left of the neutral position shown, determine the corresponding velocity $v$ of the center of the gear.                                                    *Ans.* $v = 2.65$ in./sec.

**\*147.** At the instant shown the distance $x$ between blocks $B$ and $C$ is decreasing at the rate of 10 ft./sec. Determine the instantaneous velocity of block $C$.                                      *Ans.* $v_C = 25.1$ ft./sec. to the left

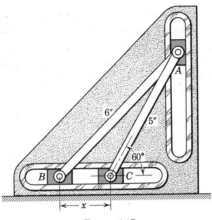

PROB. 147

**20. Instantaneous Center of Zero Velocity.** In Art. 19 the velocity of a point on a body having plane motion was determined by considering the motion in terms of a velocity due to the translation of any convenient reference point and a relative velocity due to rotation about the reference point. In the present article the problem will be solved by considering the body to be in pure rotation at any instant about a certain axis, normal to the plane of motion, which is momentarily at rest. This axis is called the *instantaneous axis* of zero velocity, and the intersection of this axis with the plane of motion is known as the *instantaneous center* of zero velocity.

The existence of the instantaneous center is easily shown. For the body in Fig. 22a let it be assumed that the directions of the velocities of any two points $A$ and $B$ are known and are not parallel. If there is a point about which $A$ has absolute circular motion at the instant considered, this point must lie on the normal to $v_A$ through $A$. Similar reasoning applies to $B$, and the intersection $C$ of these perpendiculars fulfills the requirement for an absolute center of rotation *at the instant considered*. Point $C$ is the instantaneous center and may lie on or off the body. The instantaneous center is not a fixed point in the body or body extended. Nor is it a fixed point in the plane.

If the magnitude of the velocity of one of the points, say, $v_A$, is also known, the angular velocity $\omega$ of the body and the linear velocity of every point in the body are easily obtained. Thus the angular velocity of the body, Fig. 22a, is

$$\omega = \frac{v_A}{r_A},$$

which is also the angular velocity of *every* line in the body. Therefore the velocity of $B$ is $v_B = r_B\omega = (r_B/r_A)v_A$. Once the instantaneous center is located, the direction of the instantaneous velocity of every point in the body is readily found since it is perpendicular to the radial line joining the point in question with $C$.

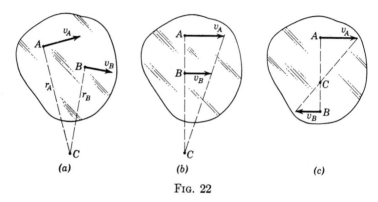

(a)                  (b)                  (c)

FIG. 22

If the velocities of two points in a body having plane motion are parallel, Fig. 22b or c, the line joining the points is perpendicular to the direction of the velocities, and the instantaneous center $C$ is located by direct proportion as shown.

In general a new instantaneous center $C$ will exist for each new position of the body during its motion. The locus of these centers in space is known as the *space centrode,* and the locus on the body (or body extended) is known as the *body centrode.* The absolute velocity of the point attached to the body which becomes the instantaneous center at a certain instant is zero at this instant, but its acceleration is *not* zero. Thus the instantaneous center of zero velocity, considered as a point attached to the body, cannot be used as an instantaneous center of zero acceleration in a manner analogous to its use for finding velocity.

*look for proportiondity*

### SAMPLE PROBLEM

**148.** Arm $OB$ of the linkage shown has a counterclockwise angular velocity of 10 rad./sec. in the position shown. Determine the velocity of $A$, the velocity of $D$, and the angular velocity of the link $AB$ at this instant.

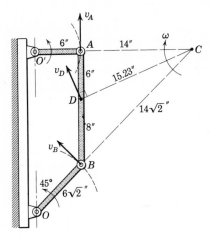

PROB. 148

*Solution.* The directions of the velocities of $A$ and $B$ are tangent to their circular paths about the fixed centers $O'$ and $O$ as shown. The intersection of the two perpendiculars to the velocities from $A$ and $B$ locates the instantaneous center $C$ for the link $AB$. The distances $AC$, $BC$, and $DC$, shown on the diagram, are scaled off the drawing or are computed as desired. The angular velocity of $BC$, which is equal to the angular velocity of $AC$, $DC$, and $AB$, is

$$\left[ \omega = \frac{v}{r} \right] \quad \omega = \frac{v_B}{\overline{BC}} = \frac{\overline{OB}\omega_{OB}}{\overline{BC}} = \frac{6\sqrt{2}}{14\sqrt{2}} \times 10 = 4.29 \text{ rad./sec. clockwise.}$$

Thus the velocities of $A$ and $D$ are

$$[v = r\omega] \qquad v_A = \tfrac{14}{12} \times 4.29 = 5.00 \text{ ft./sec.,} \qquad\qquad Ans.$$

$$v_D = \frac{15.23}{12} \times 4.29 = 5.44 \text{ ft./sec.} \qquad\qquad Ans.$$

in the directions shown.

### PROBLEMS

Solve the following problems by the method of the instantaneous center of zero velocity.

**149.** The instantaneous center of zero velocity for the link $AB$ is at $C$. If the link has a clockwise angular velocity of 4 rad./sec. in the position shown, determine the velocity of $B$ with respect to $A$.

*Ans.* $v_{B/A} = 12$ ft./sec. to the left

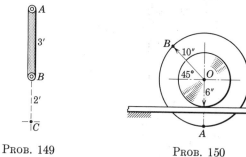

PROB. 149                     PROB. 150

**150.** The wheel rolls on its hub without slipping. If the angular velocity of the wheel is 3 rev./min. clockwise, determine the velocities of points $A$ and $B$ at the instant shown.      *Ans.* $v_A = 1.26$ in./sec., $v_B = 4.67$ in./sec.

**151.** Prob. 131.

**152.** Prob. 139.

**153.** Work Prob. 139 for $\theta = 240$ deg., and also find the velocity of a point $M$ midway between $A$ and $B$.

*Ans.* $\omega_{AB} = 36.2$ rad./sec. clockwise, $v_A = 35.6$ ft./sec., $v_M = 39.9$ ft./sec.

**154.** Rack $A$ has a velocity of 6 ft./sec. to the right, and rack $B$ has a velocity of 4 ft./sec. to the left. Find the distance $d$ of the instantaneous center for the gear from $O$ and the velocity of the point $D$ in the position shown.

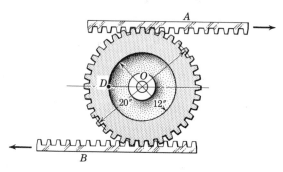

PROB. 154

**155.** Prob. 133.
**156.** Prob. 138.

  *Ans.* $\omega_{AB}$ = 3.08 rad./sec.
     counterclockwise

**157.** Construct the space centrode and the body centrode for the link $AB$ within the limits of its constrained motion. Show that its motion is described by rolling the body centrode on the space centrode.

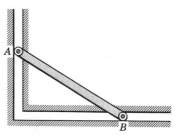

PROB. 157

**158.** A mechanism to test the wearing quality of rubbing surfaces $A$ and $B$ is shown. Determine the rubbing velocity if the link $OC$ has a velocity of 5 ft./sec. to the right at the instant when $\theta$ = 45 deg.

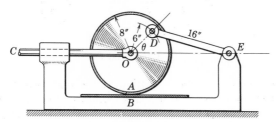

PROB. 158

**159.** The motion of the control rod attached at $G$ is governed by the upward movement of the plunger $A$ which bears against the roller at $B$. The shaft $HE$ is fixed to the base and carries the sliding collar attached to the arm at $F$. If $A$ has an upward velocity of 16 ft./sec., determine the velocity of point $G$ for the position $\theta$ = 45 deg.       *Ans.* $v_G$ = 45.7 ft./sec.

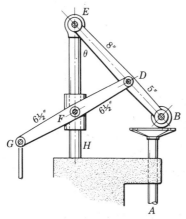

PROB. 159

**160.** The steel band $A$ is attached to the pivoted sector at $B$ and leads tangentially away from it around an idler pulley. Determine the angular velocity $\omega_{ED}$ of link $ED$ in the position shown for which the band has a velocity of 15 ft./sec.

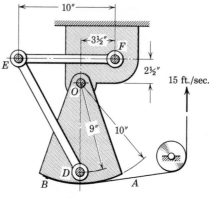

PROB. 160

**161.** Determine the angular velocity $\omega$ of the ram head $AE$ of the rock crusher in the position shown if the crank $OB$ has a clockwise angular velocity of 90 rev./min. When $B$ is at the bottom of its circle, $D$ and $E$ are on a horizontal line through $F$, and lines $BD$ and $AE$ are vertical. The dimensions are $OB = 3$ in., $BD = 30$ in., $ED = DF = 15$ in., $AE = 16$ in.

                           *Ans.*    $\omega = 0.65$ rad./sec. clockwise

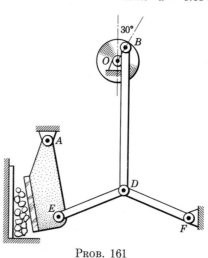

PROB. 161

**\* 162.** A shaft at $O$ drives the arm $OA$ at a speed of 60 rev./min. counterclockwise about a fixed bearing at $O$. Determine the speed of gear $B$ if ($a$) gear $D$

does not rotate, (*b*) gear *D* rotates clockwise at a speed of 40 rev./min. about *O*.
*Ans.*     (*a*) $\omega_B$ = 240 rev./min.,
(*b*) $\omega_B$ = 360 rev./min.; both counterclockwise

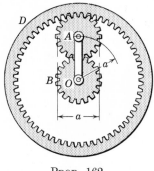
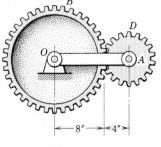

PROB. 162                    PROB. 163

*163. The gear *B* is turning 30 rad./sec. counterclockwise, and the arm *OA*
is turning 12 rad./sec. clockwise. Locate the instant center of gear *D* and find
the angular velocity of *D*. *Ans.* 1½ in. left of *A*, $\omega_D$ = 96 rad./sec. clockwise

**21. Relative Linear Acceleration.** If the relative velocity relation, Eq. 22, is differentiated with respect to the time, there results

$$\frac{dv_A}{dt} = \frac{dv_B}{dt} + \!\!\!+ \frac{dv_{A/B}}{dt}$$

or

$$a_A = a_B + \!\!\!+ a_{A/B}. \tag{24}$$

In words Eq. 24 states that the acceleration of a point *A* equals the
acceleration of a second point *B* plus (vectorially) the acceleration of
*A* measured relative to *B*. To understand this equation it is necessary
to recall that the derivative of a vector includes both the change in
direction and the change in magnitude of the vector. This fact was
developed in Art. 14. If point *B* is moving on a curved path, for
instance, then $a_B$ may be written in terms of its component normal to
the path and its component tangent to the path, or $a_B = a_{B_n} + \!\!\!+ a_{B_t}$.
Point *A* would also have normal and tangential components of acceleration if it moved on a curved path. Contrary to velocities the
accelerations $a_A$ and $a_B$ are, in general, *not* tangent to the paths described by points *A* and *B* when these paths are curvilinear.

The relative-acceleration term $a_{A/B}$ is the acceleration which would
be measured from a set of *nonrotating* axes whose origin has the same
acceleration as point *B*. From this moving set of axes attached to *B*
point *A* will, in general, appear to move on a curved path. Therefore the relative-acceleration term may be expressed in terms of its

component normal to the relative path and its component tangent to the relative path. These components are due, respectively, to the time rate of change of direction and the time rate of change of magnitude of the relative velocity $v_{A/B}$. Thus when the paths of $A$, $B$, and $A$ with respect to $B$ are curved, each of the three terms in Eq. 24 may be expressed in terms of its two components. The most useful components are those normal and tangent to the path involved although polar components or rectangular components could be used.

The most common use of Eq. 24 is its application to two points on the *same rigid body* where the distance between the points remains *fixed*. In this case the relative-acceleration term $a_{A/B}$ becomes the acceleration of $A$ measured from a nonrotating station on the same body at $B$. Since the distance $r$ between $A$ and $B$ does not change, the relative path of $A$ about $B$ is a circle of radius $r$. Thus for the purpose of determining the term $a_{A/B}$ for two points on the same rigid body, it is only necessary to consider the acceleration components due to *simple circular motion* of $A$ about the reference point $B$ which is considered to be fixed.

These relative-acceleration relations are illustrated in Fig. 23 which shows a rigid body with any motion in the plane of the figure. Points

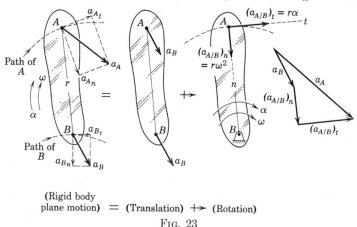

(Rigid body
plane motion)  =  (Translation) $+\!\!\!\rightarrow$ (Rotation)

Fig. 23

$A$ and $B$ are a fixed distance $r$ apart and move on the absolute paths indicated. Each point has an absolute acceleration which can be represented by its respective $n$- and $t$-components as shown in the left-hand view. Equation 24 states that the acceleration of $A$ equals the acceleration of $B$, as shown in the middle view, plus (vectorially) the relative acceleration due to rotation about $B$ considered a fixed point, as shown in the right-hand view. As in the case of any rotation with both angular velocity and angular acceleration, the relative-acceleration term will have both a normal acceleration component due to the change in the direction of the relative velocity $v_{A/B}$ and a tangential component due to the change in the magnitude of the relative velocity. The normal component of the relative acceleration is, by Eq. 17,

$$(a_{A/B})_n = \frac{(v_{A/B})^2}{r} = r\omega^2.$$

In this relation it should be noted that $\omega$ is the *absolute* angular velocity of the body. The relation $v_{A/B} = r\omega$ between the relative linear velocity and the absolute angular velocity was established in Art. 19 as Eq. 23. The normal component of relative acceleration is always directed toward the center of the rotation, from $A$ to $B$, no matter whether the rotation is clockwise or counterclockwise.

The tangential component of relative acceleration is due to the angular acceleration $\alpha$ of the line $AB$ and by Eq. 11 is

$$(a_{A/B})_t = r\alpha.$$

Again it should be noted that $\alpha$ is the *absolute* angular acceleration of the body. The observation that both $\omega$ and $\alpha$ are absolute quantities comes from the fact that the moving reference system is not rotating, so that any rotation of a line is measured as an absolute quantity.

For two points on the same rigid body Eq. 24 may be written directly as

$$a_A = a_B + (a_{A/B})_n + (a_{A/B})_t, \tag{25}$$

where the $n$- and $t$-directions are as explained and shown in Fig. 23. If $A$ and $B$ happen to have curvilinear motion, then both the normal and tangential components of the absolute acceleration of each point must be included. The vector sum of the acceleration components is shown at the extreme right in Fig. 23 for the symbolic case illustrated.

Attention is again called to the fact that plane motion of a rigid body may be analyzed as the superposition of the components of translation of the reference point and the components of pure rotation about the reference point. Any point on the body whose acceleration is known or can easily be found may be used as the reference point. The student should rewrite Eq. 25 using point $A$ as the reference point and note that the components of relative acceleration are the negative of those in Eq. 25. Particular attention is drawn to the fact that the instantaneous center of zero velocity may *not* be used as a reference point in the relative-acceleration equation on the assumption that this point has zero acceleration, which, in general, it does not. The existence and location of an instantaneous center of zero acceleration is described briefly in the next article.

The polygon which represents the sum of the several acceleration components of Eq. 25 is usually best solved graphically, although if preferred it may be used to indicate the trigonometric relations necessary for an algebraic solution. The relative-acceleration equation is, of course, a vector equation which is equivalent to two scalar equations for a two-dimensional problem in plane motion. Thus there may be as many as, but no more than, two unknown quantities in the equation for solution. These unknowns may be any combination of the magnitude or direction of the acceleration vectors. In solving Eq. 25 graphically it should be pointed out that the known vectors should be combined first.

### SAMPLE PROBLEMS

**164.** The wheel rolls to the left without slipping, and at the instant considered the center $O$ has a velocity $v_O$ and an acceleration $a_O$ to the left. Determine the acceleration of points $A$ and $C$ on the wheel.

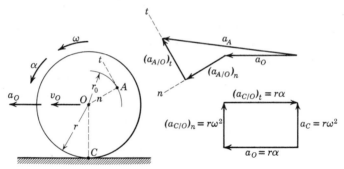

PROB. 164

*Solution.* The acceleration of $A$ will be expressed directly in terms of the known acceleration of $O$ by the relation

$$a_A = a_O \,\nrightarrow\, a_{A/O}.$$

The relative term $a_{A/O} = (a_{A/O})_n \,\nrightarrow\, (a_{A/O})_t$ depends on the angular velocity, $\omega = v_O/r$, and the angular acceleration, $\alpha = a_O/r$. (See Sample Prob. 109.) Thus

$$(a_{A/O})_n = r_0\omega^2 \qquad \text{(directed from } A \text{ to } O),$$

$$(a_{A/O})_t = r_0\alpha \qquad \text{(directed normal to } AO).$$

The absolute acceleration of $A$ is the sum of its three components as indicated in the upper of the two symbolic acceleration polygons. In a numerical problem the polygon may be drawn to scale and the answer measured from the figure; or an approximate sketch of the polygon may be made and used to deter-

# Sample Problems 93

mine $a_A$ algebraically by computing, say, its horizontal and vertical components.

The acceleration of $C$, the instantaneous center of velocity, is found by a similar process. Thus

$$a_C = a_O \mathbin{+\mkern-8mu\!\!+} a_{C/O} = a_O \mathbin{+\mkern-8mu\!\!+} (a_{C/O})_n \mathbin{+\mkern-8mu\!\!+} (a_{C/O})_t.$$

The last two terms are found by computing the acceleration due to rotation of $C$ about $O$. The first is

$$(a_{C/O})_n = r\omega^2 \qquad \text{(directed from } C \text{ to } O),$$

and the second is

$$(a_{C/O})_t = r\alpha = a_O \qquad \text{(directed to the right)}.$$

Addition of the three components produces $a_C = r\omega^2$ in the direction from $C$ to $O$ as shown in the lower acceleration polygon. Thus, although the instantaneous center on the body has zero velocity, it does *not* have zero acceleration.

**165.** Determine the acceleration of the piston $A$ and the angular acceleration of the connecting rod $AB$ for the engine described in Prob. 124 with $\theta = 60$ deg. if the crank speed is constant. Also find the acceleration of the center of gravity $G$ of the rod if $G$ is 4 in. from $B$.

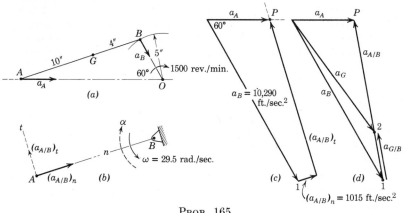

PROB. 165

*Solution.* The acceleration of $A$ may be expressed in terms of the acceleration of the crank pin $B$. Thus

$$a_A = a_B \mathbin{+\mkern-8mu\!\!+} (a_{A/B})_n \mathbin{+\mkern-8mu\!\!+} (a_{A/B})_t.$$

Point $B$ moves in the arc of the 5 in. crank circle with a constant speed, so that it has a normal acceleration equal to

$$[a_n = r\omega^2] \qquad a_B = \frac{5}{12} \times \left(\frac{1500 \times 2\pi}{60}\right)^2 = 10{,}290 \text{ ft./sec.}^2$$

in the direction from $B$ to $O$.

The normal component of relative acceleration $(a_{A/B})_n$ is calculated by considering $B$ as fixed and therefore depends on the angular velocity of the rod $AB$ and the length of $AB$. From Prob. 124 this angular velocity was found to be 29.5 rad./sec. counterclockwise, corresponding to the relative linear velocity $v_{A/B} = 34.4$ ft./sec. Using this velocity gives

$$[a_n = r\omega^2] \qquad (a_{A/B})_n = \tfrac{14}{12} \times (29.5)^2 = 1015 \text{ ft./sec.}^2$$

in the direction from $A$ to $B$ as indicated on the separate diagram of the rod in the $b$-part of the figure, which shows $B$ as fixed for the purpose of visualizing the relative acceleration. The alternate relation, $a_n = v^2/r$, may also be used for calculating the relative normal acceleration provided the relative velocity $v_{A/B}$ is used for $v$. The equivalence is easily seen when it is recalled that $v_{A/B} = r\omega$.

It may be observed now that there are only two unknowns remaining in the relative-acceleration equation, the magnitude of $a_A$ and the magnitude of $(a_{A/B})_t$. Thus the solution may be obtained. The known vectors are laid off by first starting with $a_B$ as indicated in the $c$-part of the figure. Next $(a_{A/B})_n$ is added, and then the direction of the component $(a_{A/B})_t$ is drawn through the head of this last known vector. The solution of the equation is obtained by constructing the correct direction of the sum $a_A$ through the starting point. This direction is, of course, along the axis of the cylinder in which $A$ slides. The intersection point $P$ on the polygon enables the correct magnitude of the two unknowns to be determined either by measurement from the scale drawing or by algebraic solution of the acceleration polygon. The results are

$$a_A = 3320 \text{ ft./sec.}^2 \qquad \text{and} \qquad (a_{A/B})_t = 9040 \text{ ft./sec.}^2 \qquad Ans.$$

in the directions shown.

It is not until the magnitude and sense of the component $(a_{A/B})_t$ are found that the angular acceleration of the rod may be determined. The quantities $(a_{A/B})_t$ and $\alpha$ were indicated by dotted lines in the $b$-portion of the illustration because their magnitude and sense were unknown until the solution point $P$ was found. Now it can be seen that, since $(a_{A/B})_t$ is up and slightly to the left, the angular acceleration must be *clockwise* for this position of the rod. The magnitude is

$$\left[\alpha = \frac{a_t}{r}\right] \qquad \alpha = \frac{9040}{\tfrac{14}{12}} = 7750 \text{ rad./sec.}^2 \qquad Ans.$$

The acceleration of $G$ may be determined in terms of the acceleration of either $A$ or $B$. Using $B$ gives

$$a_G = a_B +\!\!\!\!\to a_{G/B}.$$

The relative term is

$$a_{G/B} = (a_{G/B})_n +\!\!\!\!\to (a_{G/B})_t = \overline{GB}\omega^2 +\!\!\!\!\to \overline{GB}\alpha.$$

This expression is the same as that for $a_{A/B}$ except that $\overline{GB}$ replaces $\overline{AB} = r$.

Thus the two relative acceleration terms have the same direction and are related by direct ratio, or

$$a_{G/B} = \frac{\overline{GB}}{\overline{AB}} \, a_{A/B} = \frac{4}{14} \, a_{A/B}.$$

The acceleration polygon is redrawn in the $d$-part of the figure, and the vector from point 1 to $P$ is the term $a_{A/B}$. Point 2 is therefore located $\frac{4}{14}$ of the distance from point 1 to $P$. The acceleration of $G$ is then drawn to point 2 and is found to be

$$a_G = 7870 \text{ ft./sec.}^2 \qquad\qquad Ans.$$

in the direction shown. It should be noted that a point close to $B$ will have an acceleration nearly that of $B$, while a point close to $A$ will have an acceleration nearly that of $A$.

## PROBLEMS

**166.** An automobile with 28 in. diameter tires accelerates at a constant rate from rest to a speed of 30 mi./hr. in a distance of 80 ft. Determine the acceleration $a$ of a point on the top of the wheel as the car reaches the speed of 10 mi./hr. *Ans.* $a = 185.7$ ft./sec.$^2$

**167.** The cable is wrapped around the inner hub of the wheel and pulled to the right with a constant velocity of 0.5 ft./sec. If the wheel does not slip, determine the velocity and acceleration of point $A$. (Which way does the wheel roll?) *Ans.* $v_A = 2$ ft./sec. to the right, $a_A = 1$ ft./sec.$^2$ down

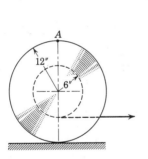

PROB. 167

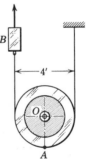

PROB. 168

**168.** The 4 ft. diameter sheave is elevated by the cable which is wrapped around it and which is attached to the block $B$. If $B$ has a constant upward acceleration of 6 ft./sec.$^2$, determine the acceleration of a point $A$ which is on the bottom of the sheave at the time when $B$ reaches an upward velocity of 4 ft./sec. *Ans.* $a_A = 5.83$ ft./sec.$^2$

**169.** The center $O$ of the wheel which rolls without slipping has a velocity of 12 in./sec. to the left at the instant shown. If this velocity is decreasing at the rate of 20 in./sec. each second, determine the acceleration of the point $A$ in the wheel at this instant. *Ans.* $a_A = 50.4$ in./sec.$^2$

PROB. 169

**170.** The rigid frame rotates about $O$ due to the action of the crank $ED$ and connecting link $CD$. If the angular velocity and angular acceleration of the frame are 0.2 rad./sec. clockwise and 0.03 rad./sec.$^2$ counterclockwise, respectively, at the instant shown, determine the acceleration of $B$ with respect to $A$.

            *Ans.*    $a_{B/A} = 0.5$ ft./sec.$^2$

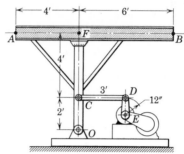

PROB. 170

**171.** If the crank $ED$ of the mechanism shown with Prob. 170 is revolving at a constant clockwise speed of 15 rev./min., determine the acceleration of point $B$ on the oscillating frame for the position represented.

**172.** The circular disk turns about its center $O$ with a constant clockwise angular acceleration of 4 rad./sec.$^2$ The bar revolves clockwise about $O$ so that $OA$ overtakes a radial line scribed on the disk once every 3 sec. during the entire period of the acceleration of the disk. In addition $O$ has a constant acceleration of 3 ft./sec.$^2$ horizontally to the right. Determine the acceleration of the end $A$ of the rod at the instant shown, for which the angular velocity of the disk is 2 rad./sec. clockwise.

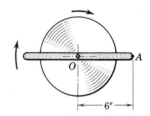

PROB. 172

          *Ans.*    $a_A = 5.74$ ft./sec.$^2$

**173.** The elements of a steam-locomotive drive are shown in the sketch. If the locomotive is traveling at a constant speed of 60 mi./hr. to the right, determine the acceleration of the crosshead $A$ when it is at the extreme left end of its stroke.

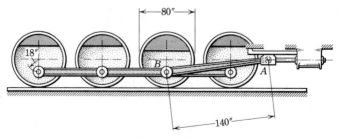

PROB. 173

**174.** The locomotive of Prob. 173 is traveling 60 mi./hr. to the right with no acceleration. Determine the angular acceleration $\alpha$ of the main rod $AB$ when in the position shown.      *Ans.* $\alpha = 90.3$ rad./sec.$^2$ clockwise

**175.** The elements of a power hacksaw are shown in the figure. The saw blade is mounted in a frame which slides along the horizontal guide. If the motor turns the flywheel at a constant counterclockwise speed of 60 rev./min., determine the acceleration of the blade for the position where $\theta = 90$ deg., and find the corresponding angular acceleration of the link $AB$.

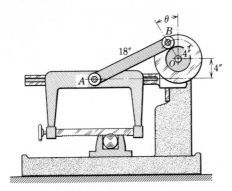

PROB. 175

**176.** Find the acceleration of the piston $A$ and the center of gravity $G$ of the connecting rod for the automobile engine described in Prob. 139 for the crank angle of $\theta = 30$ deg. and a constant clockwise engine speed of 2700 rev./min.
     *Ans.* $a_A = 13,250$ ft./sec.$^2$, $a_G = 12,850$ ft./sec.$^2$

**177.** The plane motion of the triangular plate $ABC$ is governed by the crank $OA$ and the link $BD$. In the position shown $OA$ has a counterclockwise angular

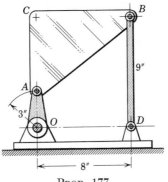

PROB. 177

acceleration of 10 rad./sec.$^2$ and a clockwise angular velocity of 4 rad./sec. Determine the angular acceleration of $BD$ at this instant.

**178.** The acceleration of pin $A$ is 6 ft./sec.$^2$ down and to the right, and its velocity is 3 ft./sec. up and to the left as the link passes the horizontal. For this position determine the angular acceleration $\alpha_{AB}$ of the link.

*Ans.* $\alpha_{AB} = 8.75$ rad./sec.$^2$ clockwise

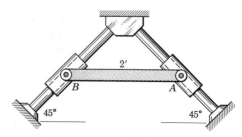

PROB. 178

**179.** If the link $AB$ shown with Prob. 178 has an angular velocity of 3 rad./sec. and a counterclockwise angular acceleration of 5 rad./sec.$^2$, find the larger of the accelerations of the two ends.

**180.** The sliding collar $A$ has a constant velocity of 10 ft./sec. to the right for an interval of its motion along the fixed bar. Determine the angular acceleration of $BC$ at the instant when $BC$ passes the horizontal.

*Ans.* $\alpha_{BC} = 185.4$ rad./sec.$^2$ counterclockwise

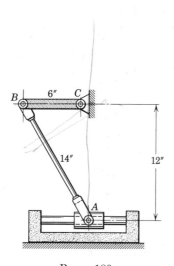

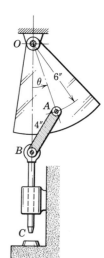

PROB. 180            PROB. 181

**181.** The sector is given a simple harmonic oscillation about the neutral position $\theta = 0$ expressed by $\theta = \theta_0 \sin 2\pi ft$, where the amplitude is $\theta_0 = 0.5$ rad., the frequency of oscillation is $f = 2$ cycles/sec., and where $t$ is the time in seconds measured from the position $\theta = 0$. Determine the acceleration of the punch $C$ for ($a$) $\theta = 0.5$ rad. and ($b$) $\theta = 0$.

$Ans.$ ($a$) $a_C = 54.7$ ft./sec.$^2$ down,
($b$) $a_C = 49.3$ ft./sec.$^2$ up

**182.** Wheel $A$ has a clockwise angular acceleration of 12 rad./sec.$^2$ and a counterclockwise angular velocity of 4 rad./sec. at the instant represented. Determine the angular acceleration $\alpha$ of wheel $B$ for this position.

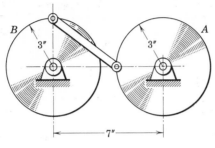

PROB. 182

**183.** The cam is rigidly bolted to the member $A$ which moves in a straight horizontal guide with an acceleration of 3 ft./sec.$^2$ to the right. The slotted arm revolves at a constant counterclockwise rate of 4 rad./sec. and guides the pin $B$ around the periphery of the cam. The cam is cut so that the path of the center of the pin relative to the slider is a limaçon $r = b - c \cos \theta$ with $b = 4$ in. and $c = 2$ in. Determine the total acceleration of the pin when $\theta = 90$ deg.

$Ans.$ $a_B = 69.9$ in./sec.$^2$

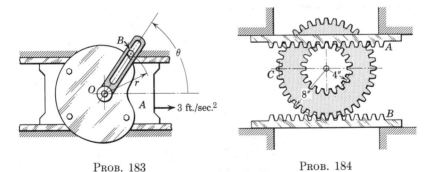

PROB. 183    PROB. 184

**184.** At the instant shown rack $A$ has a velocity of 6 ft./sec. to the right and an acceleration of 19 ft./sec.$^2$ to the left. Also at this instant rack $B$ has a velocity of 3 ft./sec. to the left and an acceleration of 4 ft./sec.$^2$ to the left. Determine the acceleration of point $C$ on the two integral gears.

$Ans.$ $a_C = 41.2$ ft./sec.$^2$

**185.** The plate $ABC$ is in the form of an equilateral triangle 12 in. on a side and moves so that the rollers at $A$ and $B$ are in contact with the vertical and horizontal surfaces. Find the acceleration of $C$ in the position shown if $B$ has an acceleration of 4 ft./sec.$^2$ to the right and a velocity of 2 ft./sec. at this instant.

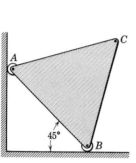

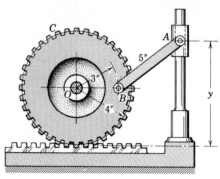

PROB. 185                                            PROB. 186

**186.** The gear $C$ rolls back and forth over a short distance on the horizontal rack, and the connecting link causes the collar $A$ to slide up and down on the fixed vertical shaft. When $A$ passes the position for which $y = 7$ in., the center $O$ of the wheel has a velocity of 0.4 ft./sec. to the right and no acceleration. Determine the acceleration $a_A$ of the collar at this position.

                                        *Ans.  $a_A = 2.26$ ft./sec.$^2$ down*

**\* 187.** The sliders at $A$ and $C$ are given an oscillatory motion in their respective parallel slots. Determine the acceleration of pin $B$ if, at the instant when $x = 6$ in., $A$ and $C$ each has a velocity of 3 ft./sec. directed away from the other and each has an acceleration of 15 ft./sec.$^2$ directed toward the other.

                                        *Ans.  $a_B = 36.8$ ft./sec.$^2$*

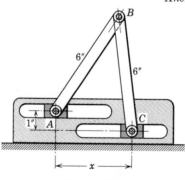

PROB. 187

**\* 188.** An oil pumping rig is shown in the figure. The flexible pump rod $D$ is fastened to the sector at $E$ and is always vertical as it enters the fitting below $D$.

The link $AB$ causes the beam $BCE$ to oscillate as the weighted crank $OA$ revolves. If $OA$ has a constant clockwise speed of 1 rev. every 3 sec., determine the acceleration of the pump rod $D$ when the beam and the crank $OA$ are both in the horizontal position shown.     *Ans.* $a_D = 1.91$ ft./sec.² down

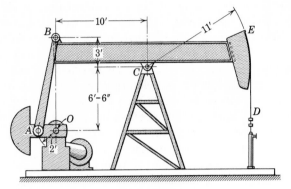

PROB. 188

* **189.** In the mechanism shown the sliding collar $A$ is connected to the pivoted arm $OD$ by the 5 in. link $AB$. If the vertical component of the acceleration of $D$ is 4 ft./sec.² down and the vertical component of the velocity of $D$ is 2 ft./sec. also down when $\theta = 30$ deg., determine the corresponding acceleration of $A$ at this position.     *Ans.* $a_A = 29.0$ ft./sec.²

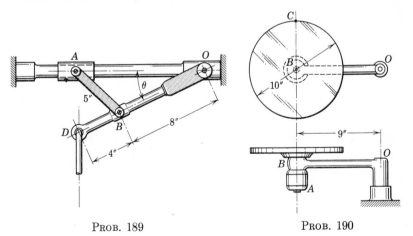

PROB. 189                PROB. 190

* **190.** The circular disk is coupled to the shaft of the electric motor $A$ so that with the arm $OB$ stationary the disk revolves at 24 rev./min. clockwise when viewed from above. The arm $OB$ is set in motion with an angular acceleration of 20 (rev./min.)/sec. clockwise when viewed from above. The current supplied to the motor is not changed, so that a point on the disk still crosses the

arm $OB$ with the same frequency. Determine the velocity $v_C$ and acceleration $a_C$ of the point $C$ if it is in the position shown when $OB$ has reached a speed of 12 rev./min.                 *Ans.*   $v_C = 1.831$ ft./sec., $a_C = 4.81$ ft./sec.²

**22. Instantaneous Center of Zero Acceleration.** In Art. 20 the velocity of a point on a rigid body moving with plane motion was determined relative to an axis, normal to the plane of motion, momentarily at rest. A counterpart of this zero-velocity axis exists for the case of acceleration. It will now be shown that, provided the angular velocity and angular acceleration of a rigid body are not both zero, a point $O$ exists in the plane of motion which has zero acceleration at any instant. The acceleration of any point other than $O$ may be computed as though the body were rotating about an axis normal to the plane of motion through $O$.

Use of the instantaneous center of zero acceleration is somewhat specialized in the study of mechanisms and will not be fully developed here. It is helpful for the critical student, however, to realize that such a point exists.

Figure 24a shows a body which has plane motion. It is assumed that the acceleration of some point $A$ on the body is known and that the angular velocity and angular acceleration of the body are also known at the instant considered. The acceleration of some other point $O$ on the body a distance $r$ from $A$ may be written as

$$a_O = a_A \;\looparrowright\; (a_{O/A})_n \;\looparrowright\; (a_{O/A})_t.$$

If $O$ has zero acceleration, it follows that

$$a_A = (a_{A/O})_n \;\looparrowright\; (a_{A/O})_t$$

$$= r\omega^2 \;\looparrowright\; r\alpha.$$

These components are shown on the figure. The magnitude of the acceleration of $A$ is $a_A = r\sqrt{\omega^4 + \alpha^2}$. Thus the distance $r$ from $A$ to $O$ and the angle $\beta$ between $a_A$ and $\overline{AO}$ are, respectively,

$$r = \frac{a_A}{\sqrt{\omega^4 + \alpha^2}}, \qquad \beta = \tan^{-1}\frac{\alpha}{\omega^2}.$$

From Fig. 24b it is observed that there are four points $O$, $O'$, $O''$, and $O'''$ on the body (or body extended) a distance $r$ from $A$ where the line joining the point to $A$ makes an angle $\beta$ with $a_A$. Point $O'$ is ruled out as the instantaneous center since the tangential component $(a_{A/O'})_t$ (perpendicular to $AO'$) is in the wrong sense for the clockwise angular acceleration. Point $O''$ is ruled out since the tangential component $(a_{A/O''})_t$ (perpendicular to $AO''$) is also in the wrong sense for clockwise $\alpha$ and additionally since the normal component $(a_{A/O''})_n$ (parallel to $AO''$) is in the wrong sense for the $r\omega^2$ term. Point $O'''$ is ruled out since the normal component $(a_{A/O'''})_n$ is in the wrong sense. Thus point $O$ is isolated as the one possible point of zero acceleration where both components fit the respective requirements for normal and tangential acceleration.

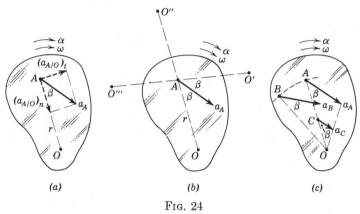

(a)          (b)          (c)

Fig. 24

With the instantaneous center $O$ of zero acceleration located it may be seen that the acceleration of all points on a radial line through $O$, such as points $A$ and $C$, of Fig. 24c, make the same angle with the radial line and are proportional to the distance from the point to $O$. Further, all points at an equal distance from $O$, such as $A$ and $B$, have accelerations of equal magnitude.

The reader who wishes to pursue further his study of the instantaneous center of zero acceleration may determine the location of the center for a number of the problems of the preceding article. ·He may also consult references which specialize in mechanism kinematics.

**23. Rotating Axes; Coriolis Acceleration.** In Arts. 19 through 22 the relative component of the motion of a point was measured from a *nonrotating* reference system which translated with the reference point to which the velocity or acceleration was referred. For problems where a point is moving along a path which itself is rotating, it is useful to introduce measurements made from a reference system which *rotates* with the path. It may be visualized, for example, that such a description will fit the problem of a fluid particle moving along the curved vane of a centrifugal pump.

In Fig. 25a is shown a body which has any plane motion and which, at the instant represented, is rotating about its instantaneous center of zero velocity $C$ with the absolute angular velocity $\omega$. The motion of a point or particle $P$ along the curved path which is *fixed* to the rotating body will be described by using point $A$ as a reference point. Point $A$ is fixed to the path and coincident with $P$ at the instant considered. The radial line from $C$ to $A$ is fixed to the body and

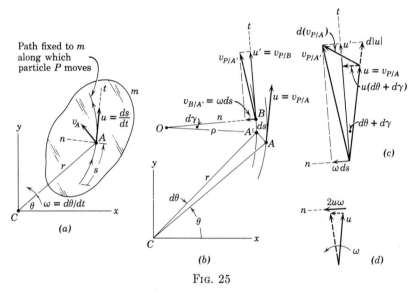

FIG. 25

constitutes the rotating reference frame. The velocity $u$ of $P$ relative to the path is directed along the path and has a magnitude given by

$$u = \frac{ds}{dt}$$

where $s$ is the distance measured along and relative to the path. This velocity is also the velocity $v_{P/A}$ of $P$ with respect to $A$. The absolute velocity of $P$ is $v_P = v_A + v_{P/A}$, and the acceleration of $P$ is the time derivative of this vector equation or

$$a_P = a_A + a_{P/A}.$$

The acceleration of $A$, a point fixed to the moving body, may be determined by any one of the methods described in the previous articles. The relative acceleration is $a_{P/A} = dv_{P/A}/dt$ and may be determined by evaluating the infinitesimal vector change in $v_{P/A}$ and dividing it by the time $dt$.

The motion which occurs during time $dt$ is shown in Fig. 25$b$.  Point $A$, fixed to the path, moves to $A'$ during the rotation $d\theta$ of the body about the instantaneous center $C$.  At the same time $P$ advances from $A$ to $B$ as it moves a distance $ds$ along the rotating path.  Point $O$ is the center of curvature of the path, and $\rho$ is the radius of curvature.  At position $A$ the velocity of $P$ with respect to $A$ is also the velocity of $P$ relative to the path, $v_{P/A} = u$.  At position $B$ the new value of this velocity relative to the reference point is the velocity of $P$ with respect to $A'$ or $v_{P/A'}$.  It is seen that $v_{P/A'}$ is *not* the same as the new velocity of $P$ relative to the path which is $u' = v_{P/B}$ where $B$ is the point fixed to the path and coincident with the new position of $P$.  The velocity of $P$ with respect to $A'$ is the same as the velocity of $P$ with respect to $B$ plus (vectorially) the velocity of $B$ with respect to $A'$.  This relative velocity relation may be obtained from the expressions relating the velocities of $P$, $B$, and $A$.  Thus

$$v_{P/A'} = v_P \rightarrow v_{A'}$$

$$= (v_B \nrightarrow v_{P/B}) \rightarrow (v_B \nrightarrow v_{A'/B})$$

$$= v_{P/B} \rightarrow v_{A'/B}$$

or

$$v_{P/A'} = v_{P/B} \nrightarrow v_{B/A'}.$$

The term $v_{B/A'}$ is the relative velocity between two points a fixed distance $ds$ apart and equals the distance $ds$ times the angular velocity of the line $A'B$ which is $\omega$, the angular velocity of the body.  Thus $v_{B/A'} = \omega\, ds$, as shown in the figure, and

$$v_{P/A'} = u' \nrightarrow \omega\, ds.$$

Figure 25$c$ shows the relative velocity vectors for the two positions.  It is seen that the angle between $u$ and $u'$ is the sum of the angle $d\theta$ due to the rotation of the path and the angle $d\gamma$ due to the change in direction of the path as $P$ moves along the arc $A'B$.  From the figure the vector difference between $v_{P/A}$ and $v_{P/A'}$ is seen to be $d(v_{P/A})$ $= [\omega\, ds + u(d\theta + d\gamma)] \nrightarrow d|u|$ where $d|u|$ is the change in the magnitude of the velocity relative to the path.  The vector $u(d\theta + d\gamma)$ is the change in $u$ due to its change in direction and is the differential arc length of radius $u$ and subtended angle $d\theta + d\gamma$.  The acceleration of $P$ relative to $A$ is, then,

$$a_{P/A} = \frac{d(v_{P/A})}{dt} = \left[ \omega \frac{ds}{dt} + u\left(\frac{d\theta}{dt} + \frac{d\gamma}{dt}\right) \right] \nrightarrow \frac{d|u|}{dt}.$$

But $ds/dt = u$, $d\theta/dt = \omega$, and $u\, d\gamma/dt = u\,(ds/\rho)/dt = u^2/\rho$ so that

$$a_{P/A} = \left(2u\omega + \frac{u^2}{\rho}\right) +\!\!\!\!\!\!\nrightarrow \frac{d|u|}{dt}.$$

This expression gives the acceleration of $P$ with respect to $A$ still measured from a *nonrotating* reference frame attached to $A$ in accordance with the relative-motion principle discussed in Art. 17 and developed in Arts. 18 through 22. If the motion of $P$ is observed from the *rotating* frame of reference attached to the body, the path appears to be fixed and the particle appears to move with curvilinear motion along the path with the instantaneous velocity $u$. Therefore the acceleration of $P$ as measured in this rotating system would be

$$a_p = \frac{u^2}{\rho} +\!\!\!\!\!\!\nrightarrow \frac{d|u|}{dt}$$

in accordance with the familiar expressions, Eqs. 17 and 18, for curvilinear motion. The apparent normal acceleration is $u^2/\rho$, and the apparent tangential acceleration is $d|u|/dt = d^2s/dt^2$. Thus the relative acceleration of $P$ to $A$ may be written

$$a_{P/A} = a_p +\!\!\!\!\!\!\nrightarrow 2u\omega.$$

The term $2u\omega$ is called the *Coriolis acceleration* * and is seen to be the difference between the acceleration of $P$ with respect to $A$ as measured from *nonrotating* axes and the acceleration of $P$ measured with respect to the *rotating* body. Figure 25c makes possible a direct visualization of the Coriolis acceleration which comes from the sum of the increments of relative velocity change $\omega\, ds$ and $u\, d\theta$. The change $\omega\, ds$ is the velocity of $B$ relative to $A'$ and is due to the angular velocity of $BA'$ which is also the angular velocity of the path and the body. The change $u\, d\theta$ is that part of the vector change in $u$ due to the rotation $d\theta$ of the path. The direction of $2u\omega$ is, consequently, always normal to the path, and the sense corresponds to the direction in which the head of the vector $u$ would move if it were rotated about its tail in the sense of $\omega$, as illustrated in Fig. 25d. If the velocity $u$ of the particle is in the direction opposite to that illustrated in Fig. 25, the Coriolis acceleration will be in the minus $n$-direction, whereas the normal component of $a_p$, namely $u^2/\rho$, will still be in the plus $n$-direction. This fact may be verified by reversing the direction of $u$ and constructing the new diagrams corresponding to those of Fig. 25.

---

* Named after the French scientist, G. Coriolis (1792–1843), who was the first to call attention to this term which is alternately called the *supplementary* or *complementary* acceleration.

The complete expression for the acceleration of $P$ may now be written. If the symbol $a$ is used for $a_P$ and $a_m$ is used for $a_A$, the acceleration of $P$ becomes

$$a = a_m \nrightarrow a_p \nrightarrow 2u\omega. \qquad (26)$$

Equation 26 expresses the so-called *theorem of Coriolis* which states that the acceleration of a particle moving on a rotating path is the sum of three terms. The first term $a_m$ is the absolute acceleration of a point on the body $m$ coincident with the particle at the instant considered. The second term $a_p$ is the acceleration of the particle which would be measured from a rotating position attached to the path which is the same as the acceleration of $P$ moving along the path considered as fixed. The third term is the Coriolis acceleration.

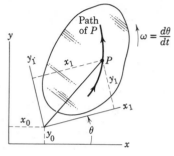

Fig. 26

An alternate approach to the results expressed by Eq. 26 may be used by writing the coordinates of the particle $P$ in terms of the coordinates measured in the rotating system and then carrying out the rather lengthy differentiations involved. Thus from Fig. 26 where the $x_1$–$y_1$ axes are attached to and rotate with the body, the coordinates of $P$ are

$$x = x_0 + x_1 \cos \theta - y_1 \sin \theta$$

$$y = y_0 + y_1 \cos \theta + x_1 \sin \theta.$$

Two time derivatives plus various combinations of terms may be carried out to obtain Eq. 26. Although quite acceptable, this approach has the disadvantage of losing the physical picture of the various terms, particularly the Coriolis acceleration.

### SAMPLE PROBLEM

**191.** Determine the angular acceleration of the link $AB$ in the position shown if $OC$ has a constant counterclockwise velocity of 4 rad./sec. The collar at $B$ is free to slide along the arm $OC$.

*Solution.* Link $OC$ will be considered as the rotating reference body, and the acceleration of $B$ will be analyzed by Eq. 26. Let $D$ be the point on $OC$ coincident with $B$ at this instant. The first term in this equation is the accelera-

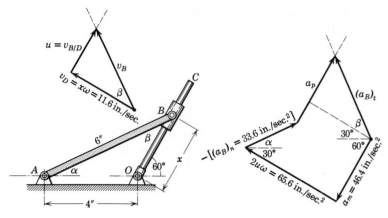

PROB. 191

tion of the coincident point on the rotating reference frame and is $a_m = a_D = \overline{OB}(\omega_{OB})^2$. Point $D$ has no tangential acceleration in this problem. The second term is the acceleration of $B$ along the path considered as not rotating. Since the path is a straight line, this acceleration is merely $a_p = d^2x/dt^2$. The last term or Coriolis acceleration is $2u\omega$, where $u = dx/dt = v_{B/D}$.

It should be apparent that the velocities involved must be obtained first. From the geometry of the triangle $AOB$ and from the solution of the equation $v_B = v_D \nrightarrow v_{B/D}$ shown in the figure, the following values are obtained:

$$x = 2.90 \text{ in.}, \qquad u = v_{B/D} = 8.20 \text{ in./sec.}, \qquad v_B = 14.20 \text{ in./sec.}$$

From these values the following computations may now be made:

$$(a_B)_n = \frac{v_B^2}{\overline{AB}} = \frac{(14.20)^2}{6} = 33.6 \text{ in./sec.}^2 \text{ from } B \text{ to } A,$$

$$a_m = a_D = x\omega^2 = (2.90)(4)^2 = 46.4 \text{ in./sec.}^2 \text{ from } B \text{ to } O,$$

$$2u\omega = (2)(8.20)(4) = 65.6 \text{ in./sec.}^2 \text{ in the direction of } v_D.$$

The magnitudes of the term $(a_B)_t$ normal to $AB$ and the term $a_p = d^2x/dt^2$ are unknown. Substituting the values just obtained into Eq. 26 and solving for $(a_B)_t$ give

$$(a_B)_t = 46.4 \nrightarrow 65.6 \rightarrow 33.6 \nrightarrow a_p.$$

The solution of this equation is shown by the acceleration polygon in the figure and results in the values

$$(a_B)_t = \overline{AB}\alpha_{AB} = 56.6 \text{ in./sec.}^2,$$

and

$$\alpha_{AB} = \frac{56.6}{6} = 9.4 \text{ rad./sec.}^2 \text{ counterclockwise} \qquad Ans.$$

## PROBLEMS

**192.** The pin $A$ moves in the slot with a constant velocity $u = 10$ ft./sec. relative to the slot in the direction shown. The disk turns clockwise about $O$ at the constant speed of $\omega = 20$ rad./sec. As $A$ passes the position indicated, determine its absolute velocity $v$ and its absolute acceleration $a$.

Ans.  $v = 0$, $a = 200$ ft./sec.²

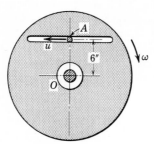

PROB. 192

**193.** When the disk shown is at rest, the pin $A$ moves counterclockwise in the circular slot at the constant speed of 12 in./sec. If the pin continues to move in the slot at this same rate relative to the disk, while the disk accelerates counterclockwise from rest at the rate of 32 rad./sec.², determine the acceleration $a$ of the pin when the disk reaches a velocity of 8 rad./sec. Solve by Eq. 26 and also by direct consideration of the absolute rotation about $O$.

Ans.  $a = 36.9$ ft./sec.²

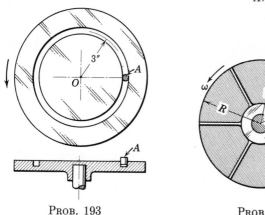

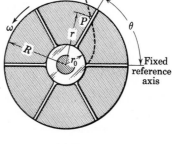

PROB. 193                                PROB. 194

**194.** Assume that a fluid particle $P$ moves with a constant velocity $u$ measured out along the radial vane of the centrifugal pump, which turns with a constant angular velocity $\omega$. Determine the acceleration $a$ of the particle when it is a distance $r$ from the axis of rotation. (Compare solution by Eq. 26 with solution by Eqs. 20.)                    *Ans.*  $a = \omega\sqrt{r^2\omega^2 + 4u^2}$

**195.** Assume that the pump impeller of Prob. 194 has a diameter of 15 in. and turns at the constant speed of 1800 rev./min. If the total acceleration of the fluid particles is tangent to the rim just before they leave the rim, find the acceleration $a_p$ of the particles along and relative to the blades at this position.                                        *Ans.*  $a_p = 22{,}200$ ft./sec.$^2$

**196.** An airplane flies north along a meridian at a constant speed of 600 mi./hr. Determine the Coriolis component of the acceleration of the airplane when a latitude of 45 deg. north is reached. The radius of the earth is very nearly 3960 mi., the angular velocity of the earth is $0.729 \times 10^{-4}$ rad./sec., and the axis of the earth may be considered fixed in space. (*Hint:* Consider the projection of the motion of the airplane on a plane of rotation of the earth.)
*Ans.*  $2u\omega = 0.0907$ ft./sec.$^2$ directed west

**197.** The slotted arm oscillates about $O$ by reason of the action of the pin $A$ which rotates with the wheel with the constant counterclockwise angular velocity $\omega = 4$ rad./sec. (This motion is used in the Geneva wheel for intermittent motion and in the quick-return mechanism of a shaper.) Determine the angular acceleration $\alpha$ of $OB$ at the instant when $\theta = 15$ deg.
*Ans.*  $\alpha = 62.6$ rad./sec.$^2$ clockwise

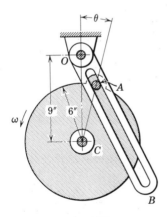

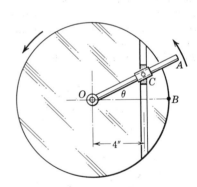

PROB. 197                                      PROB. 198

**\*198.** The slotted disk shown rotates with a constant counterclockwise angular velocity of 10 rad./sec. During a short interval of time the arm $OA$ is made to rotate counterclockwise so that its angle $\theta$ with the radial line $OB$ fixed on the disk increases at the constant rate of 4 rad./sec. Determine the total acceleration $a$ of $C$ when $\theta = 30$ deg.                    *Ans.*  $a = 838$ in./sec.$^2$

**\*199.** Find the angular acceleration of link $AB$ in Prob. 191 for the 60 deg. position shown if $OC$ has a clockwise angular velocity and acceleration of 4 rad./sec. and 8 rad./sec.$^2$, respectively, at this instant.
*Ans.*  $\alpha_{AB} = 4.70$ rad./sec.$^2$ counterclockwise

*200. The figure shows the vanes of a centrifugal pump impeller which turns with a constant clockwise speed of 300 rev./min. The fluid particles are observed to have an absolute velocity whose component in the $r$-direction is 10 ft./sec. at discharge from the vane. Furthermore, the magnitude of the

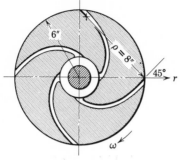

Prob. 200

velocity of the particles measured relative to the vane is increasing at the rate of 80 ft./sec.² just before they leave the vane. Determine the total acceleration $a$ of a fluid particle an instant before it leaves the impeller. The radius of curvature $\rho$ of the vane at its end is 8 in.              *Ans.*  $a = 360$ ft./sec.²

# PRINCIPLES OF KINETICS

**24. Introduction.** When a body is subjected to a force system which is unbalanced, the body has accelerated motion. *Kinetics* is a study of the relations between unbalanced force systems and the changes in motion which they produce. The properties of forces were defined and illustrated in *Mechanics, Part I, Statics.* The relations between displacement, velocity, acceleration, and time were covered in Chapter 2 of the present volume, and the remainder of the book concerns the laws which govern the combination of the two essential parts of kinetics, force and motion. The basic concepts and definitions presented in Chapter 1 are fundamental to the development of kinetics, and a review of this introduction is strongly recommended before proceeding.

**25. The Fundamental Experiment.** The basic connection between force and acceleration is stated by Newton's second law of motion. The validity of this law is entirely experimental, and the fundamental meaning of the law will be described by an ideal experiment in which force and acceleration are assumed to be measured without error. Any particle is isolated in the primary inertial system * and is subjected to the action of a single force $F_1$. The acceleration

* The primary inertial system or astronomical frame of reference is an imaginary set of reference axes attached to the mean position of the so-called fixed stars. See Art. 2, Chapter 1.

$a_1$ of the particle is measured, and the ratio $F_1/a_1$ will be some number $C_1$ whose value depends on the units used for measurement of force and acceleration. The experiment is now repeated by subjecting the same particle to a different force $F_2$ and measuring the corresponding acceleration $a_2$. Again the ratio $F_2/a_2$ will produce a number $C_2$. The experiment is repeated as many times as desired. Two important conclusions may be drawn from the results. First, the ratios of applied force to corresponding acceleration will all equal the same number, provided the units for measurement are not changed in the experiments. Thus

$$\frac{F_1}{a_1} = \frac{F_2}{a_2} = \cdots = \frac{F}{a} = C, \text{ a constant.}$$

The constant $C$ is a measure of some property of the particle which does not change. This property is the *inertia* of the particle which is the *resistance* to change in velocity. Thus for a particle with high inertia (large $C$) the acceleration will be small for a given force $F$, and, conversely, if the inertia is small, the acceleration will be large. The *mass m* is used as the quantitative measure of inertia, and therefore the expression

$$C = km$$

may be written, where $k$ is a constant to account for the units used. Thus the experimental relation becomes

$$F = kma, \tag{27}$$

where $F$ is the resultant force acting on a particle of mass $m$, and $a$ is the resulting acceleration of the particle.

The second conclusion from the ideal experiments is that the acceleration is always in the direction of the applied force. Thus Eq. 27 is a *vector* equation which expresses equality of direction as well as magnitude.

Although an actual experiment cannot be performed in the ideal manner described, the conclusions are inferred from the measurements of countless accurately performed experiments where the results are correctly predicted from the hypothesis of the ideal experiment. One of the most accurate checks lies in the precise account of the motions of planets based on Eq. 27.

It should be understood that the results of the fundamental experiment may be obtained only if measurements are made relative to the "fixed" primary inertial system. Thus, if the experiment described were performed on the surface of the earth and all measurements were made relative to a reference system attached to the earth, the measured results would show a slight discrepancy upon substitution into Eq. 27. This discrepancy would be due to the neglect of the components of acceleration of the earth and would disappear when these components were accounted for. The corrections due to the acceleration of the earth are negligible * for most practical engineering purposes which involve the motions of structures and machines on the surface of the earth. Thus accelerations measured on the earth's surface may be treated as "absolute," and Eq. 27 may be applied with negligible error to experimental measurements made on the surface of the earth.

Before 1905 the laws of Newtonian mechanics had been verified by innumerable physical experiments and were considered the final description of the motion of bodies. The concept of *time*, considered an absolute quantity in the Newtonian theory, received a basically different interpretation in the theory of relativity announced by Einstein in 1905. The new concept called for a complete reformulation of the accepted laws of mechanics. The theory of relativity was subject to early ridicule but has had experimental check and is now universally accepted by physicists the world over. Although the difference between the mechanics of Newton and that of Einstein is basic, there is no practical difference in the results given by the two theories except when velocities of the order of the speed of light (186,000 mi./sec.) are encountered.† Important problems in atomic physics and celestial

* Equation 27 may be rewritten as

$$F = m(a_r + a_e),$$

in which $k$ is taken as unity and the absolute acceleration $A$ is replaced by the vector sum of the acceleration $a_r$ of the particle measured relative to the earth, and the acceleration $a_e$ of a point on the earth's surface in the primary system.

In the case of a body falling from rest from an altitude $h$ the rotation of the earth gives rise to an eastward acceleration (Coriolis acceleration), and, neglecting air resistance, it may be shown that the body falls to the ground a distance

$$x = \frac{2}{3}\,\omega\,\sqrt{\frac{2h^3}{g}}\,\cos\gamma$$

east of the point on the ground directly under that from which it was dropped. The angular velocity of the earth is $\omega = 0.729 \times 10^{-4}$ rad./sec., and the latitude, north or south, is $\gamma$. At a latitude of 45 deg. and from a height of 200 ft., the eastward deflection is $x = 0.291$ in.

† The theory of relativity demonstrates that there is no such thing as a preferred primary inertial system and that experiments conducted in reference systems moving with constant velocity relative to one another will yield exactly the same results. On this basis, for example, the principles of relativity show that a clock carried by the pilot of an airplane flying at a constant speed of 500 mi./hr. and making a 500 mi. flight away from an airport and returning nonstop at the same speed would be slow, compared with the airport clock, by 0.00000000202 sec.

mechanics, for example, involve calculations based on the principles of relativity.

**26. Units.** It is customary to take $k$ equal to unity in Eq. 27, which puts the relation in the usual form of Newton's second law

$$F = ma. \tag{1}$$

A system of units for which $k$ is unity is known as a *kinetic* system. Thus for a kinetic system the units of force, mass, and acceleration are not independent. Also, the engineer uses a *gravitational* kinetic system in which the units of force, length, and time are considered fundamental and the units of mass are derived from these three. The British gravitational system of units, listed in the table accompanying Art. 4 of Chapter 1, is the system used universally by engineers in English-speaking countries. This table should be studied carefully before proceeding.

The pound is used frequently as a unit of mass as well as a unit of force. The legal pound in the United States is defined as 0.4535924277 times the mass of the international kilogram. A one-pound *force* would be required to support this portion of the standard kilogram at the standard conditions of absolute rest, sea level, and 45 deg. N latitude or, more precisely, any location at which the absolute acceleration of gravity is $g = 32.1740$ ft./sec.$^2$ The weight as measured on the earth's surface varies slightly with the location because of the rotation of the earth and the slight departure from a spherical shape. For practical purposes, however, it may be said that a body which "weighs" one pound on the surface of the earth has a mass of one pound. The British pound is the mass of a certain platinum cylinder kept at the Standards Office in London and is essentially identical with the United States pound.

A second example of the accepted use of the word pound as a unit of mass occurs in the expression for the heat or energy content of a unit quantity of matter. Thus the available energy of fuel is expressed as so many "B.t.u./lb." and means the number of available units of heat energy (British thermal units) per *pound* of mass (not pound of force). This double standard for the term pound is unfortunate but unavoidable. The symbols *lbf.* and *lbm.* are sometimes used to distinguish between pound-force and pound-mass, respectively. In the British absolute system the pound is the unit of mass and the poundal is the unit of force. This system finds little use because the poundal (1/32.2 times the pound force) is too small a unit for convenience.

**27. Motion of a Particle.** Consider a particle of mass $m$ subjected to the action of the concurrent forces $F_1$, $F_2$, $F_3$, $\cdots$ whose vector sum is $\Sigma F$. Equation 1 becomes

$$\Sigma F = ma, \tag{28}$$

which is a vector equation with the components

$$\Sigma F_x = ma_x,$$
$$\Sigma F_y = ma_y, \tag{29}$$
$$\Sigma F_z = ma_z,$$

where $\Sigma F = \sqrt{(\Sigma F_x)^2 + (\Sigma F_y)^2 + (\Sigma F_z)^2}$ and $a = \sqrt{a_x^2 + a_y^2 + a_z^2}$. Equation 28 is said to be the *equation of motion* for the particle, and Eqs. 29 are the three equivalent scalar equations of motion. In applying Eqs. 29 the reference axes may be oriented in any convenient manner. Thus, if the $x$-axis is chosen to coincide with the direction of the resultant acceleration $a$, Eqs. 29 become $\Sigma F_x = ma$, $\Sigma F_y = 0$, $\Sigma F_z = 0$. The particle may then be said to be in equilibrium in so far as motion in the $y$- and $z$-directions is concerned. The equation of motion may also be written as a differential equation. Thus for motion in the $x$-direction, for example, the first of Eqs. 29 becomes

$$\Sigma F_x = m \frac{d^2x}{dt^2}. \tag{30}$$

This form of the motion equation may be used to describe problems where $\Sigma F_x$ is a function of time and displacement. Two successive integrations of the differential equation produce the relation between $x$ and $t$. In particular when $\Sigma F_x$ is a function of both $x$ and $t$, solution of the equation of motion as a differential equation is indicated.

A particle may move on a free path in space without constraints, or it may be constrained to move on a plane or along a line. If free to move in space, such as the center of mass of a rocket in free flight, the particle is said to have *three degrees of freedom* which means that three independent coordinates are needed to specify the position of the particle at any instant. All three of the scalar equations of motion, Eqs. 29, would have to be applied and integrated to obtain the space coordinates in terms of the time. If a particle is constrained to move in two dimensions, such as a marble sliding on the curved surface of a bowl, only two coordinates are needed to specify its position, and in this case it is said to have *two degrees of freedom*. If a particle is constrained to move along a fixed linear path, such as a bead sliding along a fixed wire, its position may be specified by the coordinate measured along the wire. Thus the particle would have only *one degree of freedom.*

Equation 28 gives the instantaneous value of the acceleration corresponding to the forces which act at the moment considered. If the forces are variable, the acceleration will also be variable, and the changes in velocity and displacement of the particle during an interval of its motion may be computed by integrating the variable acceleration in the appropriate kinematical relations $a = dv/dt$ or $a = v\,dv/ds$ in the manner developed in Art. 11. These integrations are equivalent to the direct integration of the differential equation of motion, Eq. 30, with respect to time or displacement.

Chapter 4 is devoted to the solution of problems where attention is focused mainly upon the instantaneous relationship between the forces and the corresponding accelerations. Problems are included which also require the integration of the resulting accelerations to find changes in velocity and displacement. Equation 28 is used not only for the motion of particles, but also is extended to cover the accelerated motions of rigid bodies.

Chapter 5 is devoted to the solution of problems which involve the first integral of the equation of motion with respect to displacement. This approach is indicated when the forces are functions of displacement and leads to the principles of work and energy. These principles are applied to both particle and rigid-body motion.

Chapter 6 is devoted to problems which involve the first integral of the equation of motion with respect to time. This approach leads to the principles of impulse and momentum. These principles are developed for a particle and are extended to cover the motions of rigid bodies and the mass flow of systems of particles.

Chapter 7 is devoted to an introduction to the important topic of vibrations. Only the linear case is discussed where the forces are proportional to the displacement but of opposite sign and where they may also be periodic functions of the time.

In each of the chapters which follow a constant demand is placed on the knowledge of kinematics gained in Chapter 2. Thus the student will be well advised to conduct a continuing review of kinematics as he proceeds.

In applying Eq. 28 to the motion of a particle it is *absolutely necessary* to account for *all* forces acting on the particle. The only forces which may be neglected are those whose magnitudes are negligible compared with other forces acting. The forces of mutual attraction between particles or bodies (except that of the earth) may be neglected. The vector sum $\Sigma F$ in Eq. 28 and the corresponding scalar sums in Eqs.

29 refer to *all* forces acting *on* the particle in question. The only reliable way to account accurately for every force is to *isolate* the body or particle under consideration by drawing its complete and correct *free-body diagram* where every force, known and unknown, which acts on the particle is represented. Only after this vital step has been completed should the application of the equations of motion be attempted. The free-body diagram serves the same key purpose in kinetics as it does in statics. This purpose is simply to establish a *thoroughly reliable method* for the correct evaluation of the resultant of all real forces acting on the body in question. In statics this resultant was equated to zero, whereas in kinetics it is equated to the product of mass and acceleration. If the student recognizes that the equations of motion must be taken literally and if he respects the exact meaning of the equal sign, very little difficulty will arise.

**28. Motion of a System of Particles.** The principle of motion for a single particle will now be extended to cover a system or discrete

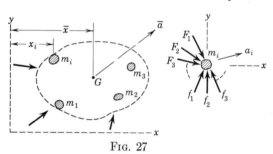

Fig. 27

number of particles. No restriction will be placed on the manner in which the particles are connected, and the analysis which follows will apply equally well to the motion of a solid body, a liquid body, or a defined system of gas molecules. Such a general system subjected to certain external forces is represented schematically in Fig. 27, where the dotted envelope encompasses and *defines the system at the instant* under consideration. Several particles only of the system are shown. The particle of mass $m_i$ will be selected as a representative particle of the system. The free-body diagram of $m_i$ is drawn to the right of the system and shows the particle under the action of forces $F_1, F_2, F_3, \cdots$, which are applied from sources *external* to the envelope, and forces $f_1, f_2, f_3, \cdots$, which are applied from sources *internal* to the envelope.

As a result of the forces acting on $m_i$ the particle has an acceleration component in the $x$-direction at the instant considered, and the first of Eqs. 29 requires

$$F_{1_x} + F_{2_x} + F_{3_x} + \cdots + f_{1_x} + f_{2_x} + f_{3_x} + \cdots = m_i a_{i_x}.$$

Similar equations may be written for *all* particles of the system, and, when added together, they give

$$\Sigma F_x + \Sigma f_x = \Sigma m_i a_{i_x}.$$

The symbol $\Sigma F_x$ stands for the algebraic sum of the $x$-components of *all* forces applied *externally* to the envelope or system. This sum of external forces includes not only mechanically applied contact forces but also all body forces applied by remote action such as gravity forces (weights) or electrical and magnetic forces if present. The term $\Sigma f_x$ is the algebraic sum of the $x$-components of all internal forces. This latter sum vanishes since, by Newton's third law, each internal action on one particle is accompanied by an equal and opposite internal reaction on its neighboring particle, and the net effect for each and all such pairs of forces is zero. The expression $\Sigma m_i a_{i_x}$ represents the algebraic sum of the products of the mass of each particle and its corresponding $x$-component of acceleration. The remaining relation is now

$$\Sigma F_x = \Sigma m_i a_{i_x}.$$

This equation may be interpreted by introducing the position of the center of mass $G$ of the system. The $x$-coordinate of $G$ is $\bar{x}$ and is located by the principle of moments which requires that

$$m\bar{x} = m_1 x_1 + m_2 x_2 + m_3 x_3 + \cdots = \Sigma m_i x_i.$$

The total mass of the system is $m = \Sigma m_i$. Two successive differentiations with respect to the time yield

$$m\frac{d^2\bar{x}}{dt^2} = \Sigma m_i \frac{d^2 x_i}{dt^2} \qquad \text{or} \qquad m\bar{a}_x = \Sigma m_i a_{i_x}.$$

All particles of the system selected are accounted for, so that the mass $m$ of the system is not a function of time. The symbol $\bar{a}_x$ is the $x$-component of the acceleration of the center of mass $G$. This last summation is identical with that in the combined motion equations so that $\Sigma F_x = m\bar{a}_x$. Similar analyses in the $y$- and $z$-directions hold, and therefore the three resulting equations are

$$\Sigma F_x = m\bar{a}_x,$$

$$\Sigma F_y = m\bar{a}_y, \qquad\qquad (31)$$

$$\Sigma F_z = m\bar{a}_z.$$

These equations express the fact that the resultant in any direction of all external forces acting on the system equals the total mass of the system times the component of the acceleration of the mass center in that direction.   Equations 31 are the three scalar components of the single vector equation

$$\Sigma F = m\bar{a}. \qquad (32)$$

Equation 32 states that the vector resultant of all external forces acting on the system equals the total mass of the system times the acceleration of the center of mass and that the acceleration is in the direction of the resultant force.   This statement, or the equivalent ones for Eqs. 31, constitutes the *principle of motion of the mass center*. This principle is one of the most important of the derived relations in mechanics because it finds direct and repeated use in most of the problems that follow.   Equation 32, although identical in form with Eq. 1 for a particle, may not be inferred from Eq. 1 but must be proved.

Equation 32 is a vector equation, and hence the equal sign signifies equality in magnitude and direction.   It must not be assumed, however, that the resultant force $\Sigma F$ passes through the center of mass $G$. There is no step in the foregoing proof which depends on the position of $\Sigma F$ or any of its components, and therefore it must be assumed that, in general, $\Sigma F$ does not pass through $G$.   The location of $\Sigma F$ for the various types of rigid-body motion will be established in *Part 2* of the following chapter.

It should be recalled from the principles of statics (see Chapter 2 of *Part I, Statics*) that the most general force system may be expressed

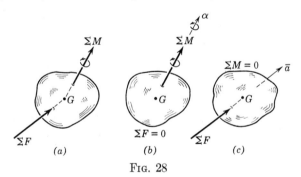

Fig. 28

in terms of the resultant force $\Sigma F$ applied at any point and the corresponding resultant couple $\Sigma M$ whose magnitude and direction depend on the line of action chosen for $\Sigma F$.   The general force system may be considered, then, as the resultant force $\Sigma F$ acting through $G$ and a corresponding resultant couple $\Sigma M$ as represented in Fig. 28a.   If $\Sigma F = 0$, Fig. 28b, there can be no acceleration $\bar{a}$ of the mass center $G$, and the effect of $\Sigma M$ is to govern the rotational motion about $G$.   Conversely, if $\Sigma M = 0$, with $\Sigma F$ passing through $G$, Fig. 28c, there will be a translational acceleration $\bar{a}$ of the system as a whole. If both $\Sigma F$ and $\Sigma M$ are zero, the system is in complete external equilibrium, whereas, if neither $\Sigma F$ nor $\Sigma M$ is zero, both linear and angular motion of the system will result. Although these conclusions hold for any material system, they are more easily visualized and find more ready application for the motion of solid bodies.

The principles developed in this chapter will now be applied to the various types of particle and rigid-body motion in the chapter which follows.

CHAPTER

4

# FORCE, MASS, AND ACCELERATION

**29. Introduction.** Part 1 of this chapter is a study of the kinetics of particles, and Part 2 deals with the kinetics of rigid bodies. Particle kinetics is concerned with concurrent force systems, whereas rigid-body kinetics involves nonconcurrent forces.

Before attempting to work the problems, the student should again read Art. 9 of Chapter 1 which outlines the essential steps in the solution of problems in mechanics. In the present chapter and in those which follow, too much emphasis cannot be placed on the vital importance of the choice of the system to be isolated. This system can be a single particle or a number of particles or bodies considered as a single body. Once a clear-cut decision has been made as to exactly what is included in the system selected, the system should be isolated by drawing a sketch of its external boundary. The student should be able to trace a *complete closed circuit around the external boundary* of the system isolated in order to define clearly everything which is or is not a part of the system chosen for isolation. Next the *free-body diagram* should be completed by indicating *all* known and unknown forces acting on the system from *external sources* in the manner developed in *Mechanics, Part I, Statics*.

In solving problems the student often wonders how to get started and what sequence of steps to follow in arriving at the solution. This difficulty may be eliminated if the student forms the habit of first recognizing some relationship between the quantity desired in the problem and other quantities, known and unknown. Additional relationships between these unknowns and other quantities, known and unknown, are then perceived. Finally the dependence upon the original data is established, and the procedure for the analysis and computation is indicated. A few minutes spent organizing the plan of attack through recognition of the dependence of one quantity upon another will be time well spent and will usually prevent groping for the answer with irrelevant calculations.

## PART 1. PARTICLE MOTION

**30. Rectilinear Motion.** For rectilinear motion in, say, the $x$-direction the equation of motion for a particle

$$\Sigma F_x = ma_x \tag{29}$$

is used to determine the acceleration which results from the action of prescribed forces or to find the forces which accompany an acceleration due to a prescribed or constrained motion. If the forces are constant, the acceleration is constant, and vice versa. If the velocity and displacement are desired, the kinematical relations, Eqs. 7, 8, and 9, may be used in the manner previously studied, or else the equation of motion written as a differential equation

$$\Sigma F_x = m \frac{d^2x}{dt^2} \tag{30}$$

may be integrated successively to find the velocity and the displacement. If the forces are variable, it will be necessary either to integrate Eq. 30 directly or else to solve Eq. 29 for the acceleration as a variable and then to integrate it in one of the kinematical equations $a = dv/dt$ or $v\,dv = a\,dx$ whichever one is appropriate. The two approaches actually amount to the same process. Integration of the equation of motion by numerical and graphical means is often required when the functional relationship between the variable forces and the coordinates cannot be written. This is frequently the case when the forces are determined experimentally or from other approximate data.

If two or more particles or bodies are connected and have the same acceleration, they may be considered together as a single system which eliminates consideration of the internal forces in the connections be-

$v = v_0 + at$      $a = \frac{dv}{dt}$

$s = v_0 t + \frac{1}{2}at^2$      $v = \frac{dx}{dt}$

$v^2 = v_0^2 + 2as$

tween them. On the other hand, if these same forces are to be found, the bodies must be considered separately in order to disclose these forces as external loads.

### SAMPLE PROBLEMS

**201.** A 161 lb. man stands on a spring scale in an elevator. During the first 3 sec., starting from rest, the scale reads 181 lb. Find the velocity of the elevator at the end of the 3 sec. and the tension $T$ in the supporting cable for the elevator during the acceleration period. The total weight of elevator, man, and scale is 1610 lb.

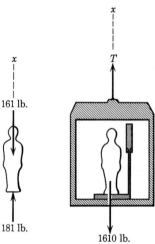

PROB. 201

*Solution.* The cable tension and the velocity acquired will depend on the acceleration which is constant since the forces are constant during the 3 sec. interval. The acceleration is obtained by considering the two forces acting on the man during the first 3 sec. The free-body diagram of the man is first drawn as indicated. Next the equation of motion is applied which is

$$[\Sigma F_x = ma_x] \qquad 181 - 161 = \frac{161}{32.2}a_x, \qquad a_x = 4 \text{ ft./sec.}^2 \text{ up.}$$

The velocity reached at the end of the 3 sec. is

$$[v = at] \qquad v = 4 \times 3 = 12 \text{ ft./sec.} \qquad Ans.$$

The tension in the cable is obtained from the free-body diagram of the elevator and its contents considered together. Thus

$$[\Sigma F_x = ma_x] \qquad T - 1610 = \frac{1610}{32.2} \times 4, \qquad T = 1810 \text{ lb.} \qquad Ans.$$

**202.** Find the vertical distance $s$ through which the 650 lb. weight has moved during 4 sec. following its release from rest and determine the tension $T$ in the cable. The friction and weight of the pulleys are negligible.

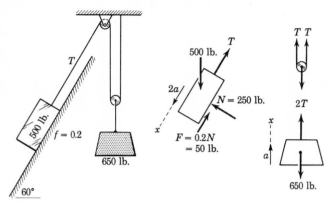

PROB. 202

*Solution.* The distance moved in the given time will depend on the acceleration, which is determined from the force analysis of each of the weights. The direction of movement of the 500 lb. block is not given so must be either assumed or determined. It may be determined by considering the system without friction, and in this event an additional force of $500 \sin 60° - (650/2) =$ 108 lb. would be thus required on the block in the direction up the plane to hold it in equilibrium. This force is greater than the friction force of $0.2N =$ $0.2 \times 500 \times 0.5 = 50$ lb., so if the supposed 108 lb. force is released, friction would be insufficient to prevent movement down the plane. Thus the direction of the friction force is established, and the correct free-body diagrams are drawn with the directions of the accelerations indicated. It should be clear that the acceleration of the 500 lb. weight is twice that of the 650 lb. weight. Also with negligible mass of the small pulleys and no appreciable friction in their bearings there is a negligible unbalance of forces and moments required for their accelerations. Hence the small pulleys may be treated as though they were in equilibrium.

The equation of motion for the 500 lb. block is

$[\Sigma F_x = ma_x]$     $500 \sin 60° - 50 - T = \dfrac{500}{32.2} \times 2a,$

and that for the 650 lb. weight is

$[\Sigma F_x = ma_x]$     $2T - 650 = \dfrac{650}{32.2}\, a.$

Solution of these two equations gives

$a = 1.41$ ft./sec.$^2$     and     $T = 339$ lb.     *Ans.*

Thus in 4 sec. the 650 lb. weight moves

$[s = \tfrac{1}{2}at^2]$     $s = \tfrac{1}{2} \times 1.41 \times 4^2 = 11.28$ ft. up.     *Ans.*

**203.** Wind-tunnel tests of the resistance of a sphere in a moving air stream for low velocities give the plotted curve shown in the full line. If the sphere weighs 4 oz. and is released from rest in still air, use these data to predict the velocity $v$ which it will acquire after dropping 10 ft. from rest.

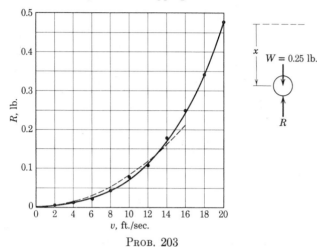

PROB. 203

*Solution.* The free-body diagram of the sphere is drawn as shown and includes the variable resistance $R$ and the constant weight $W = 0.25$ lb. The positive $x$-direction is taken down with origin at the point of release from rest. The equation of motion is

$$[\Sigma F_x = ma_x] \qquad\qquad W - R = \frac{W}{g}\,a_x.$$

Since the velocity at a particular value of displacement is required, an integration with respect to displacement is indicated. Multiplication of the equation by $dx$ yields

$$(W - R)\,dx = \frac{W}{g}\,v\,dv \qquad \text{or} \qquad (W - R)\,dx = \frac{W}{2g}\,d(v^2).$$

This step is the same as multiplying the differential equation of motion by $dx$ which gives

$$(W - R)\,dx = \frac{W}{g}\frac{d^2x}{dt^2}\,dx \qquad \text{or} \qquad (W - R)\,dx = \frac{W}{2g}\,d\left(\frac{dx}{dt}\right)^2.$$

With the substitution of the numerical values of $W$ and $g$ the equation may be written

$$d(v^2) = (64.4 - 258R)\,dx.$$

By using small but finite increments the expression may be approximated by

$$\Delta(v^2) = (64.4 - 258R)\,\Delta x.$$

In this form integration of the equation of motion may be effected by a step-by-step process as shown in the following table. The 10 ft. interval is divided into

1 ft. increments for the first 2 ft. where the velocity is changing most rapidly and into 2 ft. increments for the remaining interval. The value of $v^2$, and hence $v$, for any value of $x$ equals $v^2$ at the previous displacement plus the increment $\Delta(v^2)$ determined from the defining relation expressed in terms of $\Delta x$. Smaller increments in $\Delta x$ could be chosen for a more accurate solution. Values of $R$ are read directly from the graph for the corresponding values of $v$.

| $x$ ft. | $\Delta x$ ft. | $R$ lb. | $(64.4 - 258R)$ ft./sec.$^2$ | $\Delta(v^2)$ (ft./sec.)$^2$ | $v^2$ (ft./sec.)$^2$ | $v$ ft./sec. |
|---|---|---|---|---|---|---|
| 0 | | 0 | 64.4 | | 0 | 0 |
| | 1 | | | 64.4 | | |
| 1 | | 0.04 | 54.1 | | 64.4 | 8.0 |
| | 1 | | | 54.1 | | |
| 2 | | 0.09 | 41.2 | | 118.5 | 10.9 |
| | 2 | | | 82.4 | | |
| 4 | | 0.17 | 20.5 | | 201 | 14.2 |
| | 2 | | | 41.0 | | |
| 6 | | 0.23 | 5.0 | | 242 | 15.5 |
| | 2 | | | 10.0 | | |
| 8 | | 0.24 | 2.4 | | 252 | 15.9 |
| | 2 | | | 4.8 | | |
| 10 | | | | | 257 | 16.0 |

The velocity at $x = 10$ ft. is found to be 16.0 ft./sec. The maximum velocity reached by the sphere occurs when the increment $\Delta(v^2) = 0$ or when $64.4 - 258R = 0$. This gives $R = 0.25$ lb., which, from the graph, corresponds to a velocity of 16.1 ft./sec. Thus the calculation shows that the sphere has almost reached its maximum or terminal velocity.

An analytic solution may also be used to approximate the velocity by writing $R$ as an appropriate function of $v$. By assuming the form $R = kv^2$ the equation of motion may be integrated, upon separation of the variables, to obtain

$$\int_0^x \frac{2g}{W}\, dx = \int_0^v \frac{d(v^2)}{W - kv^2} \quad \text{or} \quad \frac{2gx}{W} = \frac{1}{k} \log \frac{W}{W - kv^2}$$

from which

$$v = \sqrt{\frac{W}{k}\left(1 - e^{-2gkx/W}\right)}.$$

An appropriate value of $k$ may be determined by assuming the function to agree with the given data at about $v = 13$ ft./sec. which represents a fair average of the resistance over the interval involved. This point on the curve gives $k = 0.83 \times 10^{-3}$ lb. sec.$^2$/ft.$^2$ and defines the dotted curve shown in the figure. Substitution of the numerical values into the expression for $v$ gives

$$v = \sqrt{\frac{0.25}{0.83 \times 10^{-3}}} (1 - e^{-\frac{2 \times 32.2 \times 0.83 \times 10^{-3} \times 10}{0.25}}) = 16.3 \text{ ft./sec.}$$

This approximation to $v$ is slightly higher than the maximum terminal velocity. A closer approximation could be achieved by using a higher degree polynomial in $v$.

## PROBLEMS

**204.** Determine the vertical acceleration $a$ of the 200 lb. weight for each of
the two cases illustrated. The mass and
friction of the pulleys are negligible.
  *Ans.*   (*a*) $a = 16.1$ ft./sec.$^2$,
      (*b*) $a = 6.44$ ft./sec.$^2$

**205.** The resultant horizontal force on
a small object of weight $W$ which moves
in a straight line on a horizontal plane is
10 lb. The displacement of the object is
given by $s = 4 + 2t + 10t^2$, where $s$ is in
feet and $t$ is in seconds. Determine $W$.
      *Ans.*   $W = 16.1$ lb.

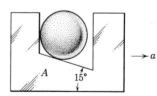

PROB. 204

**206.** The weight is attached to an arm
of negligible mass pivoted to the vertical plate at $O$. If the plate is given a
constant and steady acceleration $a$ to the right, determine the angle $\theta$ registered by the pointer.

           *Ans.*   $\theta = \tan^{-1} \dfrac{a}{g}$

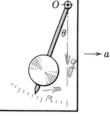

PROB. 206

PROB. 207

**207.** The frame is given a steady horizontal acceleration $a = 2g$. Determine the reaction $F$ between the 10 lb. sphere and the vertical surface.
              *Ans.*   $F = 17.32$ lb.

**208.** A car left skid marks from all four wheels on a level road for a distance of 40 ft. before coming to a stop. Determine the velocity $v$ of the car when the brakes were applied. The coefficient of kinetic friction between the tires and the pavement may be taken as 0.8.

**209.** A 150 lb. man hoists himself on a bosun's chair as shown. If, for a short interval, he exerts a pull of 60 lb. on the rope, find his acceleration.

*Ans.* $a = 6.44$ ft./sec.$^2$ up

**210.** The device shown is used as an accelerometer and consists of the 2 oz. plunger $A$ which deflects the spring a measurable amount as the unit is given an upward acceleration $a$. Specify the necessary spring constant $k$ which will limit the spring compression to $\frac{1}{4}$ in., measured from the rest position, for a steady upward acceleration of $4g$. Friction is negligible.

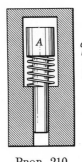

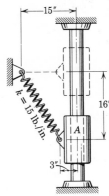

PROB. 209          PROB. 210          PROB. 211

**211.** The collar $A$ weighs 20 lb. and slides on the fixed vertical shaft. The spring is uncompressed when the collar is in the dotted position. Determine the initial acceleration $a$ of the collar when it is released from rest in the position illustrated. The coefficient of friction between the collar and the shaft is 0.2, and the stiffness of the spring is 15 lb./in.

*Ans.* $a = 99.2$ ft./sec.$^2$

**212.** The collar $A$ is free to slide along the smooth shaft $B$. Determine the acceleration $a$ of the shaft and frame necessary to maintain the collar at a fixed position on the shaft.

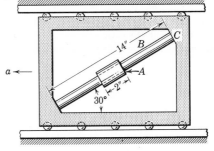

PROB. 212

**213.** The 32.2 lb. sliding block $A$ moves in the smooth vertical guide under the action of a force $P$ applied to the cable as shown. The separate cables are wound around the light pulleys, which are fastened together and which are perfectly free to turn about their common shaft mounted in the block. The diameter of the larger pulley is twice that of the smaller one. Determine the acceleration $a$ of the block for ($a$) $P = 35$ lb. and ($b$) $P = 30$ lb. (*Hint:* The integral pulley may be treated as a body in equilibrium since its mass is negligible.)   *Ans.* ($a$) $a = 2.8$ ft./sec.$^2$ up, ($b$) $a = 2.2$ ft./sec.$^2$ down

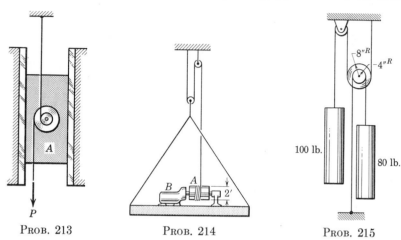

PROB. 213      PROB. 214      PROB. 215

**214.** A platform together with the load it carries weighs 600 lb. and is raised by winding the supporting cable around the drum $A$, which is driven by the motor and gear unit $B$. If this unit supplies a starting torque of 250 lb. ft. to the drum, find the initial acceleration $a$ of the platform. The weight of the drum is small and may be neglected.

**215.** Determine the acceleration $a$ of the 80 lb. weight for the system shown. The mass of the pulleys and friction are negligible, and the concentric pulleys are free to turn independently of each other about their common axle.

                 *Ans.* $a = 3.58$ ft./sec.$^2$

**216.** Small objects leave the assembly line at the rate of one every second from a conveyor belt traveling at the lineal speed of 2 ft./sec. The objects enter the chute with this initial velocity and slide to the floor below where a second conveyor belt takes them to the shipping department. The coefficient

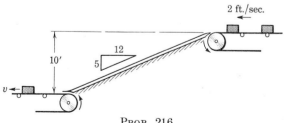

PROB. 216

of friction for the parts on the steel chute is found to be ⅓. What would be the required velocity $v$ of the lower conveyor in order that there be no slipping of the parts when they are deposited horizontally on the belt?

*Ans.* $v = 11.52$ ft./sec.

**217.** If the coefficient of friction between the 50 lb. weight and the 300 lb. weight is 0.5, determine the acceleration of each weight for (*a*) $P = 12$ lb. and

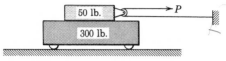

PROB. 217

(*b*) $P = 16$ lb. The 300 lb. weight is free to roll, and the weight and friction for the pulley are negligible.

**218.** Determine the acceleration of each weight. The pulleys have negligible weight and friction.

*Ans.* $a_A = \frac{1}{31} g$ down, $a_B = \frac{9}{31} g$ up, $a_C = \frac{7}{31} g$ down

**219.** The elevator in a vertical mine shaft weighs 3000 lb. loaded and requires 24 sec. to descend 300 ft. from rest until it stops at the bottom. The velocity of the elevator is 15 ft./sec. except during the starting and stopping periods. If the tension in the cable supporting the elevator is 2700 lb. during the starting period, what is its value during the stopping period, assuming constant deceleration?

**220.** In the Scotch-yoke mechanism shown the 2 lb. piston and the 5 lb. connecting link are driven by the pin $A$ of the crank $AO$. In the $\theta = 45$ deg. position the angular velocity and angular acceleration of the crank are 18 rad./sec. and 72 rad./sec.$^2$, respectively, both counterclockwise. Determine the force $A$ exerted by the pin on the smooth slotted link and find the force $B$ exerted by the piston pin on the piston for this position.

*Ans.* $A = 9.67$ lb., $B = 2.76$ lb.

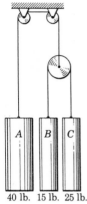

40 lb. 15 lb. 25 lb.

PROB. 218

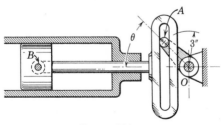

PROB. 220

**221.** A chain of length $2l$ and weight $\mu$ per unit length is hanging in the equilibrium position shown when end $B$ is given a slight downward displacement which causes an unbalance of forces. Determine the acceleration $a$ of the chain in terms of the upward displacement $x$ of end $A$ from its equilibrium position. Also find the velocity $v$ of the chain when end $A$ reaches the top position. Neglect the mass, friction, and diameter of the pulley.

$$Ans. \quad a = \frac{x}{l}\,g, \; v = \sqrt{gl}$$

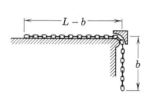

PROB. 221                          PROB. 222

**222.** The chain is released from rest in the position shown and slides on the smooth surface through the opening and over the edge. Determine the velocity $v$ of the chain when the last link has left the edge.

**223.** Assume that the surface on which the chain of Prob. 222 slides is not smooth and that the coefficient of friction is $f$. Determine the velocity $v$ of the chain when the last link leaves the edge if the chain was started from rest with a sufficient number of links over the edge to overcome friction on the remaining links and barely initiate motion. Neglect friction at the edge.

$$Ans. \quad v = \sqrt{\frac{gL}{1 + f}}$$

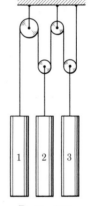

**224.** Determine the acceleration of each of the identical metal cylinders if the pulleys and cables have negligible weight and friction is too small to be considered.

**225.** A small block is given an initial velocity $v$ measured along the floor of an elevator moving with a downward acceleration $a$. Because of friction the block moves a distance $s_1$ measured along the floor before it stops sliding. The experiment is repeated with the same initial velocity relative to the floor when the elevator has an upward acceleration of the same magnitude $a$, and the block slides a shorter distance $s_2$. Determine the elevator accelerations $a$.

$$Ans. \quad a = g\,\frac{s_1 - s_2}{s_1 + s_2}$$          PROB. 224

**226.** Assume that the frame and shaft in Prob. 212 are in the horizontal plane and that the collar $A$ weighs 1.61 lb. If the frame is given an acceleration of 10 ft./sec.$^2$ to the right, determine the force $F$ exerted by the smooth shaft on the collar and the time $t$ required for the collar to move across the frame if it starts from $C$ at rest relative to the frame.

**227.** The total resistance $R$ to the horizontal motion of a rocket test sled is shown in the figure. Approximate the resistance by the straight dotted line

shown, and determine the distance $x$ which the sled must travel along the track
from rest to reach a velocity of 1600 ft./sec.  The forward thrust of the rockets
is assumed to be constant at 60,000 lb., and the total weight of the sled is also
assumed to be constant at 4000 lb.                    *Ans.*  $x = 5160$ ft.

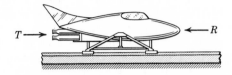

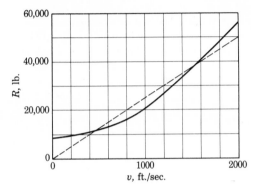

PROB. 227

**228.** A small ship displaces 350 tons (1 long ton $= 2240$ lb.) and is powered
with engines which produce a maximum forward propeller thrust of 12,000 lb.
The total resistance of the ship to motion through the water is shown in the
graph as a function of the speed of the ship in knots (1 knot $= 1.69$ ft./sec.).

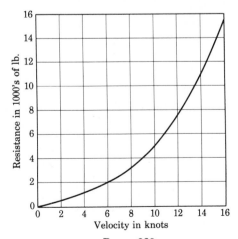

PROB. 228

If the ship starts from rest and maintains maximum propeller thrust, determine its speed $v$ after it has moved 360 ft. (*Suggestion:* Take displacement increments in the finite-difference equation of 20, 20, 40, 40, and the remainder 60 ft.)                                                                    *Ans.* $v = 10$ knots

**229.** A small steel block is "weighed" by a spring balance in the gondola of a balloon which is at rest at an altitude of 20 mi. above the earth, and a value of 1.200 lb. is recorded. The block is placed on a perfectly smooth horizontal surface in the gondola and subjected to a horizontal force of ½ lb. Find the acceleration $a$ of the block. Take the radius of the earth to be 4000 mi. and the acceleration of gravity at the surface of the earth to be 32.17 ft./sec.$^2$

*Ans.* $a = 13.26$ ft./sec.$^2$

**230.** In theory an object projected vertically up from the surface of the earth with a sufficiently high velocity $v$ can escape from the earth's field of influence. Calculate this velocity on the basis of the absence of an atmosphere to offer resistance due to air friction. The radius $R$ of the earth is very nearly 4000 mi.                    *Ans.* $v = \sqrt{2gR} = 6.98$ mi./sec.

**231.** Tests of a certain 8 lb. shell show that the air resistance varies with the velocity according to the graph shown. If the shell is fired vertically up

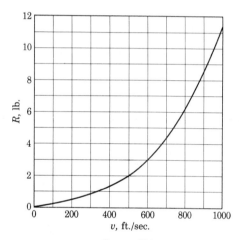

PROB. 231

with an initial velocity of 1000 ft./sec., determine the maximum height $x$ to which it ascends and the total time $t$ from firing until return to the ground. Neglect the effect of altitude on both air resistance and gravitational attraction.                                        *Ans.* $x = 11,000$ ft., $t = 52$ sec.

**\* 232.** A small steel ball of weight $W$ and diameter $D$ is released from rest on a smooth horizontal surface with its center a distance $s$ from the vertical pole face of a magnet. Determine the velocity $v$ with which the ball strikes the face. The opposite pole of the magnet is assumed to be at a considerable distance from the ball so that the attractive force varies inversely as the square of the distance from the pole face to the center of the ball. Also, a force $P$, normal to the pole face, is required to dislodge the ball when it rests against the face.

$$Ans. \quad v = \sqrt{\frac{PDg}{2W}}\left(2 - \frac{D}{s}\right)$$

\* **233.** The polishing disk shown rotates counterclockwise. A small metallic specimen is placed on the disk at $A$ in the smooth slot of the fixed supporting rail and released from rest. Determine the velocity $v$ of the specimen as it passes the vertical center line of the disk if the coefficient of friction between the specimen and the disk is $f$. Assume that $\omega$ is large so that the velocity of the point on the disk under the specimen is large compared with $v$ and hence that the friction force is always normal to the radial line joining $A$ with the center of the disk.

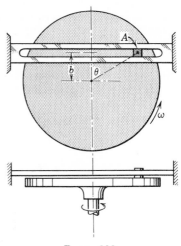

$$Ans. \quad v = \sqrt{fgb \log \frac{1 + \sin\theta}{1 - \sin\theta}}$$

\* **234.** The total mass of a small rocket prior to firing is $m_0$ which includes the fuel of mass $m_f$. The mass of the rocket decreases at a rate $m'$ which equals the constant rate at which fuel is burned. Determine the maximum upward velocity $v$ which the rocket could reach in vertical

Prob. 233

flight if there were no air resistance. The upward thrust $T$ is constant, and the altitude is small compared with the radius of the earth so that the variation in gravitational attraction is negligible.

$$Ans. \quad v = \frac{1}{m'}\left[T \log \frac{m_0}{m_0 - m_f} - gm_f\right]$$

\* **235.** The hoisting drum $D$ of diameter $d$ turns counterclockwise with a constant angular velocity $\omega$. Determine the tension $T$ in the vertical section of cable which attaches $W$ to $B$ in terms of $x$. The size, weight, and friction of the pulleys at $A$ and $B$ are negligible.

$$Ans. \quad T = W\left(1 + \frac{\omega^2 d^2 b^2}{16gx^3}\right)$$

\* **236.** The motion of the 2 lb. block $A$ in its guide is controlled by the rotation of the slotted arm in a vertical plane about $O$. If the arm has an angular velocity of 6 rad./sec. and an angular acceleration of 20 rad./sec.$^2$ both clockwise, in the vertical position shown, determine the force $F$ exerted by the arm on the pin mounted in

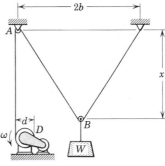

Prob. 235

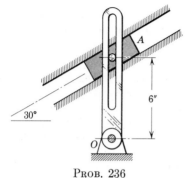

$A$ and find the normal force $N$ between the block and its 30 deg. guide. Friction is negligible on all surfaces. (*Caution:* The acceleration of $A$ is not equal to $(6 \times 20)/\cos 30°$ in./sec.²)

*Ans.* $F = 3.70$ lb., $N = 3.58$ lb.

\* **237.** A projectile of mass $m$ is fired with a muzzle velocity $u$ at an angle $\theta$ with the horizontal. If the resistance to motion is proportional to the first power of the velocity $R = kv$, determine the horizontal and vertical coordinates $x$ and $y$ of the projectile in terms of the time $t$

PROB. 236

after firing. What is the greatest possible value which $x$ may have assuming $y$ has no limits?

$$\text{Ans.} \qquad x = \frac{mu}{k}\cos\theta\,(1 - e^{-kt/m}),$$

$$y = \frac{m}{k}\left[\left(u\sin\theta + \frac{mg}{k}\right)(1 - e^{-kt/m}) - gt\right],$$

$$x_{max.} = \frac{mu}{k}\cos\theta$$

\* **238.** Set up the differential equation for the powered vertical flight of a rocket under the following conditions. The initial total mass is $m_0$ which includes the fuel of mass $m_f$. The fuel is burned at a constant rate $m'$ which produces a constant thrust $T$. The atmospheric resistance is a known function of both velocity $v$ and altitude $h$. The reduction in gravitational attraction must be accounted for. Rewrite the differential equation in the form of a finite-difference equation by expressing the increment in vertical velocity $\Delta v$ in terms of the corresponding time increment $\Delta t$, and indicate the procedure for a step-by-step solution for the altitude as a function of the time.

**31. Curvilinear Motion; $n$–$t$ Components.** When a particle moves along a curved path, its components of acceleration both normal and tangent to the path must be accounted for when writing the equation of motion of the particle. The basic vector equation of motion, Eq. 28, is

$$\Sigma F = ma = m(a_n \nrightarrow a_t)$$

where $a$ is the resultant vector acceleration of the particle and $a_n$ and $a_t$ are its components normal and tangent to the curve, respectively. These components of acceleration were studied in Art. 14 of Chapter 2, and it was found that $a_n = v^2/\rho = \rho\omega^2 = v\omega$ and $a_t = d|v|/dt = d|\rho\omega|/dt = \rho\alpha + \omega\,d\rho/dt$ where the meaning of the symbols is the same as that established in Chapter 2.

The vector equation of motion may be written in terms of its $n$- and $t$-components. Thus

$$\Sigma F_n = ma_n = m\frac{v^2}{\rho},$$

$$\Sigma F_t = ma_t = m\frac{d|v|}{dt}. \tag{33}$$

The significance of these relations is illustrated in Fig. 29 which shows a particle of mass $m$ moving along any plane curve with increasing speed $|v|$ in the direction shown. The summation of the $n$-components of *all* forces acting on the particle is $\Sigma F_n$. This sum is always directed toward the center of curvature $O$ since it must have the same direction as $a_n$ which is always toward the center of curvature. The summation of the $t$-components of *all* forces acting on the particle is $\Sigma F_t$. This sum agrees in direction with the tangential acceleration $a_t$ which is the

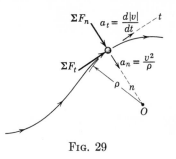

FIG. 29

direction of the velocity if the speed is increasing. If the speed is decreasing, $a_t$ and hence $\Sigma F_t$ will be in the direction opposite to the velocity.

When the motion is circular, the radius of curvature $\rho$ is constant, and the tangential acceleration is merely $a_t = \rho\alpha$. This relation also holds for points on a curved path for which the radius of curvature is a maximum or a minimum given by $d\rho/dt = 0$.

### SAMPLE PROBLEMS

**239.** *Conical Pendulum.* A small weight $W$ is suspended by a light arm or wire of length $l$ and made to revolve in a horizontal circle with a constant angular velocity $\omega$. Locate the plane of the circular motion by finding $h$, and calculate the tension $T$ in the supporting member.

*Solution.* For constant speed of rotation the conical pendulum will assume a position for which $\theta$, $h$, and $r$ will have fixed values. The free-body diagram of the particle in this position discloses *only two real forces* acting on it, its weight $W$ and the tension $T$. The first of Eqs. 33 and the equilibrium requirement for the vertical direction give

$$[\Sigma F_n = ma_n] \qquad T\sin\theta = \frac{W}{g}r\omega^2,$$

$$[\Sigma F_y = 0] \qquad T\cos\theta = W.$$

Substitution of $r = l \sin \theta$ into the first equation gives

$$T = \frac{W}{g} l \omega^2. \qquad Ans.$$

Division of the first equation by the second and substitution of $h = l \cos \theta$ give

$$h = \frac{g}{\omega^2}. \qquad Ans.$$

This last result shows that the distance $h$ from the plane of rotation to the point of support is the same for all conical pendulums which rotate at the same rate, irrespective of their length $l$.

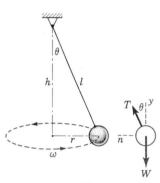

The term "centrifugal force" is often used (misused) in connection with this and similar problems of rotating bodies. Examination of the free-body diagram of the particle discloses the two forces $T$ and $W$ only. Neither of these forces is centrifugal, which means *"away from the center."* The word "centripetal" means "toward the center," and therefore the component $T \sin \theta$ is properly known as a *centripetal force*. There is *no actual centrifugal force* acting on the particle.

(If the particle is analyzed by D'Alembert's principle, described briefly in Art. 38,

PROB. 239

a fictitious force $ma_n = (W/g)r\omega^2$ called an *inertia force* is added in the direction opposite to the acceleration to produce "equilibrium" with the actual forces $W$ and $T$. This hypothetical inertia force is away from the center of rotation and is referred to as the *centrifugal force*. It must be clearly understood that this so-called centrifugal force is *not* a real force. The horizontal component of the tension $T$ which acts *on* the support is away from the center and may be properly called a centrifugal force. D'Alembert's principle offers no advantage in the analysis of this problem or other similar problems.)

**240.** A small object slides on a smooth vertical curve and has an initial velocity $v_0$ at a point $A$ as shown. Determine the velocity $v$ of the object after it has descended a vertical distance $h$, and write the expression for the normal force acting on the particle at any position.

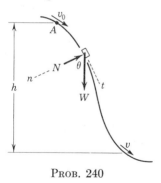

PROB. 240

*Solution.* The free-body diagram of the particle shows the weight $W$ and the normal force $N$. The equation of motion in the tangential direction gives

$$[\Sigma F_t = ma_t] \qquad W \sin \theta = \frac{W}{g} a_t, \qquad a_t = g \sin \theta.$$

The velocity change along the path is given by

$$[v\,dv = a_t\,ds] \qquad\qquad v\,dv = g\,ds\sin\theta = g\,dh.$$

Integration between the appropriate limits gives

$$v^2 = v_0^2 + 2gh. \qquad\qquad Ans.$$

This equation shows that for a path without friction the velocity does not depend on the shape of the path but only on the vertical change in position.

The normal force is given by

$$[\Sigma F_n = ma_n] \qquad W\cos\theta - N = \frac{W}{g}\frac{v^2}{\rho}, \qquad N = W\left(\cos\theta - \frac{v^2}{g\rho}\right). \qquad Ans.$$

The value of $N$ may be obtained in any particular problem where the radius of curvature $\rho$ is known or can be computed. If friction is present, the problem is complicated considerably. (See Prob. 274.)

**241.** A small sphere of weight $W$ is attached to one end of a light rod freely pivoted about the other end as shown. If the rod and sphere are released from rest in the vertical position, find the angle $\theta$ for which the force in the rod is zero, and determine the force in the rod when $\theta$ reaches 90 deg.

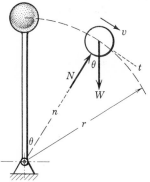

PROB. 241

*Solution.* The free-body diagram of the sphere is shown for the general position $\theta$. In addition to the weight $W$ there is the force $N$ which is exerted by the bar on the sphere. This force is along the bar since the bar, if light, may be considered a two-force member. The required answers may be determined when the expression for $N$ as a function of $\theta$ is obtained. This expression will depend upon the equations of motion, which are

$$[\Sigma F_n = ma_n] \qquad W\cos\theta - N = \frac{W}{g}\frac{v^2}{r}, \qquad N = W\left(\cos\theta - \frac{v^2}{gr}\right),$$

$$[\Sigma F_t = ma_t] \qquad W\sin\theta = \frac{W}{g}a_t, \qquad a_t = g\sin\theta.$$

The velocity $v$ of the sphere depends on the tangential acceleration and its change with $\theta$. Thus

$$[v\,dv = a_t\,ds] \qquad \int_0^v v\,dv = \int_0^\theta g\sin\theta\,r\,d\theta, \qquad v^2 = 2gr(1 - \cos\theta).$$

Substitution of this value for $v^2$ in the first equation of motion gives

$$N = (3\cos\theta - 2)W.$$

The force in the rod is clearly zero when

$$\theta = \cos^{-1}\tfrac{2}{3}, \qquad \theta = 48°\,11'. \qquad\qquad Ans.$$

When $\theta = 90$ deg., $\cos \theta = 0$ and

$$N = -2W. \qquad\qquad Ans.$$

Hence the force in the rod at this position is a tension equal to twice the weight of the sphere. The similarity between this problem and Prob. 240 should be noted.

## PROBLEMS

**242.** A small 4 lb. weight is swung in a vertical circle of 3 ft. radius with slowly increasing speed on the end of a light steel wire of 100 lb. breaking strength. Determine the velocity $v$ of the weight when the wire breaks.

$Ans.$   $v = 48.2$ ft./sec.

**243.** The simple pendulum weighs 4 lb. and is given an initial swing so that its velocity is 10 ft./sec. when $\theta = 30$ deg. Find the tension $T$ in the supporting wire at this instant.        $Ans.$   $T = 9.67$ lb.

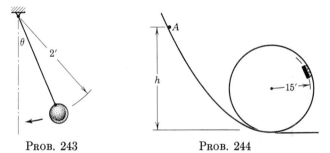

PROB. 243                 PROB. 244

**244.** A small car starts from rest at $A$ and rolls freely down the track and around the vertical loop. Determine the minimum height $h$ so that the car does not leave the rails when upside down.        $Ans.$   $h = 37.5$ ft.

**245.** Determine the proper angle of bank $\theta$ for an airplane flying at 300 mi./hr. and making a horizontal turn of 1 mi. radius.      $Ans.$   $\theta = 48.7$ deg.

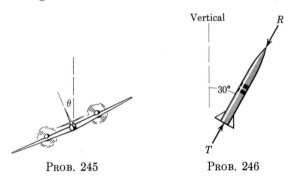

PROB. 245                 PROB. 246

**246.** A rocket which moves on a vertical curved path is being propelled by a thrust $T$ of 2000 lb. and is subjected to an atmospheric resistance $R$ of 600 lb.

If the rocket has a velocity of 10,000 ft./sec. and if the acceleration of gravity is 20 ft./sec.² at the altitude of the rocket, find the radius of curvature ρ of its path when in the position shown. *Ans.* ρ = 10⁷ ft.

**247.** The design of a space ship to operate beyond the earth's effective gravitational field is under consideration. If it has the form of a cylindrical shell of 10 ft. radius, determine the angular velocity ω of the shell about its central axis O which should be maintained in order to simulate the effect of the earth's gravity for a passenger. Assume the center of gravity of the passenger is 3 ft. from his feet in the standing position as shown. Take g to be 32.2 ft./sec.²

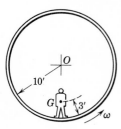

**248.** At the bottom of a vertical loop the test pilot of an experimental airplane notices that his accelerometer indicates an absolute linear acceleration of the airplane of 5g normal to its path and that his speed is 600 mi./hr. If the pilot weighs 161 lb., find the radius

PROB. 247

of curvature ρ of the bottom of the loop and the force N exerted by the man on the seat. *Ans.* ρ = 4810 ft., N = 966 lb.

**249.** A 3220 lb. car traveling at 30 mi./hr. passes over (a) a hump and (b) a dip in the road. If the radius of curvature of both the top of the hump and the bottom of the dip is 80 ft., determine the total normal force N between the tires and the road when the car passes over each contour.

**250.** The position of the small 1 lb. block in the smooth radial slot of the flywheel depends on the speed of rotation and is used as an activating device for the speed-control mechanism. If the axis of the flywheel is vertical and the block moves from a radius r of 6 in. to one of 7 in. while the speed changes slowly from 300 to 400 rev./min., find the constant k of the spring.

*Ans.* k = 16.46 lb./in.

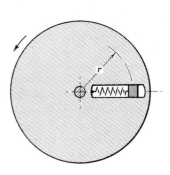

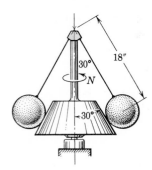

PROB. 250      PROB. 251

**251.** Compute the angular velocity N of the assembly about the vertical axis so that the force of contact R between each 15 lb. sphere and the conical surface is reduced to 4 lb.

**252.** The pendulum is held at rest in the position shown by the light horizontal string. What is the ratio $R$ of the tension in the wire $OA$ immediately after the string is cut to that in the wire before the string is cut?

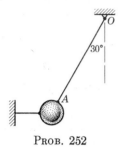

PROB. 252        PROB. 254

**253.** If the pendulum of Prob. 243 is released from rest at $\theta = 90$ deg., find the tension $T$ in the supporting wire when it passes the bottom position.

*Ans.* $T = 12$ lb.

**254.** The small collar $A$ has a weight $W$ and slides down the fixed circular shaft $BC$ with negligible friction. If the collar is released from rest at $\theta = 0$, determine the force $N$ exerted by the shaft on the collar as a function of $\theta$.

**255.** A small object is given an initial horizontal velocity $v$ at the bottom of a smooth slope. The angle made by the slope with the horizontal varies according to $\sin \theta = ks$, where $k$ is a constant and $s$ is the distance measured along the slope from the bottom. Find the maximum distance $s$ which the object slides up the slope.

*Ans.* $s = \dfrac{v}{\sqrt{kg}}$

**256.** A spring scale is suspended from a hook in the ceiling of a railway mail car. A package is weighed while the car is rounding a curve of 600 ft. radius at 30 mi./hr., and the scale reads 9.20 lb. What is the true weight of the package? Neglect the mass of the moving parts of the scale.

**257.** A small block of weight $W$ is placed on the horizontal surface of a circular disk at a radius $r$ from the axis of rotation. If the coefficient of friction is $f$ and the disk starts from rest with a constant angular acceleration $\alpha$, find the angular velocity $\omega$ at which the block begins to slip.

*Ans.* $\omega = \left[ \left( \dfrac{fg}{r} \right)^2 - \alpha^2 \right]^{1/4}$

**258.** A rocket is fired in near vertical flight. As it reaches the top of its trajectory at $A$ at an altitude of 1000 mi., it still has a horizontal velocity of 300 mi./hr. Determine the radius of curvature $\rho$ of its path at $A$. The radius of the earth is 3960 mi., and the acceleration of gravity at the surface of the earth may be taken as 32.17 ft./sec.$^2$

PROB. 258

*Ans.* $\rho = 9440$ ft.

**259.** A 1 lb. particle $P$ slides on a smooth curve in the vertical plane under the action of its own weight. The angular acceleration $\alpha$ of the radial line $PO$ to the center of curvature $O$ for this point on the curve is 5 rad./sec.² counterclockwise, and the radius of curvature to the moving particle is increasing at the rate of 2 ft./sec. Determine the angular velocity $\omega$ of $PO$ and the normal force $N$ on the particle at this instant.

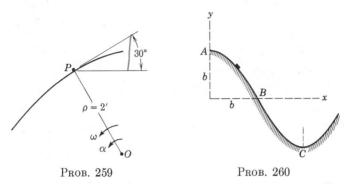

PROB. 259                    PROB. 260

**260.** A small object of weight $W$ initially at rest at $A$ is given a slight displacement and slides down the smooth guide which has a shape given by $y = b \cos (\pi x/2b)$. Determine the force $N$ exerted by the path on the object (a) at point $B$ and (b) at point $C$. The radius of curvature is given by $\rho = [1 + (dy/dx)^2]^{3/2}/(d^2y/dx^2)$.

$Ans.$   (a)  $N = 0.537W$,   (b)  $N = (1 + \pi^2)W$

**261.** The slotted disk revolves in a horizontal plane about its center $O$. The position of the smooth 1 lb. slider $A$ in the slot is controlled by the spring and the angular velocity of the disk. If the spring has a stiffness of 2 lb./in. and is

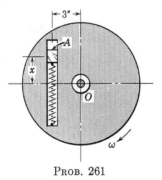

PROB. 261

unstretched when $x = 1$ in., determine $x$ for a constant disk speed of 230 rev./min. Also determine the corresponding normal force $N$ exerted by the slot on the slider. What effect has the direction of rotation on the answer? (*Suggestion:* Write equations of motion along and perpendicular to the slot.)

**262.** Determine the rotational speed $N$ necessary to maintain the given configuration of the flyball governor. The weights of the links may be neglected.

*Ans.* $N = 81.5$ rev./min.

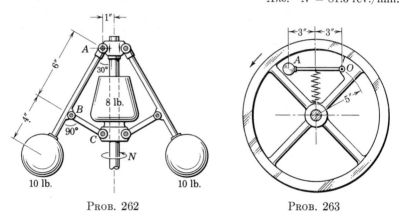

PROB. 262                    PROB. 263

**263.** An inertia type of speed governor on a flywheel with vertical axis consists of the small 1 lb. weight $A$ attached to the light arm $AO$. The position of $AO$ is used to activate the speed control, and this position depends on the speed of the flywheel and the stiffness $k$ of the spring. Determine $k$ if the governor is to assume the position shown where the spring is stretched $\frac{3}{4}$ in. for a constant speed of 600 rev./min.

**264.** The 10 lb. weight $C$ is carried on the two triangular plates $A$ by the shaft through $G$, the center of gravity of $C$. The motion of the plates is controlled by the rotation of the identical links $B$ in the vertical plane. If the links

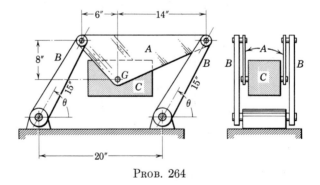

PROB. 264

have a counterclockwise angular acceleration of $\alpha = 12$ rad./sec.[2] and a clockwise angular velocity of $\omega = 4$ rad./sec. at the instant when $\theta = 60$ deg., find the force $P$ exerted by the shaft at $G$ on *each* plate $A$. *Ans.* $P = 4.98$ lb.

**265.** The motion of the 4 oz. pin $A$ in the circular slot is controlled by the guide $B$ which has a constant upward velocity of 4 ft./sec. for an interval of its motion. Calculate the force $N$ exerted on the pin by the guide $B$ as the pin passes the position for which $\theta = 30$ deg. All surfaces are smooth.

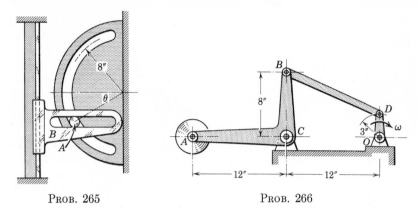

PROB. 265         PROB. 266

**266.** The oscillation of the bell crank $ACB$ in a vertical plane about its bearing $C$ is controlled by the connecting link $BD$ and the rotating crank $DO$. The bell crank carries a cylindrical 10 lb. weight at $A$. Determine the force $A$ exerted by the crank on the weight at $A$ in the position shown if the crank $OD$ has a constant clockwise angular velocity of 8 rad./sec. *Ans.* $A = 12.25$ lb.

**267.** The small pin $A$ weighs 1.61 lb. and is attached to the face of the wheel which rolls on a horizontal track. If the wheel is given a constant angular acceleration of 2 rad./sec.² clockwise, find the force $R$ exerted by the wheel on the pin after the wheel has rolled without slipping through ¼ turn from the rest position shown. *Ans.* $R = 1.540$ lb.

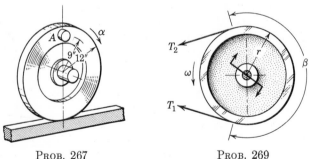

PROB. 267         PROB. 269

**268.** If the collar of Prob. 254 is released from rest at $\theta = 0$, set up the expression for the time $t$ required for it to reach the bottom position. (The resulting integral can be transformed into an elliptic integral and its value found from tables of elliptic integrals.)

**269.** A flat, flexible belt of weight $\mu$ per unit length drives the pulley at a constant high speed $\omega$. The relation $T_2 = T_1 e^{f\beta}$ derived for the impending slippage of stationary belts must now be modified to account for the "centrifugal" effect. Derive this new relation between the tensions $T_2$ and $T_1$ in terms of the given quantities and the coefficient of friction $f$. (The resulting relation may be adapted to the case of V-belts by replacing $f$ by $f/\sin(\alpha/2)$, where $\alpha$ is the angle of the V-section. See Art. 52 and Prob. 562 of *Part I*.)

$$Ans. \quad T_2 - \frac{\mu r^2 \omega^2}{g} = \left(T_1 - \frac{\mu r^2 \omega^2}{g}\right) e^{f\beta}$$

* 270. The radius $r$ of the earth is about $20.9 \times 10^6$ ft., and the distance $R$ between the centers of the earth and the moon is $12.54 \times 10^8$ ft. Determine the period $\tau$ of the rotation of the moon about the earth considered as fixed.

$$Ans. \quad \tau = \frac{2\pi R}{r}\sqrt{\frac{R}{g}}, \ \tau = 27.2 \text{ days}$$

* 271. Derive an expression for the mass $m_0$ of the sun by considering the earth to travel in a circular orbit of radius $a$ and period $\tau$ about the sun. Compute the sun's mass by using the values $\tau = 365\frac{1}{4}$ days, $\gamma = 6.67 \times 10^{-8}$ cm.$^3$/(gm. sec.$^2$) for the universal gravitational constant, and $a = 92.6 \times 10^6$ mi. Also compute the orbital velocity $v$ of the earth about the sun.

$$Ans. \quad m_0 = \frac{4\pi^2 a^3}{\gamma \tau^2} = 1.97 \times 10^{33} \text{ gm.}, \ v = 66{,}400 \text{ mi./hr.}$$

* 272. Derive an expression for the velocity $v$ of an artificial satellite which is to operate in a circular orbit at an altitude $h$ above the surface of the earth. The altitude is sufficiently great to neglect the effect of atmospheric resistance to motion. The radius $R$ of the earth is 3960 mi. What is the period $\tau$ of its motion? Compute $v$ and $\tau$ for $h = 400$ mi.

$$Ans. \quad v = R\sqrt{\frac{g}{R+h}}, \ \tau = 2\pi \frac{(R+h)^{3/2}}{R\sqrt{g}},$$

$$v = 16{,}830 \text{ mi./hr.}, \ \tau = 1 \text{ hr. } 37 \text{ min. } 30 \text{ sec.}$$

* 273. The pipe $A$ of weight $W$ is welded to the rim of a circular hoop of radius $r$ and negligible weight which is free to roll on a horizontal plane. If the hoop is released from rest with the pipe initially in a horizontal plane through the center of the hoop, determine the initial angular acceleration $\alpha$ of the hoop if the coefficient of friction between the hoop and the plane is ($a$) greater than unity and ($b$) less than unity. (*Hint:* The resultant of all forces acting on the hoop and pipe taken together passes through the center of the pipe which may be considered to be a particle.)

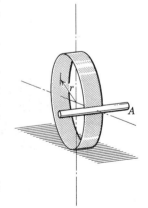

Prob. 273

$$Ans. \quad (a) \ \alpha = \frac{g}{2r}, \ (b) \ \alpha = \frac{g}{r}$$

* 274. A small object is released from rest at $A$ and slides with friction down the circular path. If the coefficient of friction is $\frac{1}{3}$, determine the velocity of the object as it passes $B$. (*Hint:* Write the equations of motion in the $n$- and $t$-directions, eliminate $N$, and substitute $v \, dv = a_t \, r \, d\theta$ first chang-

ing variables to $u = v^2$ so that $du = 2a_t\, r\, d\theta$. The resulting equation is a linear nonhomogeneous differential equation of the form $dy/dx + f(x)y = g(x)$, the solution of which is well known.)       *Ans.*   $v = 18.2$ ft./sec.

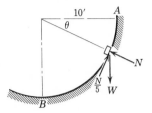

PROB. 274

**32. Polar Coordinates and Rotating Axes.** There are important problems involving curvilinear motion where the acceleration is more easily described in polar coordinates with respect to a fixed origin (Art. 15). For a particle of mass $m$ Eqs. 20, then, require

$$\Sigma F_r = m\left[\frac{d^2r}{dt^2} - r\left(\frac{d\theta}{dt}\right)^2\right],$$

$$\Sigma F_\theta = m\left[r\frac{d^2\theta}{dt^2} + 2\frac{dr}{dt}\frac{d\theta}{dt}\right].$$

$$(34)$$

Equations 34 are the basic equations used to describe the motion of earth satellites, planets, and rockets. They also find application in the dynamics of certain machine motions.

If the acceleration of the particle is described in terms of its motion relative to a rotating path (Art. 23), Eq. 26 may be used. Thus

$$\Sigma F = m(a_m \leftrightarrow a_p \leftrightarrow 2u\omega). \qquad (35)$$

The term $a_p$ is the acceleration of the particle $P$ along the path considered as fixed, $a_m$ is the acceleration of a point fixed to the rotating path and momentarily coincident with $P$, and $2u\omega$ is the Coriolis acceleration, where $u$ is the velocity of $P$ relative to the path and $\omega$ is the angular velocity of the path. The resultant force $\Sigma F$ on the particle has the same direction as the resultant of the three acceleration terms.

If Eq. 35 is applied to the motion of a particle relative to the earth, it is more convenient to write the equation as

$$ma_p = \Sigma F \rightarrow ma_m \rightarrow 2mu\omega, \qquad (36)$$

where $a_p$ is the measured acceleration of the particle relative to the

earth.  The acceleration $a_m$ for a reference point attached to the earth
on its surface is $R\omega^2 \cos \phi$, where $R$ is the radius of the earth, $\omega$ is the
angular velocity of the earth, and $\phi$ is the latitude.  This expression
neglects the extremely small acceleration of the center of the earth.
The term in $R\omega^2 \cos \phi$ is itself usually neglected since the square of
the small angular velocity $\omega = 0.729 \times 10^{-4}$ rad./sec. is even smaller.
With the neglect of $a_m$ the equation of motion for a particle falling in
space (air friction neglected) becomes

$$a_p = g \to 2u\omega, \qquad (37)$$

where $\Sigma F$ has been replaced by the product of the mass $m$ and the
absolute acceleration of gravity $g$.  Thus the measured acceleration
$a_p$ will be the vector difference between $g$ and the Coriolis acceleration.

### SAMPLE PROBLEMS

**275.**  The slider block of weight $W$ starts from rest at time $t = 0$ with $r$ essentially zero and slides down the rod under the action of its own weight.  The
rod has a constant clockwise angular velocity $\omega$ and passes the horizontal position when $t = 0$.  Set up the equations of motion for the block neglecting friction.

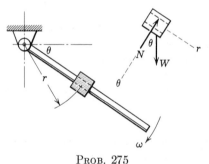

PROB. 275

*Solution.*  The free-body diagram of the block discloses the two forces $N$ and
$W$.  Application of Eqs. 34 gives

$$[\Sigma F_r = ma_r] \qquad\qquad W \sin \theta = \frac{W}{g} \left( \frac{d^2r}{dt^2} - r\omega^2 \right),$$

$$[\Sigma F_\theta = ma_\theta] \qquad\qquad W \cos \theta - N = \frac{W}{g} \left( 2\omega \frac{dr}{dt} \right).$$

Solution of the first of these equations for $r$ is prerequisite to the determination
of $N$ from the second.

The identical formulation of the problem is made by using Eq. 35. The term $a_m$ is the acceleration of a fixed point on the rod coincident with the block at the instant considered, and is therefore $a_m = r\omega^2$ in the negative $r$-direction. The term $a_p$ is the acceleration of the block relative to the straight rod and is $a_p = d^2r/dt^2$ in the positive $r$-direction. The Coriolis acceleration is $2u\omega = 2(dr/dt)\omega$ and, by the rule established in Art. 23, is in the direction of increasing $\theta$. Thus the first two terms are $a_m \mapsto a_p = a_r$ and the third term is $2u\omega = a_\theta$.

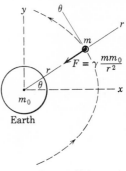

PROB. 276

* **276.** Derive the equations of motion for an earth satellite, and find its period. Take the orbit sufficiently far from the earth so that atmospheric resistance is negligible.

*Solution.* The free-body diagram of the satellite of mass $m$ shows the single central force of attraction due to the earth's gravity. The equations of motion from Eqs. 34 are

$$[\Sigma F_r = ma_r] \qquad -\gamma \frac{mm_0}{r^2} = m\left[\frac{d^2r}{dt^2} - r\left(\frac{d\theta}{dt}\right)^2\right],$$

$$[\Sigma F_\theta = ma_\theta] \qquad 0 = m\left[r\frac{d^2\theta}{dt^2} + 2\frac{dr}{dt}\frac{d\theta}{dt}\right].$$

The last expression may be written as $\dfrac{1}{r}\dfrac{d}{dt}\left(r^2\dfrac{d\theta}{dt}\right) = 0$ which is easily verified by differentiation. Integrating the exact differential gives

$$r^2\frac{d\theta}{dt} = h$$

where $h$ is a constant. (This expression is Kepler's second law of planetary motion. It states that the rate at which the radius vector $r$ to the body $m$ sweeps through area is constant. The area $dA$ swept by $r$ during a change $d\theta$ is the area of a differential triangle of altitude $r$ and base $r\,d\theta$ or $dA = \frac{1}{2}r^2\,d\theta$, which neglects the higher-order terms that disappear in the limit. Thus the time rate at which $r$ sweeps through area is $\frac{1}{2}r^2\,d\theta/dt$ which is constant. This expression also states that the angular momentum of the satellite about the fixed center of the earth is constant.) The derivative of $r$ may be written as

$$\frac{dr}{dt} = \frac{dr}{d\theta}\frac{d\theta}{dt} = \frac{dr}{d\theta}\frac{h}{r^2} = -h\frac{du}{d\theta} \quad \text{where } u = \frac{1}{r} \text{ and } du = -\frac{dr}{r^2}.$$

Thus

$$\frac{d^2r}{dt^2} = -h\frac{d^2u}{d\theta^2}\frac{d\theta}{dt} = -h^2u^2\frac{d^2u}{d\theta^2}.$$

Substitution of the derivatives into the first equation of motion gives

$$-\gamma m_0 u^2 = -h^2 u^2 \frac{d^2 u}{d\theta^2} - \frac{1}{u} h^2 u^4$$

or

$$\frac{d^2 u}{d\theta^2} + u = \frac{\gamma m_0}{h^2}.$$

This expression is a nonhomogeneous linear equation of second order. The solution, which may be easily verified by differentiation and substitution, contains two constants of integration $A$ and $\delta$ and is

$$u = \frac{1}{r} = A \cos (\theta + \delta) + \frac{\gamma m_0}{h^2}.$$

The constant $\delta$ may be taken to be zero by choosing the axis $\theta = 0$ to coincide with the condition of minimum $r$. Thus

$$\frac{1}{r} = A \cos \theta + \frac{\gamma m_0}{h^2}.$$

This expression has the same form as the equation of a conic section in polar coordinates with origin at the focus which is $1/r = 1/(ed) + (1/d) \cos \theta$ where $e$ is the eccentricity and $d$ is the distance from the focus to the directrix. For an ellipse $e < 1$, and the equation becomes

$$\frac{1}{r} = \frac{1}{a(1 - e^2)} + \frac{e \cos \theta}{a(1 - e^2)}$$

where $a$ is the semi-major axis. Thus $A = e/a(1 - e^2)$ and $1/a(1 - e^2) = \gamma m_0/h^2$ from which $A = e\gamma m_0/h^2$. Thus the equation of the orbit is

$$\frac{1}{r} = \frac{\gamma m_0}{h^2} (1 + e \cos \theta).$$

The values of $e$ and $h$ depend upon the particular velocity and altitude used to establish the orbit.

The period $\tau$ of the satellite is the total area of the ellipse $\pi a^2 \sqrt{1 - e^2}$ divided by the constant rate at which area is generated by the radius vector. Thus $\tau = \pi a^2 \sqrt{1 - e^2}/(h/2)$. Substituting $a(1 - e^2) = h^2/\gamma m_0$ gives

$$\tau = \frac{2\pi a^{3/2}}{\sqrt{\gamma m_0}}.$$

This last expression gives Kepler's third law of planetary motion which says that $\tau^2$ is proportional to $a^3$.

The foregoing relations hold not only for satellite motion, but also for general planetary motion governed by the inverse-square law of attraction.

## PROBLEMS

**277.** A body at rest relative to the surface of the earth rotates with the earth and therefore moves in a circular path about the polar axis of the earth considered as fixed. Derive an expression for the ratio $n$ of the apparent weight of such a body as measured by a spring scale at the equator (calibrated to read the actual force) to the true weight of the body which is the absolute gravitational attraction to the earth. The absolute acceleration of gravity at the equator is $g = 32.20$ ft./sec.[2] The radius of the earth is $r = 3960$ mi., and the angular velocity of the earth is $\omega = 0.729 \times 10^{-4}$ rad./sec. If the true weight is 100 lb., what is the apparent measured weight $W'$?

$$Ans. \quad n = 1 - \frac{r\omega^2}{g}, \ W' = 99.655 \text{ lb.}$$

**\*278.** A plumb bob of mass $m$ is suspended from a point on the surface of the earth at a latitude $\phi$. Prove that the apparent weight or tension $W'$ in the supporting string is equal to $mg'$ where $g'$ is the acceleration of gravity as measured relative to the earth at the onset of motion for a freely falling body at the same latitude. Also determine the expression for the small angle $\theta$ between the direction of the plumb bob string and the line joining the bob with the center of the earth. Assume the earth to be a sphere of radius $r$ rotating with an angular velocity $\omega$ about its polar axis considered as fixed. (*Hint:* Express $g'$ in terms of $g$, $r$, $\omega$, and $\phi$ by Eq. 26 where the absolute acceleration $a$ is $g$ and the relative acceleration $a_p$ is $g'$. The Coriolis term $2u\omega$ is zero since the relative velocity $u$ is zero. Then apply Eq. 35.) $\quad Ans. \quad \theta = \sin^{-1}\left(\dfrac{r\omega^2}{2g'}\sin 2\phi\right)$

**\*279.** The slotted disk rotates in a horizontal plane about its shaft at $O$, and the 1 lb. slider $P$ is free to move in the slot. The disk is given a clockwise angular acceleration of 40 rad./sec.[2] starting from rest with the slider initially at rest in the position shown. Determine the horizontal force $F$ exerted on $P$ by the slot at the start of the motion.      *Ans.* $F = 0.311$ lb.

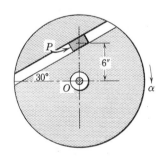

PROB. 279

**\*280.** In the pump described in Prob. 108 an element of fluid is assumed to be a particle $P$ which moves outward along the smooth radial vane. If the weight of the particle is $W$ and if the impeller rotates about a vertical axis at the constant angular velocity $\omega$, find the force $N$ exerted by the vane on $P$ as a function of $r$.

$$Ans. \quad N = \frac{2W\omega^2}{g}\sqrt{r^2 - r_0^2}$$

**\*281.** Solve the equations of motion of Sample Prob. 275 for $r$ and $N$ as functions of $\theta$ where the initial conditions of motion are defined in the problem statement. $\quad Ans. \quad r = \dfrac{g}{2\omega^2}(\sinh\theta - \sin\theta), \ N = W(2\cos\theta - \cosh\theta)$

*282. Derive the relation given in the footnote on p. 114 for the deflection from the vertical of a freely falling body. The result is based on Eq. 37, which neglects the acceleration of the center of the earth and the square of the angular velocity $\omega$ of the earth.

*283. The slotted arm in Prob. 102 rotates in a horizontal plane around the fixed cam with a constant counterclockwise velocity $K = 10$ rad./sec. The spring has a constant of 10 lb./in. and is uncompressed when $\theta = 0$. If $b = 4$ in., $c = 2$ in., and the small smooth roller $A$ weighs 8 oz., find the force $P$ exerted on $A$ by the smooth sides of the slot when $\theta = 60$ deg.

*Ans.* $P = 6.07$ lb.

# PART 2. RIGID-BODY MOTION

**33. Translation.** The various types of plane motion of rigid bodies were identified in Art. 16, and translation was defined as any motion in which every line in the body remains parallel to its original position. This requirement means that there can be no angular velocity or angular acceleration of a translating body, and therefore each point in the body has the same acceleration. If a point in such a body moves in a straight line, the body moves with *rectilinear translation*. If the point moves along a curve, the body is said to have *curvilinear translation*. The principles of kinetics which apply to these two motions are identical.

Figure 30a shows the free-body diagram of a body which has translation in the plane of the figure under the action of external forces $F_1, F_2, F_3, \cdots$. The mass center $G$, and hence all points in the body, has a total or absolute acceleration $\bar{a}$. From the principle of motion of the mass center of any system of particles, Eq. 32 of Art. 28, it is known immediately that the resultant of all external forces is $R = m\bar{a}$, so that two of the equations of motion are $\Sigma F_x = m\bar{a}_x$ and $\Sigma F_y = m\bar{a}_y$ where the $x$- and $y$-axes are chosen arbitrarily. The principle of Eq. 32, which applies to all motions, defines the magnitude and direction of $R$ but does not establish its line of action.

The line of action of $R$ is determined by considering the moment requirement of the forces. The resultant of all forces which act on a representative particle of mass $m_i$ of the body, Fig. 30a, is $m_i a_i = m_i \bar{a}$. The moment of this force about $G$ is $m_i \bar{a} d_i$, and the sum of the moments about $G$ of all forces acting on all particles is

$$\Sigma \overline{M} = \Sigma m_i \bar{a} d_i = \bar{a} \Sigma m_i d_i.$$

By the principle of moments $\Sigma m_i d_i = \bar{d}m$ where $\bar{d}$, the distance to the mass center, is zero. Thus $\Sigma \overline{M} = 0$. In the derivation the moment sum includes the moments of internal and external forces. But since the internal forces always occur in pairs of equal and opposite forces, their net moment is necessarily zero about any point, and $\Sigma M$ therefore represents merely the sum of the moments of all *external* forces on the body. From the principle of moments it follows that the moment of the resultant $R$ is also zero, which means that the resultant $R = m\bar{a}$ must pass through the mass center for a translating rigid body as shown in Fig. 30b.

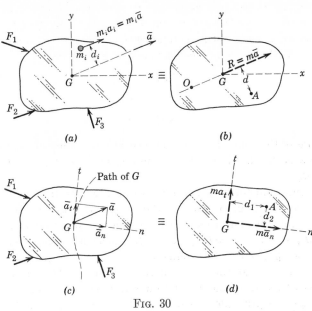

FIG. 30

The location of the resultant force through the mass center is the *essential characteristic of the forces on a translating body.* It may now be observed from Fig. 30b that the sum of the moments of all external forces is zero about any point such as $O$ on the line of action of the resultant $R = m\bar{a}$. The moment sum about some point not on this line, such as $A$, is merely $m\bar{a}d$. This sum is clockwise in the illustration but would be counterclockwise if $A$ were chosen on the opposite side of $R$. Thus the three equations of motion for a translating rigid body may be written as

$$\Sigma F_x = m\bar{a}_x$$

$$\Sigma F_y = m\bar{a}_y \tag{38}$$

$$\Sigma \overline{M} = 0 \quad \text{or} \quad \Sigma M_O = 0 \quad \text{or} \quad \Sigma M_A = m\bar{a}d.$$

It is advisable to represent the resultant $R = m\bar{a}$ either on the free-body diagram or on a separate sketch of the body isolated as in Fig. 30b. Consistent use of a dotted line for the resultant vector will always avoid confusing it with one of the actual applied loads which are represented by full lines. When the resultant is so drawn, the three equations of motion become obvious from the diagram. It is seen that the moment principle may be applied about any point which is convenient, and any desired orientation of axes may be used.

When the translation is curvilinear, the mass center will move on a curve with a total acceleration $\bar{a}$ which for convenience is usually represented in terms of its components in the $n$- and $t$-directions, Fig. 30c. Thus the motion equations may be written as

$$\Sigma F_n = m\bar{a}_n$$
$$\Sigma F_t = m\bar{a}_t \qquad (39)$$
$$\Sigma \overline{M} = 0.$$

In terms of the velocity $v$ of the mass center and the radius of curvature $\rho$ of its path, the acceleration components are $\bar{a}_n = v^2/\rho$ and $\bar{a}_t = d|v|/dt$.

The resultant-force diagram, shown in Fig. 30d, may be represented by the $n$- and $t$-components of the resultant. It then becomes clear that a moment sum about some convenient point such as $A$ would be $\Sigma M_A = m\bar{a}_t d_1 - m\bar{a}_n d_2$ where the clockwise sense is chosen arbitrarily as positive. The signs in the moment equation will differ depending on the choice of moment center. The student should recognize that the moment equation is nothing more than an application of Varignon's principle which means that the sum of the moments of the external forces shown on the free-body diagram equals the moment of the sum or resultant shown on the resultant-force diagram.

When a translating rigid body is composed of two or more distinct geometrical parts, it is often convenient to replace the resultant $R = m\bar{a}$ by the resultants $R_1 = m_1\bar{a}$, $R_2 = m_2\bar{a}$, $\cdots$ for each of the separate parts. Each resultant equals the mass of the part times the common acceleration and passes through the mass center of its respective part.

### SAMPLE PROBLEMS

**284.** The 3220 lb. car shown has a forward acceleration on the level road of 16.1 ft./sec.[2] Determine the normal reactions $N_1$ and $N_2$ under each pair of wheels, and find the coefficient of friction $f$ between the tires and the road if the rear wheels are on the verge of slipping.

*Solution.* The free-body diagram of the translating car is drawn as indicated. The resultant of the external forces is shown acting through the center of gravity $G$ in the diagram to the right. It will be assumed that the weight of the wheels is small compared with the total weight of the car; otherwise it would be necessary to consider the forces required to produce the angular acceleration of the wheels. The third of the alternate moment relations of Eqs. 38 will

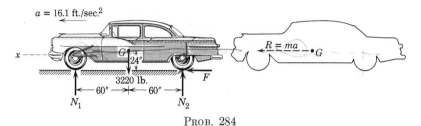

PROB. 284

eliminate $N_2$ and $F$ when applied about the rear wheel contact as a moment center. The direction for positive $\Sigma M$ is counterclockwise about this point since the resultant $ma$ is directed to the left through $G$. Thus

$$[\Sigma M_{N_2} = mad] \qquad 3220 \times 5 - 10N_1 = 100 \times 16.1 \times 2, \qquad N_1 = 1288 \text{ lb.}$$
$$Ans.$$

The remaining two principles give

$$[\Sigma F_x = ma_x] \qquad F = 100 \times 16.1 = 1610 \text{ lb.,}$$

$$[\Sigma F_y = 0] \qquad 1288 + N_2 - 3220 = 0, \qquad N_2 = 1932 \text{ lb.} \qquad Ans.$$

If the rear wheels are on the verge of slipping, the friction force $F$ is the limiting value, and hence the coefficient of friction is

$$f = \frac{F}{N_2} = \frac{1610}{1932} = 0.834. \qquad Ans.$$

**285.** The 300 lb. homogeneous log is supported by the two parallel 10 ft. ropes. It is released from rest in the position for which $\theta = 30$ deg. and swings past the bottom position. Determine the tensions $T_1$ and $T_2$ in the ropes $(a)$ an instant after release and $(b)$ as the bottom position is reached.

*Solution.* The tensions are disclosed by the free-body diagrams of the log for each position. Points $A$ and $B$, and hence $G$, have identical curvilinear motion, so that the log moves with curvilinear translation, always parallel to its original position. For condition $(a)$ immediately after release the velocity of $G$ is essentially zero, so that its acceleration has no $n$-component. The resultant-force diagram on the right shows $m\bar{a}_t$ acting through $G$ in the direction of the tangential component of acceleration. For condition $(b)$ the forces are vertical, and the resultant has an $n$-component only as shown on the resultant-force diagram for this case.

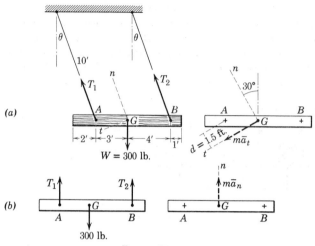

PROB. 285

The tangential acceleration is obtained from the first free-body diagram. Thus

$$[\Sigma F_t = m\bar{a}_t] \qquad W \sin\theta = \frac{W}{g}\bar{a}_t, \qquad \bar{a}_t = g\sin\theta$$

which for $\theta = 30$ deg. is $\bar{a}_t = 0.5g$ ft./sec.$^2$  A moment equation about $A$ will yield $T_2$, or one about $B$ will yield $T_1$.  With $A$ as a moment center the resultant-force diagram shows that the moment sum is clockwise.  Thus for the 30 deg. position

$$[\Sigma M_A = m\bar{a}_t d] \quad 300 \times 3 - 7T_2 \cos 30° = \frac{300}{g} \times 0.5g \times 1.5, \qquad T_2 = 111 \text{ lb.}$$
Ans.

The tension $T_1$ may be found by a similar moment equation about $B$ or by a force summation in the $n$-direction.  The latter step gives

$$[\Sigma F_n = 0] \qquad T_1 + 111 = 300 \cos 30°, \qquad T_1 = 149 \text{ lb.} \qquad Ans.$$

The forces acting at condition (b) depend upon the normal acceleration which, in turn, depends upon the velocity.  The velocity is obtained by integrating the tangential acceleration.  Thus

$$[v\,dv = a_t\,ds] \qquad \int_0^v v\,dv = \int_{30°}^0 g\sin\theta\,(-10\,d\theta), \qquad v^2 = 2.68g \text{ (ft./sec.)}^2$$

and $\bar{a}_n = v^2/\rho = 2.68g/10 = 0.268g$ ft./sec.$^2$  A moment sum about $B$ is clockwise as seen from the resultant-force diagram.  Hence

$$[\Sigma M_B = m\bar{a}_n d] \quad 7T_1 - 300 \times 4 = \frac{300}{g} \times 0.268g \times 4, \qquad T_1 = 217 \text{ lb.} \quad Ans.$$

The tension $T_2$ is obtained from

$$[\Sigma F_n = m\bar{a}_n] \qquad 217 + T_2 - 300 = \frac{300}{g} \times 0.268g, \qquad T_2 = 163 \text{ lb.} \quad Ans.$$

A moment equation about $A$ will yield the same result. It should be noted that a moment sum given by $\Sigma \overline{M} = 0$ could have been applied for either position but would have necessitated a simultaneous solution with the force equation since each relation would involve both unknown tensions. Other choices of moment centers may be noted. For instance, in case $(a)$ a zero moment summation would result about the point of intersection of $T_1$ and the resultant $m\bar{a}_t$ or about the intersection of $T_2$ and $m\bar{a}_t$. Either of these two points would represent a good choice of moment center and would permit the direct calculation of a tension without involving the acceleration.

**286.** Investigate the relations between the angle to which a curved road is banked and the tendency for a car rounding the curve to tip over or slide.

*Solution.* The rear view of a car rounding an inwardly banked curve of mean radius $r$ at a constant speed $v$ is shown. The velocity of the car is normal to the plane of the figure, but the acceleration, $a_n = v^2/r$, is toward the center of the curve and is in the plane of the paper. If $r$ is large compared with the dimensions of the car, each point in the car may be assumed to have the same acceleration. Thus the car may be analyzed by the principles of translation applied in the plane of the figure even though the actual motion is normal to this plane. The forces acting on the car may be

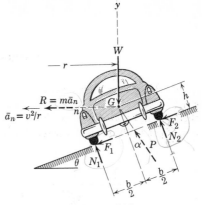

PROB. 286

represented by the weight $W$ and the force $P$ which is the resultant of the normal forces $N_1$ and $N_2$ and the lateral friction forces $F_1$ and $F_2$. Each of these wheel forces is, of course, the sum of the front- and rear-wheel forces. The force $P$ must pass through $G$ since the resultant of $P$ and $W$ is $R = m\bar{a}_n$ which passes through $G$. The equations of motion are

$$[\Sigma F_n = m\bar{a}_n] \qquad\qquad P \sin(\theta + \alpha) = \frac{W}{g}\frac{v^2}{r},$$

$$[\Sigma F_y = 0] \qquad\qquad P \cos(\theta + \alpha) = W.$$

Dividing gives

$$\tan(\theta + \alpha) = \frac{v^2}{gr} \qquad \text{or} \qquad v^2 = gr\,\frac{\tan\theta + \tan\alpha}{1 - \tan\theta\tan\alpha}.$$

The angle of bank which produces no tendency to tip or slip for a particular speed $v$ is that angle for which there is no side friction. Thus $\alpha = 0$, $N_1 = N_2$, and

$$\tan\theta = \frac{v^2}{gr}.$$

This relation shows that a road can be properly banked for one speed only.

The speed at which the car overturns occurs when the reaction $P$ acts entirely at the outside wheels. In this event $\tan \alpha = (b/2)/h$, and thus

$$v^2 = gr\,\frac{\tan \theta + (b/2h)}{1 - (b/2h)\tan \theta}.$$

This relation assumes sufficient friction to allow $P$ to act at the outer wheels and is valid provided the coefficient of friction $f$ is greater than $(b/2)/h$.

The car will slide before it will tip, on the other hand, if the coefficient of friction $f$ is less than $(b/2)/h$. Thus $\tan \alpha = f$, and the speed at which sliding begins is given by

$$v^2 = gr\,\frac{\tan \theta + f}{1 - f \tan \theta}.$$

## PROBLEMS

**287.** The device shown consists of a vertical frame $A$ to which are pivoted a geared sector at $O$ and a balanced gear and attached pointer at $C$. Determine the relation between the steady horizontal acceleration $a$, expressed as a fraction of $g$, and the angle $\theta$ registered by the pointer. Friction may be neglected.

$$Ans. \quad \frac{a}{g} = \tan 0.214\theta$$

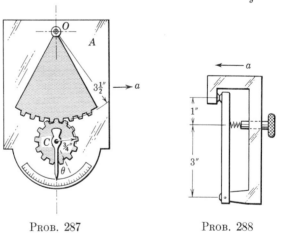

PROB. 287          PROB. 288

**288.** One type of instrument for measuring accelerations is known as a classifying accelerometer and indicates whether an acceleration is greater or less than some prescribed value. The device shown may be used as such an instrument. When the acceleration to the left exceeds a certain critical value, the uniform bar of weight $W$ rotates slightly against the spring and opens the electrical contacts. If the bar weighs 8 oz. and the spring has a stiffness of 20 lb./in., how many turns $N$ of the adjusting screw from the position of initial contact of the spring with the bar are required to preset the device for an acceleration of $12g$? The screw has 40 single threads per inch. *Ans.* 8 turns

**289.** At what speed can a car round a turn of 100 ft. radius on a flat unbanked road without slipping if the coefficient of friction between the tires and the road is 0.80 and if the center of gravity of the car is sufficiently low to prevent over-turning? *Ans.* $v = 34.6$ mi./hr.

**290.** The center of gravity of a certain car is 2 ft. from the road, and the tread (transverse distance between wheels) is 6 ft. Also the coefficient of friction between the tires and the road is 0.80. What is the maximum speed $v$ with which the car can enter a turn of 100 ft. radius banked inward at an angle of 15 deg. without tipping or sliding? Which would occur first?

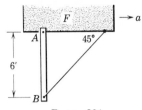

*Ans.* $v = 45.1$ mi./hr., sliding

**291.** The uniform bar $AB$ weighs 100 lb. and is pinned at $A$ and fastened by a cable at $B$ to the frame $F$. If the frame is given an accelera-tion $a = 0.5g$, determine the tension $T$ in the cable and the total force exerted by the pin at $A$ on the bar. *Ans.* $T = 35.4$ lb., $A = 79.1$ lb.

PROB. 291

**292.** What is the minimum turning radius $r$ which a bicycle can make on a horizontal road with a speed of 15 mi./hr. if the coefficient of friction between the tires and the road is 0.70? Find the corresponding angle $\theta$ with the vertical at which the cyclist must lean. Measure $r$ to the center of gravity of rider and bicycle.

**293.** What are the minimum speed $v$ and corresponding angle $\theta$ in order that the motorcycle may ride on the vertical wall of the cylindrical track? The coefficient of friction between the tires and the wall is 0.70.

*Ans.* $v = 25.3$ mi./hr., $\theta = 55$ deg.

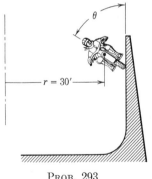

PROB. 293

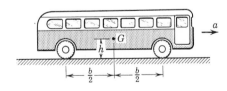

PROB. 294

**294.** Find the maximum velocity $v$ which the bus can reach in a distance $s$ from rest without slipping its rear driving wheels if the coefficient of friction between the tires and the road is $f$. Neglect the weight of the wheels.

$$Ans. \quad v = \sqrt{\frac{fbgs}{b - fh}}$$

**295.** By reversing the pitch of its propellers upon landing, the transport plane reduces its speed from 100 mi./hr. to 30 mi./hr. in 800 ft. of runway length with constant deceleration. Determine the force $P$ on the front wheels at the end of this interval if no mechanical braking forces are applied to the wheels. The plane weighs 150,000 lb. with center of gravity at $G$. The aerodynamic forces at 30 mi./hr. may be neglected except for the resultant negative propeller thrust which passes through $G$. Does $P$ depend on the acceleration?

PROB. 295

**296.** If the 150,000 lb. transport plane shown with Prob. 295 is brought to a stop from a velocity of 30 mi./hr. in 80 ft. with its wheel brakes, determine the normal force $P$ under the front wheels. The propellers are idling, and other aerodynamic forces are negligible at the low speed involved.

*Ans.  P = 27,000 lb.*

**297.** Assume that the driver of the car shown with Sample Prob. 284 applies the brakes so that all four wheels slide when the car is going down a slope of 1 to 4. Find the total normal force $N_1$ under the front pair of wheels if the coefficient of friction between the tires and the road is 0.80.

**298.** A water heater is placed on the horizontal bed of a truck. The base of the four legs forms a 12 in. square as shown, and the center of gravity of the heater is 3 ft. above its base. The coefficient of friction between the legs and the truck bed is 0.25. If the driver forgets to secure the heater with the ropes shown, find the forward acceleration $a$ at which the heater tips or slips.

*Ans.   a = 5.37 ft./sec.² tips*

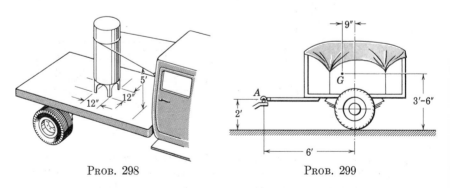

PROB. 298            PROB. 299

**299.** The loaded trailer weighs 2500 lb. with center of gravity at $G$ and is attached to a rear-bumper hitch at $A$. If the car and trailer reach a velocity of 30 mi./hr. in 75 ft. with constant acceleration starting from rest, determine the horizontal and vertical components of the force exerted by the trailer on the bumper at $A$ during this motion. Assume that the horizontal friction force exerted by the road on the relatively light wheels is small and can be neglected.

**300.** A 3000 lb. milling machine with center of gravity at $G$ is to be hoisted on rollers from the position shown to the bed of the truck. When the power for the winch is applied, the cable tension is momentarily 50 per cent greater than that necessary to maintain equilibrium of the milling machine with both rollers on the incline. Determine the reactions on the rollers $A$ and $B$ at the instant of this maximum tension. Neglect friction on the rollers compared with the other forces acting.     *Ans.*  $A = 831$ lb., $B = 2530$ lb.

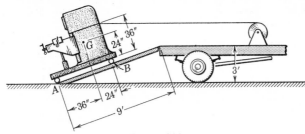

PROB. 300

**301.** The side rod on a small locomotive weighs 86 lb., and its center of gravity is located as shown. Find the maximum values of the forces on the crank pins $A$ and $B$ while the locomotive is traveling at the constant speed of 20 mi./hr.

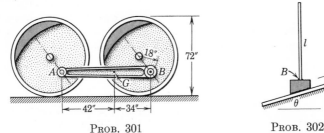

PROB. 301                PROB. 302

**302.** A small cantilever beam of weight $\mu$ per unit length and of length $l$ is welded in the vertical position to a movable base $B$. If the base is given an acceleration $a$ in a direction which makes an angle $\theta$ with the horizontal, determine the bending moment $M$ acting on the beam at its support.

$$Ans. \quad M = \frac{\mu l^2 a}{2g} \cos \theta$$

**303.** The collar $A$ and attached rods $B$ are given a simple harmonic oscillation $x = x_0 \sin pt$ along the horizontal shaft. The amplitude of the motion measured from the middle position of the oscillation is $x_0 = 0.25$ in., and the frequency of the vibration is $p = 40$ cycles/sec. Each rod weighs 0.20 lb. per inch of length. Determine an expression for the bending moment $M$ in each rod in pound inches in terms of the distance $r$ in inches from the shaft axis at the instant of time when the bending is greatest.

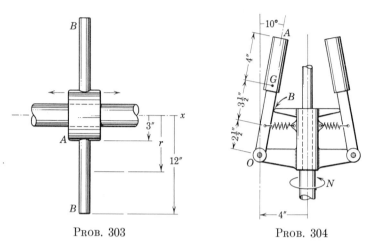

PROB. 303                    PROB. 304

**304.** In the rest position shown each spring, which has a modulus of 5 lb./in., is under a tension of 6 lb. and holds the weighted arms $OA$ against the stops $B$. Determine the speed $N$ of rotation which will bring the arms into a vertical position. Each arm weighs 4 lb. and has a center of gravity at $G$. The small angle and its sine may be interchanged in computing the added stretch of the spring.                    *Ans.* $N = 86.5$ rev./min.

**305.** A force $P$ is applied to the homogeneous rectangular box of weight $W$. If the coefficient of friction is $f$, determine the limiting values of $h$ so that the box will slide without tipping about either the front edge or the rear edge.

$$Ans. \quad h = \frac{1}{2}\left[ b - \frac{W}{P}(fb \pm c) \right]$$

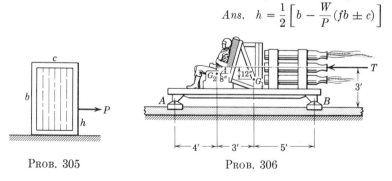

PROB. 305                    PROB. 306

**306.** The rocket sled shown is used to test human reactions to large accelerations. The initial weight of the sled and rocket motors is 3000 lb. with center of gravity at $G_1$, and the weight of the man and instrumentation carried is 500 lb..with center of gravity at $G_2$. If the rockets provide a thrust $T$ of 25,000 lb. and the initial frictional resistance at the runners is 25 per cent of the total weight, determine the normal reaction $N_A$ under the front pair of runners as the rocket sled starts its motion. *Ans.* $N_A = 3720$ lb.

**307.** The proposed overhead monorail car shown is to be driven by one of its two wheels. Select the one for which the acceleration of the car would be the greater without slipping the wheel, and compute the corresponding maximum acceleration if the coefficient of friction between the wheels and the rail is 0.30. The center of gravity of the car is to be at $G$. Neglect the weight and radius of each wheel. *Ans.* $a = 5.22$ ft./sec.$^2$

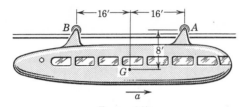

PROB. 307

**308.** Determine the maximum counterweight $W$ so that the empty 300 lb. skip with center of gravity at $G$ will not overturn about its upper wheels. Neglect the weights of the pulleys and wheels and any friction in the bearings. *Ans.* $W = 346$ lb.

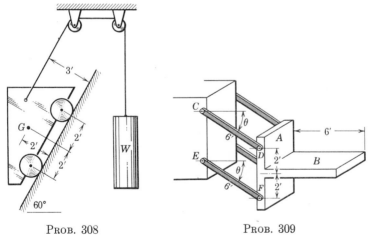

PROB. 308             PROB. 309

**309.** The T-shaped platform consists of member $A$ which weighs 350 lb. and member $B$ which weighs 500 lb. It is supported by the four identical light links and is held in the position $\theta = 30$ deg. by a cable from $C$ to F. If the cable suddenly breaks, determine the forces in $CD$ and $EF$ an instant after the cable breaks.

**310.** Each of the two uniform and identical links has a weight $W$. Find the angle $\theta$ when they are accelerating under a constant force $P$. Neglect the weight of the wheels.

$$Ans. \quad \theta = 2 \tan^{-1} \frac{P}{W}$$

**311.** The tandem unit $A$ of the road grader weighs 6500 lb. and is freely pivoted to the motive unit $B$ at $O$, which is also the center of gravity of $A$. Unit $B$ alone weighs 22,000 lb. including wheels $C$, and its center of gravity is

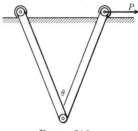

PROB. 310

54 in. above the road and 81 in. to the right of $O$. The diameter of each of the tires is 48 in. Find the minimum distance $s$ in which the grader can stop when

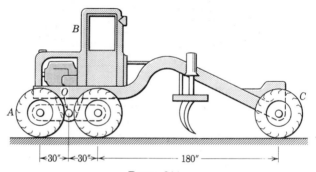

PROB. 311

traveling on a level highway at 25 mi./hr. (blade retracted and engine disengaged) so that the rear pair of wheels of the tandem unit $A$ will not lift off the road.                     $Ans. \quad s = 27.1$ ft.

\* **312.** The homogeneous triangular plate weighs 50 lb. and is attached to the two arms shown whose weights may be neglected. Determine the total force on pin $A$ as the mechanism starts from rest in the position shown under a tension $T$ of 100 lb. in the control cable.

$$Ans. \quad A = 187.8 \text{ lb.}$$

\* **313.** The horizontal member $ACG$ weighs 300 lb. and is elevated by the constant moment $M = 1200$ lb. ft. applied to the supporting link $CD$ through its shaft at $D$. The links $AB$ and $CD$ have negligible weight. If the mechanism is at rest

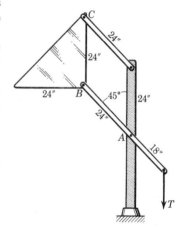

PROB. 312

at $\theta = 0$, determine the force supported by each pin at $A$ and $C$ when the position $\theta = 30$ deg. is reached.  *Ans.* $A = 342$ lb., $C = 809$ lb.

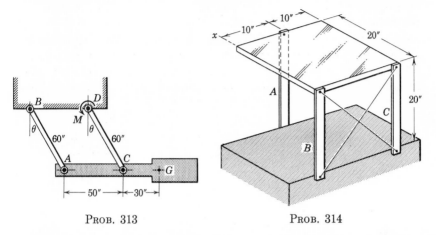

PROB. 313 PROB. 314

\* **314.** The uniform square plate weighs 100 lb. and is supported in the horizontal position by the three light legs shown. Each leg is hinged at each end by a pin whose axis is parallel to the $x$-direction. The frame is prevented from collapsing by the two diagonal wires. If one wire breaks, find the force in each leg just before the plate hits the horizontal base.

*Ans.* $A = 100$ lb., $B = C = 50$ lb., all tension

\* **315.** In the mechanism shown the light arms with connecting tie rod rotate in unison in a vertical plane with a constant counterclockwise angular accelera-

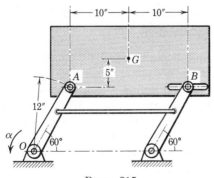

PROB. 315

tion $\alpha = 10$ rad./sec.$^2$ The center of gravity of the 45 lb. rectangular member is at $G$. If the angular velocity of the arms is 4 rad./sec. in the position shown, find the forces on pins $A$ and $B$ at this instant.

*Ans.* $A = 25.5$ lb., $B = 22.1$ lb.

**34. Fixed-Axis Rotation.**  Consider any rigid body, Fig. 31*a*, which rotates about a fixed axis through point $O$. The plane of rotation is normal to this axis and passes through the center of mass of the body. At the instant considered the body is assumed to have an angular velocity $\omega$ and an angular acceleration $\alpha$. The projections of the external forces acting on the body onto the plane of rotation are indicated by the full arrows on the free-body diagram, Fig. 31*b*, and include the reaction exerted by the bearing on the body at $O$. If the

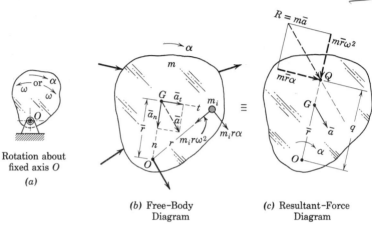

Rotation about
fixed axis $O$

(a)

(b) Free-Body
Diagram

(c) Resultant-Force
Diagram

Fig. 31

plane of rotation is other than horizontal, the weight $W$ of the body will appear on the free-body diagram. The acceleration $\bar{a}$ of the mass center $G$ has the components $\bar{a}_n = \bar{r}\omega^2$ and $\bar{a}_t = \bar{r}\alpha$. Thus from the principle of motion of the mass center, Eq. 32 of Art. 28, it is known immediately that the resultant $R$ of all external forces acting on the body is $\Sigma F = R = m\bar{a}$ and is in the same direction as $\bar{a}$. The resultant is represented by its two components in Fig. 31*c*, so that $\Sigma F_n = m\bar{r}\omega^2$ and $\Sigma F_t = m\bar{r}\alpha$. The principle of Art. 28 tells nothing about the line of action of the resultant, and it must *not* be assumed that the resultant passes through $G$ for rotation as it does for translation. The location of the line of action of $R$ is determined by evaluating the sum of the moments of all forces about $O$.

The moment relation is obtained by considering the forces acting on a representative particle of mass $m_i$. The resultant of these forces may be represented by its two components $m_i r\omega^2$ and $m_i r\alpha$ as shown in Fig. 31*b*. Of the two components only the tangential one exerts a moment about $O$, and the magnitude of this moment is $m_i r^2 \alpha$. If this moment is added to those for the remaining particles in the body, the sum

$$\Sigma M_O = \Sigma m_i r^2 \alpha = \alpha \Sigma m_i r^2$$

results.  The acceleration $\alpha$ is common to all terms and may be factored outside the summation sign.  The sum $\Sigma M_O$ includes moments due to internal forces (actions and reactions between particles) and moments due to external forces.  Since each internal action is accompanied by an equal and opposite internal reaction, it follows that the net contribution to $\Sigma M_O$ by the internal forces is zero.  Therefore the expression represents the algebraic sum of the moments about the axis of rotation of all external forces.  The summation $\Sigma m_i r^2$ depends on the radial distribution of mass about the axis and is known as the *mass moment of inertia I* of the body about *O*.

The three equations of motion for a rigid body rotating about a fixed axis through $O$ may now be written as

$$\Sigma F_n = m\bar{r}\omega^2,$$

$$\Sigma F_t = m\bar{r}\alpha, \tag{40}$$

$$\Sigma M_O = I_O \alpha.$$

The use of these equations of motion is straightforward when they are applied exactly and literally with the aid of a complete and correct free-body diagram.

In terms of the differential element of mass $dm$, the mass density $\rho$, and the volume element $dV$ the defining expression for mass moment of inertia may be written as

$$I_O = \Sigma m_i r^2 = \int r^2\, dm = \int \rho r^2\, dV,$$

where the integral is evaluated over the entire volume of the body.  The radius of gyration $k$ of the body about the axis through $O$ is defined by

$$k_O{}^2 = \frac{I_O}{m}.$$

Moments of inertia are involved in all problems of bodies which have rotational acceleration, and it is necessary to be familiar with them in order to proceed further.  A detailed discussion of mass moments of inertia is presented in Appendix $C$.

The line of action of the resultant $R$ for a rotating rigid body, Fig. 31$c$, may be found by locating point $Q$.  The principle of moments requires that the sum of the moments of all external forces on the body must equal the moment of their sum or resultant. Thus

$$I_O\alpha = qm\bar{r}\alpha, \qquad k_O^2 m\alpha = qm\bar{r}\alpha$$

so that

$$q = \frac{k_O^2}{\bar{r}}. \tag{41}$$

The point $Q$, located by the distance $q$ from $O$, is known as the *center of percussion about O*. With $Q$ located two alternate moment equations which are often convenient may be written. The first, a moment sum about $Q$, is clearly zero. The second, a moment sum about the mass center $G$, is obtained by multiplying $\Sigma F_t = m\bar{r}\alpha$ by $q - \bar{r}$ which gives

$$m\bar{r}\alpha(q - \bar{r}) = m\alpha(k_O^2 - \bar{r}^2) = m\bar{k}^2\alpha = \bar{I}\alpha.$$

Thus two alternate moment equations of motion for a rigid body rotating about a fixed point are

$$\Sigma M_Q = 0 \qquad \text{and} \qquad \Sigma\bar{M} = \bar{I}\alpha.$$

Points other than $O$, $G$, or $Q$ may be used as moment centers if desired, and the correct expression for the moment sum may be determined from the resultant-force diagram by using the principle of moments. For the special case of rotation of a rigid body about a fixed centroidal axis $\bar{r} = 0$, $M_O$ is replaced by $\bar{M}$ and $I_O$ by $\bar{I}$. Thus for rotation about a fixed axis through the mass center Eqs. 40 become

$$\Sigma\bar{M} = \bar{I}\alpha,$$
$$\Sigma F_x = 0, \tag{42}$$
$$\Sigma F_y = 0,$$

where the $x$- and $y$-directions are arbitrary. Such a body may be said to be in translational equilibrium ($\bar{a} = 0$) but not in rotational equilibrium. For this case of centroidal rotation it may be observed, since the resultant force is zero, that the resultant of all forces acting on the body is a couple equal to $\bar{I}\alpha$. Hence $\Sigma\bar{M}$ is the same as a moment sum about any axis parallel to the centroidal axis.

### SAMPLE PROBLEMS

**316.** The radius of gyration about the axis of the uniform integral pulleys is 12 in., and their combined weight is 96.6 lb. If friction in the bearing is negligible, find the distance $s$ through which the 32.2 lb. weight has moved 4

sec. after release from rest.  The cables are wrapped securely around the
pulleys.  Also find the bearing reaction at $O$ during this interval.

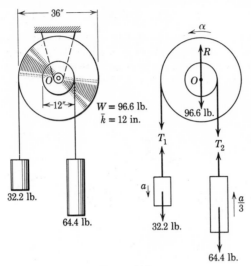

PROB. 316

*Solution.*  Comparison of the static moments about $O$ shows that the 32.2
lb. weight accelerates down.  If the acceleration of this weight is $a$, the acceleration of the 64.4 lb. weight is $6a/18$ upward.  Also the centroidal moment of
inertia of the combined pulleys is

$[I = k^2 m]$ $\qquad\qquad$ $\bar{I} = \left(\dfrac{12}{12}\right)^2 \dfrac{96.6}{32.2} = 3$ lb. ft. sec.$^2$

The free-body diagram of each of the three members is shown.  For the two
weights

$[\Sigma F = ma]$ $\qquad\qquad$ $32.2 - T_1 = \dfrac{32.2}{32.2}\, a; \qquad T_2 - 64.4 = \dfrac{64.4}{32.2}\dfrac{a}{3}.$

For centroidal rotation of the pulleys

$[\Sigma \bar{M} = \bar{I}\alpha]$ $\qquad\qquad$ $\dfrac{18}{12} T_1 - \dfrac{6}{12} T_2 = 3\dfrac{a}{18/12}.$

Solution of the three equations gives

$\qquad\qquad a = 4.20$ ft./sec.$^2$, $\qquad T_1 = 28.0$ lb., $\qquad T_2 = 67.2$ lb.

With the constant acceleration known the distance dropped by the 32.2 lb.
weight in 4 sec. is

$[s = \tfrac{1}{2}at^2]$ $\qquad\qquad$ $s = \tfrac{1}{2} \times 4.20 \times 4^2 = 33.6$ ft. $\qquad\qquad\qquad$ *Ans.*

The bearing reaction is obtained from the vertical equilibrium of forces on the drum and is

$$[\Sigma F_y = 0] \qquad R - 96.6 - 28.0 - 67.2 = 0, \qquad R = 191.8 \text{ lb.} \qquad Ans.$$

**317.** The center of gravity of the 3.10 lb. connecting rod shown in the $a$-part of the figure is at $G$, and the radius of gyration of the rod about the pivot axis $O$ is 9.14 in. If the rod is released from rest with $\theta = 0$, find the total force on the bearing $O$ when the position $\theta = 45$ deg. is passed. Neglect any friction in the bearing.

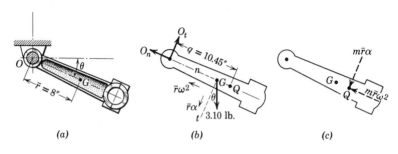

(a)                          (b)                         (c)

PROB. 317

*Solution.* The free-body diagram of the rod in an intermediate position $\theta$ is shown in the $b$-part of the figure, and the resultant of the external forces is represented in the $c$-part of the figure. The bearing reaction is indicated by its $n$- and $t$-components where the sense of these components may be assumed for the present. The normal component $O_n$ is found from a force equation in the $n$-direction which involves the normal acceleration $\bar{r}\omega^2$. Since $\omega$ is found from the integral of the angular acceleration and since $O_t$ depends on the tangential acceleration $\bar{r}\alpha$, it follows that $\alpha$ must be obtained first. The moment equation about $O$ gives

$$[\Sigma M_O = I_o \alpha] \qquad 3.10 \times \frac{8}{12} \cos \theta = \left(\frac{9.14}{12}\right)^2 \frac{3.10}{32.2} \alpha,$$

Then

$$\alpha = 37.0 \cos \theta.$$

$$[\omega \, d\omega = \alpha \, d\theta] \qquad \int_0^\omega \omega \, d\omega = \int_0^{\pi/4} 37.0 \cos \theta \, d\theta,$$

$$\omega^2 = 52.3 \text{ (rad./sec.)}^2.$$

The remaining two equations of motion applied to the 45 deg. position yield

$$[\Sigma F_n = m\bar{r}\omega^2] \qquad O_n - 3.10 \times 0.707 = \frac{3.10}{32.2} \times \frac{2}{3} \times 52.3, \qquad O_n = 5.55 \text{ lb.,}$$

$$[\Sigma F_t = m\bar{r}\alpha] \quad 3.10 \times 0.707 - O_t = \frac{3.10}{32.2} \times \frac{2}{3} \times 37.0 \times 0.707, \qquad O_t = 0.51 \text{ lb.}$$

The total bearing force is

$$O = \sqrt{(5.55)^2 + (0.51)^2} = 5.57 \text{ lb.} \qquad Ans.$$

The proper sense for $O_t$ may be observed at the outset by applying the alternate moment equation, $\Sigma \overline{M} = \overline{I}\alpha$. This relation eliminates all forces but $O_t$ and requires a clockwise moment to agree with the known direction of $\alpha$. Also, the component $O_t$ may be found directly with the aid of the second alternate moment equation and the distance $q$, which is $k_O{}^2/\bar{r} = (9.14)^2/8 = 10.45$ in. Thus

$$[\Sigma M_Q = 0] \quad 10.45 O_t - 3.10 \times 0.707 \times (10.45 - 8) = 0, \quad O_t = 0.51 \text{ lb.}$$

### PROBLEMS

**318.** If the connecting rod of Sample Prob. 317 is given an initial swing which carries it over the top position ($\theta = 270$ deg.) with an angular velocity of 10 rad/sec., find the bearing reaction $O$ at this position. *Ans.* $O = 3.31$ lb.

**319.** The solid cylindrical pulleys weigh 32.2 lb. each and are mounted in bearings with negligible friction. The 10 lb. force on pulley $A$ is constant. Determine the angular acceleration $\alpha$ of each pulley.

*Ans.* $\alpha_A = 20$ rad./sec.$^2$, $\alpha_B = 12.34$ rad./sec.$^2$

**320.** The radius of gyration of a 40 lb. flywheel about its vertical shaft is 6 in., and the center of gravity of the wheel is 0.003 in. from the axis of the shaft. If a constant moment of 10 lb. ft. is applied to the flywheel through its shaft, find the components of the horizontal force $F$ exerted on the bearing 5 sec. after the wheel starts from rest.

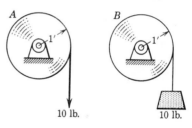

10 lb.          10 lb.

PROB. 319

*Ans.* $F_n = 8.05$ lb., $F_t = 0.010$ lb.

**321.** The rim of the flywheel shown in section is welded to the central web which in turn is welded to the hub. The weights of the web and hub are negligible compared with the 100 lb. rim. If the maximum safe shearing force which

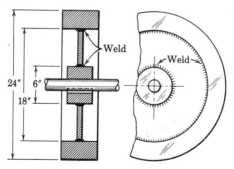

24"   6"
18"

Weld

Weld

PROB. 321

the rim weld and hub weld can each support is 4000 lb. per inch of weld length, find the maximum safe acceleration $\alpha$ which can be given to the flywheel by a torque suddenly applied to the shaft.

**322.** Gears $A$ and $B$ weigh 6 lb. and 30 lb., respectively, and may be treated as circular disks. If the motor accelerates gear $B$ from rest to a speed of 920 rev./min. in 1.2 sec., find the torque $M$ to which the motor shaft is subjected where it is attached to the pinion.        *Ans.*   $M = 5.61$ lb. ft.

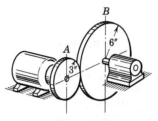

PROB. 322

**323.** The large mixing drum consists of a cylindrical shell and two flat circular ends all made from 1 in. thick steel plate. The drum is supported on two coaxial rings by two guide rollers at $A$ and two at $B$. Determine the initial angular acceleration $\alpha$ of the empty drum if a starting torque of 60 lb. ft. is applied to each of the two guide rollers $B$. Assume that friction is sufficient to prevent slipping of the driving rollers. The mass of the rollers and the mass of the rings are small and may be neglected.

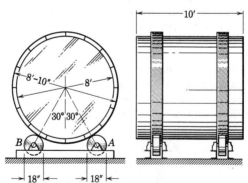

PROB. 323

**324.** The motor pinion $A$ of the log hoist has a negligible moment of inertia and is subjected to a counterclockwise starting torque of 40 lb. ft. Determine the tension $T$ in the cable if the coefficient of friction between the 500 lb. log and the incline is 0.80.        *Ans.*   $T = 722$ lb.

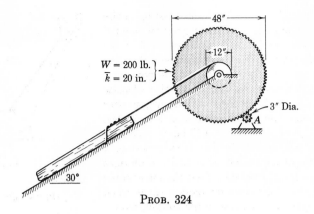

PROB. 324

**325.** The gear weighs 10 lb. and has a radius of gyration of 4 in. Each rack weighs 12 lb. and slides against the smooth vertical guide. Determine the

torque $M$ required on the shaft of the gear to give an angular acceleration of 8 rad./sec.²

**326.** A 50 lb. horizontal component of the bearing reaction at $O$ is recorded when the uniform slender rod is struck with a force $F$. Determine the magnitude of $F$ at the instant that the 50 lb. reaction was measured.

*Ans.* $F = 250$ lb.

**327.** The mast $OA$ is a uniform pole weighing 3750 lb. It is hinged at $O$

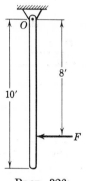

and is to be hoisted by the winch at $B$. If the winch supplies a starting

PROB. 325                    PROB. 326

torque of 2500 lb. ft., determine the total force exerted by the bearing on the mast at $O$ as the winch is activated.

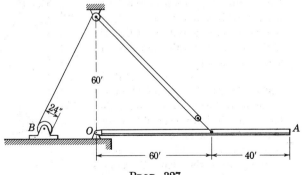

PROB. 327

**328.** The pendulum for the impact testing device weighs 75 lb. and has a radius of gyration about $O$ of 26 in. The pendulum is designed so that the force on the bearing at $O$ is the least possible value during impact with the specimen at the bottom of the swing. Determine the distance $b$. Also calculate the total force on the bearing at $O$ an instant after the pendulum is released from rest at $\theta = 60$ deg.

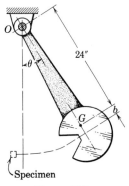

Ans.    $b = 4.17$ in., $O = 38.7$ lb.

**329.** The uniform 10 lb. link is subjected to a constant frictional moment of 5 lb. ft. in its tight bearing at $O$ during rotation. Find the force on the bearing at $O$ an instant after motion starts when the link is released from rest in the position shown.

PROB. 328

**330.** If the support at $A$ is suddenly removed, find (a) the momentary reaction at $B$ in the horizontal position and (b) the reaction at $B$ as the bar swings through the vertical. The weight of the uniform slender bar is 16.1 lb.

Ans.    (a) $B = 12.08$ lb., (b) $B = 24.2$ lb.

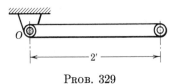

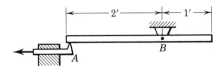

PROB. 329                    PROB. 330

**331.** The bar is suspended by a light cord from its end and swings as a pendulum. With the aid of a free-body diagram show that the bar cannot remain in line with the cord during the motion.

**332.** Determine the starting torque $M$ which a motor must supply to the light pinion $A$ in order to raise the weighted arm with an initial angular acceleration of 2 rad./sec.² from the position shown. The radius of gyration of the 10 lb. arm assembly about its pivot is 12 in., and its center of gravity is at $G$. The 20 lb. rack moves with negligible friction in its guides.

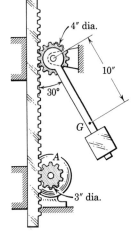

Ans.    $M = 13.4$ lb. in.

**333.** The 64.4 lb. cylindrical rotor $A$ is mounted freely on the shaft $BC$. The arms $D$ have negligible weight and are rigidly attached to the vertical shaft $E$ with fixed axis. Through a motor drive the shaft $E$ exerts a torque of 20 lb. ft. on the arm as-

PROB. 331

PROB. 332

sembly. Determine the angular acceleration $\alpha$ of the arms ($a$) when the locking pin $F$ is in place and ($b$) when the pin is removed.

$Ans.$   ($a$) $\alpha = 8.89$ rad./sec.$^2$, ($b$) $\alpha = 10$ rad./sec.$^2$

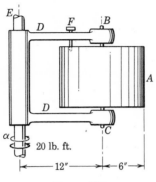

PROB. 333

**334.** A large pendulum consists of the 50 lb. circular metal disk $A$ welded to the uniform shaft $B$, which weighs 40 lb. Determine the reaction on the bearing $O$ an instant after release from rest in the horizontal position shown.

$Ans.$   $O = 21.7$ lb.

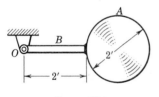

PROB. 334                          PROB. 335

**335.** A horizontal force $F$ is applied to the end of the slender bar of length $l$ at an angle $\theta$ to the bar. The bar is initially at rest on a smooth horizontal surface. Locate the point $O$ about which the bar is momentarily in rotation by finding the distance $\bar{r}$ from the center of mass of the bar to point $O$.

$Ans.$   $\bar{r} = \dfrac{l}{6} \csc \theta$

**336.** A horizontal shaft of radius $r_0$ turns about its fixed axis through $O$ with a constant angular acceleration $\alpha_0$. A ring of negligible thickness and of weight $W$ and radius $r$ rests on the shaft and turns with it. If friction is sufficient to prevent slipping, determine the angle $\theta$ with the vertical assumed by the normal to the surfaces of contact

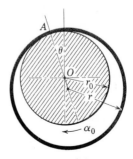

PROB. 336

at $A$ during a constant acceleration $\alpha_0$ of the shaft.  What is the minimum coefficient of friction $f$ to prevent slipping for a given $\alpha_0$?

$$Ans. \quad \theta = \sin^{-1}\frac{r_0\alpha_0}{g}, \ f_{min.} = \frac{1}{\sqrt{\left(\dfrac{g}{r_0\alpha_0}\right)^2 - 1}}$$

**337.** The 50 lb. bar $AB$ is mounted on wheels of negligible weight and rolls down the circular guide under the action of its own weight.  The bar is started in such a way that its angular velocity at the position $\theta = 45$ deg. is 3 rad./sec.  Determine the forces $A$ and $B$ under the wheels at this position.  Observe that the bar executes rotation about point $O$.

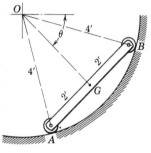

**338.** The 6 lb. uniform bar hinged at $A$ is given an initial angular velocity of 4 rad./sec. as it passes the position for which $\theta = 45$ deg. It continues to fall under the action of its own weight until it strikes the spring $S$ as it reaches the vertical position.  A maximum deflection of 0.2 in. is recorded for the spring which has a stiffness of 1050 lb./in.  Determine (a) the

PROB. 337

force exerted by the pin $A$ on the bar an instant before contact with the spring and (b) the horizontal component of the force at $A$ at the instant of maximum spring deformation.          $Ans.$   (a) $A_n = 9.0$ lb., (b) $A_t = 30.0$ lb.

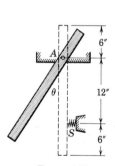

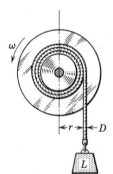

PROB. 338          PROB. 339

**339.** Find the moment $M$ required to rotate the drum at a constant speed $\omega$ if the diameter $D$ of the rope is small compared with $r$ and if there is negligible friction in the bearings.          $Ans.$   $M = Lr\left(1 + \dfrac{D\omega^2}{2\pi g}\right)$

**340.** A long heavy cable of length $L$ and weight $\mu$ per unit length is wound around a light drum with negligible friction in the bearings of its horizontal shaft.  One end of the cable hangs down a very small distance, and the resulting unbalance causes the drum to rotate and unwind the cable with increasing speed.  Determine the velocity $v$ of the cable as it leaves the drum completely.

**341.** The direction of rotation of an electric motor for a high-speed computing device may be reversed quickly with negligible energy loss by engaging the positive clutch in the connecting shaft when the power is shut off. The shaft twists in bringing the rotor to a stop and then untwists in returning the rotor to the same speed in the opposite direction, at which instant the clutch is disengaged. The moment acting on the shaft is proportional to the angle of twist of the shaft and equals 2 lb. ft. for each degree of twist. If the moment of inertia of the rotor is 0.008 lb. ft. sec.$^2$ and that of the

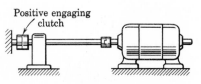

Positive engaging clutch

PROB. 341

shaft is negligibly small, find the maximum moment $M$ in the shaft due to reversing the direction of rotation from a speed of 1800 rev./min.

$Ans.$ $M = 180.4$ lb. ft.

**342.** Determine the force on the bearing $O$ for the link described in Prob. 329 as it swings past the vertical position.

\* **343.** Determine the force $R$ and the moment $M$ supported by the weld, joining parts $A$ and $B$ of the pendulum in Prob. 334, an instant after release from rest in the horizontal position. $Ans.$ $R = 3.9$ lb., $M = 12.9$ lb. ft.

\* **344.** The curved bar of weight $W$ is hinged to the rotating disk at $O$ and bears against one of the smooth pins $A$ and $B$ which are fastened to the disk. If the disk rotates about its vertical axis $C$, determine the force exerted on the bar by the hinge at $O$ and the reaction $A$ or $B$ on the bar $(a)$ if the disk has a constant angular velocity $\omega$ and $(b)$ as the disk starts from rest with a counterclockwise angular acceleration $\alpha$.

$$Ans. \quad (a)\ O = \frac{2Wr\omega^2}{\pi g}, \quad A = \frac{2Wr\omega^2}{\pi g},$$

$$(b)\ O = \frac{Wr\alpha}{g}\sqrt{1 + \frac{4}{\pi^2}}, \quad B = \frac{Wr\alpha}{g}\left(1 - \frac{2}{\pi}\right)$$

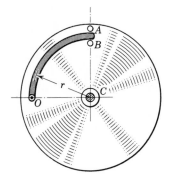

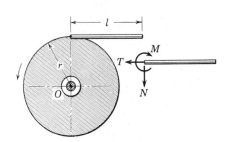

PROB. 344

PROB. 345

\* **345.** The uniform slender rod of length $l$ and weight $W$ is welded at its end tangent to the rim of the circular disk of radius $r$ which rotates about a vertical axis through $O$. Determine the bending moment $M$, the shear force $N$, and the axial force $T$ which the weld exerts on the rod $(a)$ for a constant angular velocity $\omega$ of the disk and $(b)$ as the disk starts from rest with a counterclockwise angular acceleration $\alpha$.

$$Ans. \quad (a) \quad M = \frac{Wrl\omega^2}{2g}, \quad N = \frac{Wr\omega^2}{g}, \quad T = \frac{Wl\omega^2}{2g},$$

$$(b) \quad M = -\frac{Wl^2\alpha}{3g}, \quad N = -\frac{Wl\alpha}{2g}, \quad T = \frac{Wr\alpha}{g}$$

*346. The pendulum has a weight $W$ with center of gravity $G$ a distance $\bar{r}$ from the axis of rotation $O\!-\!O$. The radius of gyration of the pendulum about $O\!-\!O$ is $k$. If the pendulum is released from rest at $\theta = 0$, derive expressions for the torsional moment $M_z$ and the bending moment components $M_x$ and $M_y$ in the supporting pipe at its base $B$ in terms of $\theta$.

$$Ans. \quad M_z = -\frac{3W\bar{r}^2 b}{2k^2} \sin 2\theta, \quad M_x = -\frac{3W\bar{r}^2 c}{2k^2} \sin 2\theta,$$

$$M_y = Wb \left[ 1 + \frac{\bar{r}^2}{k^2} (2 - 3 \cos^2 \theta) \right]$$

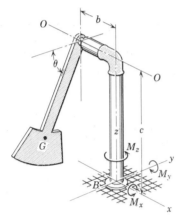

PROB. 346                    PROB. 347

*347. The uniform slender bar of weight $W$ and length $l$ is released from rest in the vertical position and pivots on its square end about the corner $O$. $(a)$ If the bar is observed to slip when $\theta = 30$ deg., find the coefficient of friction $f$. $(b)$ If the end of the bar is notched so that it cannot slip, find the angle $\theta$ at which contact between the bar and the corner ceases.

$$Ans. \quad (a) \; f = 0.188, \quad (b) \; \theta = 53°\,8'$$

**35. Distributed Forces in Rotation.** The internal forces induced in a body by reason of high rotative speeds or appreciable accelerations are usually important design considerations. The calculation of the internal forces which result from such motions is often very involved. However, when the body is essentially uni-dimensional, such as a slender rod or a thin ring, it is usually possible to calculate the internal forces without undue difficulty. The general procedure is to isolate a differential element or a finite portion of the body with a free-body diagram and to write the motion equations for the forces acting on the part isolated.

### SAMPLE PROBLEM

**348.** Determine the variation of the centrifugal tension in the slender rod of weight $W$ and length $2l$ which rotates in a horizontal plane about an axis through $O$ normal to the rod.

*Solution.* The free-body diagram of an element of length $dx$ shows a tension $T$ acting on the left-hand section, where the coordinate is $x$, and a tension $T + dT$ on the right-hand section, where the coordinate is $x + dx$. The weight of the element

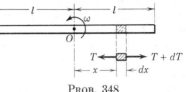

PROB. 348

is assumed small compared with the tension $T$. If $\mu$ stands for the weight of the bar per unit length, the equation of motion for this element gives

$$[\Sigma F_n = mr\omega^2] \qquad T - (T + dT) = \frac{\mu \, dx}{g} x\omega^2,$$

$$-dT = \frac{\mu\omega^2}{g} x \, dx.$$

At the center of the bar the tension will be designated by $T_0$, so that the integration limits give

$$\int_{T_0}^{T} - dT = \frac{\mu\omega^2}{g} \int_0^x x \, dx,$$

$$T = T_0 - \frac{\mu\omega^2 x^2}{2g}.$$

Since the tension is zero at $x = l$, the tension at the center becomes $T_0 = (\mu\omega^2 l^2)/(2g)$. This value for $T_0$ may also be obtained by considering the acceleration of the mass center of half the bar, which is $(l/2)\omega^2$. Thus the force $T_0$ is $\frac{1}{2}(W/g)(l/2)\omega^2 = (\mu\omega^2 l^2)/(2g)$. The tension at any value of $x$ becomes

$$T = \frac{\mu\omega^2}{2g}(l^2 - x^2) = \frac{Wl\omega^2}{4g}\left(1 - \frac{x^2}{l^2}\right). \qquad\qquad Ans.$$

The stress at any position in the bar is the tension $T$ divided by the cross-sectional area of the bar and is known as a *centrifugal stress.*

It is left for the student to show that the same results may be obtained by isolating a finite portion of the rod from $x$ to $l$ and writing the appropriate equation of motion.

## PROBLEMS

**349.** Determine the centrifugal stress $\sigma$ in the rim of a flywheel of weight density $\mu$ rotating with a constant rim speed $v$. Assume the radial thickness of the rim to be small compared with the radius of the wheel and neglect the effect of the web or spokes. Solve, first, by considering one half of the rim as a free body and, second, by considering the free body as an element of the rim subtending an angle $d\theta$.

$$Ans. \quad \sigma = \frac{\mu}{g}v^2$$

**350.** The ring of weight $W$ and radius $r$ rotates about a diametral axis with an angular velocity $\omega$. Determine the tension $T$ in the ring at $A$ and $B$ if the dimensions of its rim are small compared with $r$. Analyze one half of the ring on either side of the axis as a free body. Compare with Prob. 349.

**351.** The hub and attached blades are given an angular acceleration $\alpha$ about the vertical shaft at $O$. Derive expressions for the shear force $Q$ and bending moment $M$ in the blade in terms of $r$. The blade is a uniform slender bar with a mass $\rho$ per unit length.

PROB. 350

$$Ans. \quad Q = \frac{\rho\alpha}{2}(R^2 - r^2), \quad M = \frac{\sigma\alpha}{6}(2R + r)(R - r)^2$$

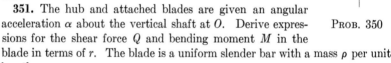

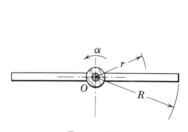

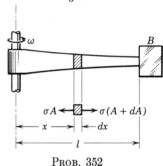

PROB. 351                          PROB. 352

*__352.__ A slender rod of mass density $\rho$ and variable cross-sectional area $A$ is to be designed to support the rotation of body $B$ at an angular velocity $\omega$. The centrifugal force applied to the end of the rod by $B$ divided by a desired design stress $\sigma$ gives an area $A_l$ for the end section of the rod. Determine the necessary variation of the cross-sectional area $A$ as a function of $x$ in order that the stress $\sigma$ be constant over the length of the rod. (*Hint:* The free-body diagram of an element of the rod is shown.)

$$Ans. \quad A = A_l e^{\frac{\rho\omega^2}{2\sigma}(l^2 - x^2)}$$

*__353.__ Derive an expression for the bending moment $M$ in the rod of Prob. 345 in terms of the distance $x$ measured along the rod from the welded end for the case of constant angular velocity $\omega$ of the disk.

$$Ans. \quad M = \frac{Wr\omega^2}{2gl}(l - x)^2$$

\* **354.** The split ring of radius $r$ is rotating about a vertical axis through its center $O$ with a constant angular velocity $\omega$. Use a differential element of the ring and derive expressions for the shear force $N$ and rim tension $T$ in the ring in terms of the angle $\theta$. Determine the bending moment $M_0$ at point $C$ by using one half of the ring as a free body. The mass of the ring per unit length of rim is $\rho$.     *Ans.*  $N = \rho r^2 \omega^2 \sin \theta, \ T = \rho r^2 \omega^2(1 + \cos \theta), \ M_0 = 2\rho r^3 \omega^2$

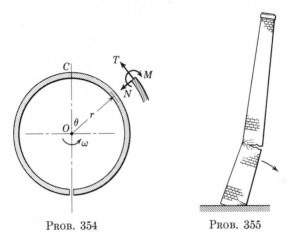

PROB. 354                    PROB. 355

\* **355.** A falling chimney, such as the one shown, will usually crack, before it hits the ground, at a point where the bending moment is greatest. Show that this position of maximum moment always occurs at the center of percussion relative to the upper end for a slender chimney of constant cross section if the restraining moment at the bottom is neglected.

**36. Fixed-Axis Rotation of a Body with Axial Dimensions.** When a rotating body is not symmetrical with respect to a single plane of rotation, the dimensions in the direction of the axis of rotation must be considered. Problems of this type may be solved by locating the resultant of the forces on each part of the rotating assembly and using the principle of moments in one or both coordinate planes which contain the axis of rotation. If the resultant is not known, the resultant force for a differential element of mass must be determined and integrated over the body.

Although general equations of motion may be written to cover this case of rotation, it is usually just as convenient to work out the necessary force and moment relations directly from the equivalence of the system of applied forces and their resultants.

## SAMPLE PROBLEMS

**356.** The identical rotors each of weight $W$ shown in cases $(a)$ and $(b)$ are mounted eccentrically on their shafts with their centers of gravity a distance $e$ from the shaft axis. Determine the bearing reactions due to the unbalance which exists at a constant rotational speed $\omega$.

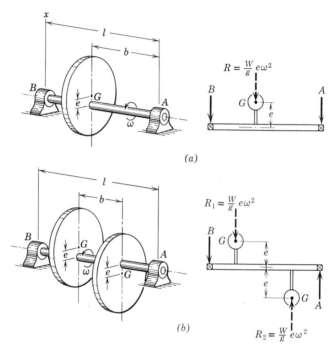

(a)

(b)

PROB. 356

*Solution. Case* $(a)$. The bearing reactions due to the rotational unbalance of the rotor may be computed independently of the reactions due to the static weight of the rotor. In so far as the forces on the shaft are concerned the mass of the rotor may be assumed to be concentrated at the center of gravity as shown in the free-body diagram. The two bearing reactions $A$ and $B$ produce the resultant $R = m\bar{a}_n = (W/g)e\omega^2$ shown as a dotted vector. The principle of moments permits the direct calculation of either bearing reaction. The force resultant is then determined. Thus

$$[\Sigma M_A = m\bar{a}d] \qquad Bl = \frac{W}{g}e\omega^2 b, \qquad B = \frac{b}{l}\frac{W}{g}e\omega^2, \qquad Ans.$$

$$[\Sigma F_x = m\bar{a}_x] \qquad A + \frac{b}{l}\frac{W}{g}e\omega^2 = \frac{W}{g}e\omega^2, \qquad A = \left(1 - \frac{b}{l}\right)\frac{W}{g}e\omega^2. \quad Ans.$$

The addition of a weight $W_0$ on the opposite side of the shaft from $W$ and at a distance $e_0$ from the axis will balance the rotor and produce zero bearing forces if $W_0 e_0 = We$. If the shaft with rotor and balancing weight is mounted in frictionless bearings, a static equilibrium of moments will exist about the shaft axis, and a condition of *static balance* is said to exist. Such a test for static balance will not be influenced by the location of the balancing weight with respect to its position along the shaft.

*Solution. Case (b).* The free-body diagram of the shaft is shown with the weights of the rotors concentrated at their centers of gravity. The resultants $R_1$ and $R_2$ of all forces acting on each rotor are shown by the dotted vectors. The two bearing reactions $A$ and $B$ must be equivalent to these resultants. Since the resultants constitute a couple in this particular problem, it is clear that the bearing reactions constitute an equal couple, and the magnitude of each is

$$A = B = \frac{b}{l} \frac{W}{g} e\omega^2 \qquad Ans.$$

This couple is called a *rocking couple* and exists only when the shaft is rotating. The shaft is in static balance since a static test discloses that the sum of the moments of the eccentric weights about the shaft axis is zero. The shaft would be in *dynamic balance* if two additional eccentric weights were added so as to produce an equal and opposite resultant couple.

Static balance requires the equilibrium of resultant *forces*, whereas dynamic balance requires, in addition, the equilibrium of the resultant *couples*. Most balancing problems involve a combination of the two requirements and also involve resultant forces which do not all lie in a single plane containing the axis of rotation.

**357.** A flywheel is mounted so that its geometric axis makes an angle $\phi$ with the axis of rotation through its center as shown. Find the moment $M$ (rocking couple) exerted on the shaft at a rotational speed $\omega$. Neglect the effect of the hub and spokes and consider the flywheel to be a rotating hoop of weight $W$ and radius $r$ with a rim of small cross section.

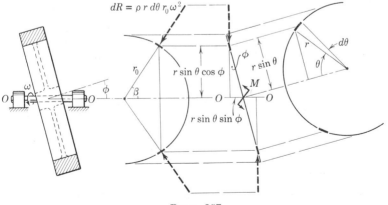

PROB. 357

*Solution.* The diagrams to the right of the flywheel show the edge view of the wheel and the orthogonal projection on either side. The center line only of the rim is shown. The moment $M$ applied by the shaft to the wheel must equal the sum of the moments of the resultant forces for all elements of the wheel. If $\rho$ stands for the mass of the rim per unit length, the resultant force for an element $r\ d\theta$ of the rim is in the direction of its centripetal acceleration and is $\rho r\ d\theta\ r_0\omega^2$, where $r_0$ is the actual radius of rotation for this element. The resultant force for a symmetrically spaced element below the axis is also shown. From the edge view of the disk it is seen that only the vertical components of these forces contribute to $M$. Each vertical component is

$$\rho r\ d\theta\ r_0\omega^2 \sin \beta = \rho r^2\omega^2 \cos \phi \sin \theta\ d\theta,$$

and the couple produced by both of them is the force multiplied by $2r \sin \theta \sin \phi$ or

$$dM = 2\rho r^3\omega^2 \sin \phi \cos \phi \sin^2 \theta\ d\theta.$$

Integration from $\theta = 0$ to $\theta = \pi$ includes the couples due to all pairs of elements. Thus

$$M = 2\rho r^3\omega^2 \sin \phi \cos \phi \int_0^\pi \sin^2 \theta\ d\theta = \frac{Wr^2\omega^2 \sin 2\phi}{4g}, \qquad Ans.$$

where the weight of the rim is $W = 2\pi r\rho g$ and the integral equals $\pi/2$. If the angle $\phi$ is very small, the sine may be replaced by the angle, and the moment becomes

$$M = \frac{Wr^2\omega^2\phi}{2g}.$$

## PROBLEMS

**358.** The shaft and 10 lb. disk of the air turbine rotate at a constant speed of 12,000 rev./min. If the center of mass of the disk is off center by 0.002 in., determine the horizontal forces supported by the bearings due to the unbalance.          *Ans.*   $A = 54$ lb., $B = 136$ lb.

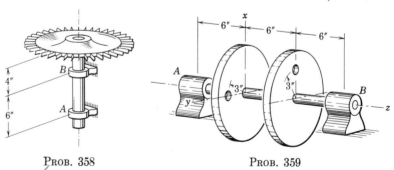

PROB. 358                    PROB. 359

**359.** Two circular steel disks 1 in. thick are mounted on the shaft shown. A 1 in. diameter hole is drilled in each disk in the location indicated. Determine the magnitude of the bearing reactions due to the rotational unbalance of the system for a speed of 1000 rev./min.

*Ans.* $|A| = |B| = 14.12$ lb.

**360.** At the instant represented the uniform 16.1 lb. arm $OC$ has an angular velocity of 4 rad./sec. and an angular acceleration of 16 rad./sec.$^2$ about the shaft $AB$. Compute the total lateral forces on the bearings due to the rotation of the rod only. *Ans.* $A = 9\sqrt{2}$ lb., $B = 3\sqrt{2}$ lb.

**361.** The arm $A$ of a large radial drilling machine weighs 4200 lb. and has a center of gravity at $G_1$. The drilling head $B$ weighs 960 lb. with center of gravity at $G_2$ and is in its extreme outward position.

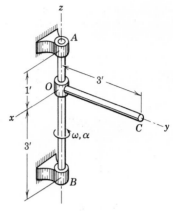

PROB. 360

Determine the horizontal forces exerted by the arm on the column, assuming contact at $C$ and $D$ with the entire weight supported at $D$, if the arm and head are being rotated about the vertical column at the constant rate of 2 rad./sec.

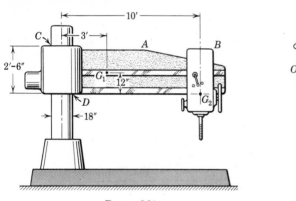

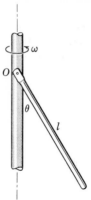

PROB. 361                            PROB. 362

**362.** The slender rod of weight $W$ and length $l$ is hinged at $O$ to the vertical shaft which rotates with a constant angular velocity $\omega$. Find the angle $\theta$ assumed by the bar. (*Question:* Why does the resultant force not act through the center of gravity of the bar?)

$$Ans. \quad \theta = \cos^{-1}\frac{3g}{2l\omega^2}$$

**363.** If the bar in Prob. 362 is welded to the shaft at $O$ at an angle $\theta$, find the bending moment $M$ in the bar at $O$ due to the angular velocity $\omega$ of the vertical shaft.

$$Ans. \quad M = \frac{Wl\sin\theta}{6}\left(\frac{2l\omega^2}{g}\cos\theta - 3\right)$$

**364.** Determine the bending moment $M$ in each of the rods where they attach to the hub at $A$ due to a rotation of 3000 rev./min. about the vertical axis. Each rod weighs 0.60 lb. per foot of length.    *Ans.*   $M = 1056$ lb. in.

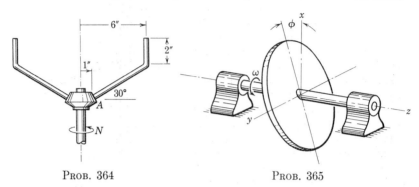

PROB. 364                         PROB. 365

*365. Use the results of Sample Prob. 357 to determine the rocking couple $M$ exerted on the shaft by the rotating circular disk of weight $W$ and radius $r$ whose plane makes an angle $\phi$ with the plane normal to the shaft through its center.

$$Ans. \quad M = \frac{Wr^2\omega^2 \sin 2\phi}{8g}$$

*366. A square plate of weight $W$ and length $a$ on a side is mounted on a central shaft in the manner shown. Determine the rocking couple $M$ which the plate exerts on its shaft at a rotational speed $\omega$.

$$Ans. \quad M = \frac{Wa^2\omega^2 \sin 2\phi}{24g}$$

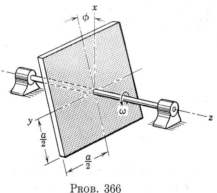

PROB. 366

*367. Determine the moment $M$ exerted on the shaft by the flywheel of Sample Prob. 357 because of an angular acceleration $\alpha$ as the wheel starts from rest.

$$Ans. \quad M = \frac{Wr^2\alpha \sin 2\phi}{4g}$$

**37. Plane Motion.** The kinematics of a body having plane motion was discussed in Chapter 2 beginning with Art. 16, and it was found that such motion may be considered a combination of translation and rotation. This same combination will be evident in the kinetics of plane motion.

Consider a body, Fig. 32, which has any general motion in the plane of the figure. This motion is determined entirely by the projections on this plane of all forces acting on the body. Let point $O$ be any convenient reference point whose acceleration $a_O$ is known. A set of $x$–$y$ reference axes with origin at $O$ is selected. The acceleration of any particle of mass $m_i$ may be expressed by the principles of relative motion in terms of the acceleration components of $O$ added vectorially to the normal and tangential acceleration components of $m_i$ with respect to $O$. It follows that the resultant force on $m_i$ may be expressed in terms of components each of which is the mass of the particle times the corresponding acceleration. These components of the resultant force on $m_i$ are shown in the free-body diagram of the particle in Fig. 32. A sum

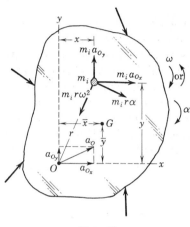

Fig. 32

of the moments of these force components about $O$ is now made, and the similar expressions for these moments for all particles are added together to give the sum

$$\Sigma M_O = \Sigma m_i r^2 \alpha + \Sigma m_i a_{O_x} y - \Sigma m_i a_{O_y} x.$$

When the expressions $I_O = \Sigma m_i r^2$, $m\bar{y} = \Sigma m_i y$, and $m\bar{x} = \Sigma m_i x$ are substituted, the moment sum is

$$\Sigma M_O = I_O \alpha + m\bar{y} a_{O_x} - m\bar{x} a_{O_y}. \qquad (43)$$

The moment sum of the actual forces acting on the particles involves the internal forces of action and reaction between the particles and forces external to the body. The internal forces occur in pairs of equal and opposite forces, so their moment sum is zero. Thus $\Sigma M_O$ is the sum of the moments about $O$ of *all external forces* applied to the body.

Equation 43 is one of the three motion equations for plane motion. The principle of the motion of the mass center, expressed by Eqs. 31, provides the additional two equations of motion, $\Sigma F_x = m\bar{a}_x$ and $\Sigma F_y = m\bar{a}_y$, for this two-dimensional case.

In most problems of plane motion the mass center $G$ is used as the reference point. In this case $\bar{x}$ and $\bar{y}$ in Eq. 43 are zero, $I_O$ becomes $\bar{I}$, and the three equations of motion for a body having plane motion are

$$\Sigma F_x = m\bar{a}_x,$$

$$\Sigma F_y = m\bar{a}_y, \tag{44}$$

$$\Sigma \bar{M} = \bar{I}\alpha.$$

The first two of these equations are the scalar equivalents of the single vector equation which relates the resultant external force $\Sigma F$ on a body to the mass $m$ and translational acceleration $\bar{a}$ of the mass center. The third of Eqs. 44 represents the relation between the moment sum $\Sigma \bar{M}$ of all external forces about the center of mass, the moment of inertia $\bar{I}$ with respect to the centroidal axis through $G$ normal to the plane of motion, and the angular acceleration $\alpha$ which has the same sense as $\Sigma \bar{M}$. Thus the kinetics of plane motion is represented in terms of the *translation* of the mass center and the *rotation* about the mass center. The conclusions here are represented in Fig. 33, where

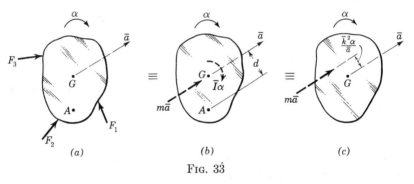

(a)                    (b)                    (c)

FIG. 33

the $a$-part of the figure represents the free-body diagram of any body having plane motion. The external forces acting may be replaced by a single resultant force $m\bar{a}$ through the mass center and the resulting couple $\bar{I}\alpha$ as shown in Fig. 33b.

Figure 33 illustrates one of the most important and useful of the conclusions in dynamics. The equivalence between the external force system which produces plane motion of a rigid body, Fig. 33a, and the resultants of this system, Fig. 33b, makes it possible to write the necessary equations which establish the instantaneous relations between the forces and the accelerations for any given problem. Representation of the resultants $m\bar{a}$ and $\bar{I}\alpha$ for every problem in plane motion will insure that the force and moment sums as disclosed from the free-body diagram are equated to their proper resultants. This representation permits complete freedom of choice of a convenient moment center. If point $A$ in Fig. 33 is such a convenient point, the summation of moments of the external forces about $A$ would give

$$\Sigma M_A = \bar{I}\alpha + m\bar{a}d. \tag{45}$$

If a moment center is chosen on the opposite side of $m\bar{a}$, it is clear that the sign of the $m\bar{a}d$ term would be negative for a clockwise summation in the sense of $\alpha$. Equation 45 is merely an expression of the principle of moments. It states that the sum of the moments about some point $A$ of all external forces acting on the body in the plane of motion equals the moment of their resultant. The resultant is expressed as the force $m\bar{a}$ through $G$ and the couple $\bar{I}\alpha$. Equation 45 may be considered to be the *general moment relation* for plane motion. Equations 43 and 45 are fully equivalent, but the latter is simpler to visualize and use.

Application of the moment principle of Eqs. 43 or 45 to two special cases in plane motion deserves attention. The first case occurs when the moment center has zero acceleration. With the notation of Eq. 43 it is seen that the moment relation for this case becomes

$$\Sigma M_O = I_O\alpha,$$

which is the same as the third of Eqs. 40 for the rotation of a rigid body about a fixed axis through $O$. However, it is seen now that this moment equation derived for a fixed axis holds for a reference point which has zero acceleration but moves with constant velocity.

The second special case occurs when the acceleration of the reference point $O$ is directed *toward* or *away from* the mass center as represented in Fig. 34a. With the $x$-axis oriented through $G$ it is seen that $\bar{y} = 0$ and $a_{O_y} = 0$ in Eq. 43, and thus

$$\Sigma M_O = I_O\alpha.$$

This result may be applied to a rolling wheel, Fig. 34b, which does not slip and whose center of mass coincides with the geometric center of the wheel. Under these conditions point $C$, the instant center of zero velocity, has an acceleration $a_C$ toward the center of the wheel through $G$, and therefore

$$\Sigma M_C = I_C\alpha. \tag{46}$$

In the case of an unbalanced wheel, such as shown in Fig. 34c, this moment equation about the instant center $C$ may *not* be applied except in the two positions where $G$ crosses the vertical center line.

The equivalence between forces and their resultants may be used to analyze two or more connected bodies in plane motion. Two links hinged together at a common point may be analyzed as a single system even though their angular accelerations and the linear accelerations of their mass centers are different. A force summation in the $x$-direction for the entire system must equal the sum of the $x$-components of their resultants $m_1 \bar{a}_{1_x}$ and $m_2 \bar{a}_{2_x}$. A similar relation holds for the $y$-direction. The sum of the moments about any axis normal to the

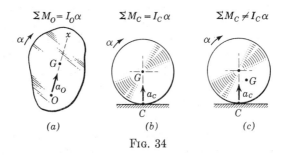

$$\Sigma M_O = I_O \alpha \qquad \Sigma M_C = I_C \alpha \qquad \Sigma M_C \neq I_C \alpha$$

(a)          (b)          (c)

FIG. 34

plane of motion of all forces external to the system must equal the moment of their resultants which would be $(\bar{I}_1 \alpha_1 + m_1 \bar{a}_1 d_1)$ plus $(\bar{I}_2 \alpha_2 + m_2 \bar{a}_2 d_2)$. In both the force and moment summations the forces at the connecting hinge are internal to the system isolated so do not appear in the equations.

Enough emphasis cannot be placed on the importance of a clear choice of the body to be isolated and the representation of this isolation by a correct free-body diagram. Only after this vital step has been completed can the equivalence between the external forces and their resultants be properly evaluated. Of equal importance in the analysis of plane motion is a clear understanding of the kinematics involved. Very often the difficulties experienced by students at this point have to do with kinematics. The student will find that a thorough review of the relative acceleration relations for plane motion will be most helpful. In formulating the solution to a problem it should be recognized that the directions of certain forces or accelerations may not be known at the outset, so that it may be necessary to make initial assumptions whose validity will be proved or disproved when the solution is carried out. It is essential, however, that all assumptions made are consistent with the principle of action and reaction and with any kinematical requirements, which are also called conditions of constraint. Thus if a wheel is rolling on a horizontal surface, its center is constrained to move in a horizontal line. Furthermore if the unknown linear acceleration $a$ of the center of the wheel is assumed positive to the right, the unknown angular acceleration $\alpha$ must be positive in a clockwise sense in order that $a = +r\alpha$, assuming the wheel does not slip.

### SAMPLE PROBLEMS

**368.** If the coefficient of friction between the 322 lb. wheel and the plane is 0.20, determine the acceleration $a$ of the center $G$ of the wheel if the force $P$ in the cable which is wrapped around the central hub is (a) 60 lb. and (b) 100 lb.

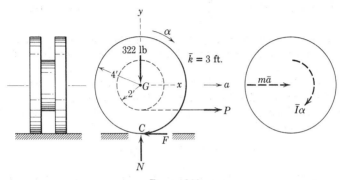

PROB. 368

*Solution.* The free-body diagram and the resultant-force diagram of the wheel are drawn as shown. If the wheel rolls without slipping, it must roll to the *right* because of the clockwise unbalance of moments about $C$. The friction force is therefore seen to act to the left in order that the moment equation for clockwise angular acceleration about $G$ may be satisfied. If the wheel slips, the friction force will still be to the left to oppose this slipping. Irrespective of whether the wheel slips or not, the three equations of plane motion, Eqs. 44, hold. Equating the moments and the force to their resultants gives

$$[\Sigma \bar{M} = \bar{I}\alpha] \qquad\qquad 4F - 2P = 3^2 \frac{322}{32.2}\alpha$$

$$[\Sigma F_x = m\bar{a}_x] \qquad\qquad P - F = \frac{322}{32.2}a,$$

$$[\Sigma F_y = 0] \qquad\qquad N = 322 \text{ lb.}$$

*Case* (a). Assume that the wheel does not slip with $P = 60$ lb. With this assumption $a = r\alpha$, where $r = 4$ ft., and, with these values, solution of the equations of motion just written yields

$$F = 40.8 \text{ lb.}, \qquad a = 1.92 \text{ ft./sec.}^2$$

The assumption of no slipping must now be checked. The maximum friction force which the surfaces can support is

$$F = fN = 0.20 \times 322 = 64.4 \text{ lb.},$$

which is greater than the 40.8 lb. needed to support the rolling of the wheel without slipping. Thus the assumption of no slipping was correct, and the answers are as calculated.

Since the wheel does not slip, the moment equation, Eq. 46, about the instant center $C$ of zero velocity may be used. Thus

$$[\Sigma M_C = I_C \alpha] \qquad 60 \times 2 = \frac{322}{32.2} (3^2 + 4^2) \frac{a}{4}, \qquad a = 1.92 \text{ ft./sec.}^2 \qquad Ans.$$

This equation may be used only if the acceleration of $C$ is toward the mass center $G$, which occurs for a nonslipping wheel with center of gravity $G$ at the geometrical center.

*Case (b).* Although it may be suspected now that the wheel will slip with $P = 100$ lb., for the sake of illustration let it be assumed again that the wheel rolls without slipping. With $a = 4\alpha$ and the new value of $P$ solution of the equations of motion gives

$$F = 68.0 \text{ lb.}, \qquad a = 3.20 \text{ ft./sec.}^2$$

The assumption of no slipping is seen to be invalid since 68.0 lb. represents more friction force than can possibly be supported. Thus the wheel slips and $a \neq r\alpha$. With $P = 100$ lb. and the correct value of $F = 64.4$ lb. the equations of motion yield

$$\alpha = 0.640 \text{ rad./sec.}^2 \qquad \text{and} \qquad a = 3.56 \text{ ft./sec.}^2 \qquad Ans.$$

**369.** Determine the forces on the piston pin $A$ and crank pin $B$ of the connecting rod of the reciprocating engine for the crank position of 60 deg. and for a constant crank speed of 1500 rev./min. clockwise. The connecting rod weighs 6 lb. with center of gravity at $G$ and has a centroidal radius of gyration of $\bar{k} = 4.20$ in. The pressure of the expanding gases on the 5 lb. piston at this position is 100 lb./in.$^2$

*Solution.* The forces acting on the connecting rod will depend on its acceleration. In Sample Prob. 165 for the same position of this same connecting rod the acceleration of $A$ was found to be $a_A = 3320$ ft./sec.$^2$ to the right, and the angular acceleration of the rod was found to be $\alpha = 7750$ rad./sec.$^2$ clockwise. The angular velocity of the connecting rod was determined in Prob. 124 and is $\omega = 29.5$ rad./sec. counterclockwise. In addition the angle $\phi$ may be scaled from the graphical solutions of these sample problems or calculated by the law of sines which gives

$$\phi = \sin^{-1} \left( \tfrac{5}{14} \sin 60° \right) = \sin^{-1} 0.309 = 18° \ 0'.$$

One of the forces acting on the rod is determined by the motion of the piston.

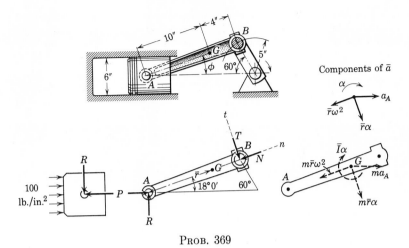

PROB. 369

From the free-body diagram of the piston the horizontal component of the piston-pin force is found from the equation

$$[\Sigma F = ma] \qquad 100 \times \frac{\pi \times 6^2}{4} - P = \frac{5}{32.2} \times 3320, \qquad P = 2310 \text{ lb.}$$

The free-body diagram of the connecting rod is drawn, and the forces at $A$ and $B$ are represented by their components. The weight of the rod is negligible in this problem compared with the remaining forces and is therefore omitted. The resultant-force diagram is shown to the right of the free-body diagram. Here it is convenient to represent the resultant force $m\bar{a}$ in terms of its components. The components of $\bar{a}$ are shown and are obtained from the relative acceleration relation written with respect to point $A$ which is

$$\bar{a} = a_A +\!\!\!\!+ \bar{r}\omega^2 +\!\!\!\!+ \bar{r}\alpha.$$

Consequently the corresponding components of $m\bar{a}$ are

$$ma_A = \frac{6}{32.2} \times 3320 = 619 \text{ lb.,}$$

$$m\bar{r}\omega^2 = \frac{6}{32.2} \frac{10}{12} \times (29.5)^2 = 135.2 \text{ lb.,}$$

$$m\bar{r}\alpha = \frac{6}{32.2} \frac{10}{12} \times 7750 = 1204 \text{ lb.}$$

Also the resultant moment about $G$ has the value

$$\bar{I}\alpha = \frac{6}{32.2} \left(\frac{4.20}{12}\right)^2 \times 7750 = 177 \text{ lb. ft.}$$

The three remaining unknown forces on the rod may now be found by the three equations of motion. In evaluating the first equation it is noted that the $m\bar{a}d$ term is found in terms of its components.

$$[\Sigma M_B = \bar{I}\alpha + m\bar{a}d]$$

$$R \times 14 \cos 18° - 2310 \times 5 \sin 60° = 177 \times 12 - 619 \times 4 \sin 18° - 1204 \times 4,$$

$$R = 492 \text{ lb.},$$

$$[\Sigma F_n = m\bar{a}_n] \quad N - 2310 \cos 18° - 492 \sin 18° = 135.2 - 619 \cos 18°,$$

$$N = 1895 \text{ lb.},$$

$$[\Sigma F_t = m\bar{a}_t] \quad T - 492 \cos 18° + 2310 \sin 18° = 1204 + 619 \sin 18°,$$

$$T = 1149 \text{ lb.}$$

The total forces on the two pins are therefore

$$A = \sqrt{(2310)^2 + (492)^2} = 2360 \text{ lb.,} \qquad Ans.$$

$$B = \sqrt{(1895)^2 + (1149)^2} = 2220 \text{ lb.} \qquad Ans.$$

## PROBLEMS

**370.** Find the acceleration $a$ of the center of the homogeneous cylinder if it rolls without slipping down the incline. Also find the minimum coefficient of friction $f$ to prevent slipping. $\qquad Ans. \quad a = \dfrac{2}{3} g \sin \theta, f = \dfrac{\tan \theta}{3}$

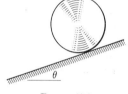

**371.** If the coefficient of friction for Prob. 370 is less than $\frac{1}{3} \tan \theta$, write the expression for the acceleration $a$ of the center of the cylinder. Also find the angular acceleration $\alpha$.

$$Ans. \quad a = g(\sin \theta - f \cos \theta), \alpha = \frac{2fg \cos \theta}{r}$$

PROB. 370

**372.** What should be the radius $r_0$ of the small circular groove in order that there be no friction force acting between the wheel and the surface irrespective of the magnitude of the horizontal force $P$ applied to the cord? The centroidal radius of gyration of the wheel is $\bar{k}$.

$$Ans. \quad r_0 = \frac{\bar{k}^2}{r}$$

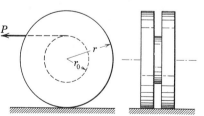

PROB. 372

**373.** The circular cylinder with a cord wrapped around its periphery and fastened as shown is released on the incline. If the coefficient of friction $f$ is less than $\frac{1}{2}\tan\theta$, find the acceleration $a$ of the center of the cylinder.

*Ans.* $a = \frac{2}{3}(\sin\theta - 2f\cos\theta)g$

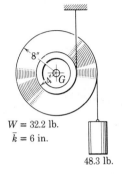

$W = 32.2$ lb.
$\bar{k} = 6$ in.

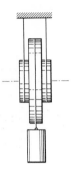

48.3 lb.

Prob. 373        Prob. 374

**374.** Determine the acceleration $a$ of the center $G$ of the attached wheels for the system shown. Each cable is wrapped securely around its respective wheel.

*Ans.* $a = 3.39$ ft./sec.$^2$

**375.** The unbalanced wheel shown weighs 100 lb. and has a center of gravity $G$ which is 0.25 in. away from the geometric center $O$. The radius of gyration of the wheel about $O$ is 12 in. If the wheel rolls down the inclined plane with increasing speed, find the minimum angular velocity $\omega$ at which it first hops (contact with the plane becomes zero). Specify the position of $G$ relative to $O$ when this happens.

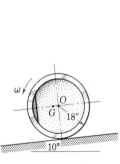

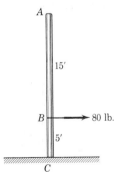

Prob. 375        Prob. 376

**376.** The uniform pole $ABC$ weighs 100 lb. and is balanced in the vertical position when a horizontal force of 80 lb. is suddenly applied to the cable at $B$. If the coefficient of friction between the pole and the ground is 0.3, determine the initial acceleration of $A$ at the instant the 80 lb. force is applied.

*Ans.* $a_A = 6.44$ ft./sec.$^2$ to the right

**377.** A 25 lb. roll of heavy wrapping paper in the form of a solid cylinder with a diameter of 12 in. is resting on a horizontal table top. If a horizontal force of 10 lb. is applied evenly to the paper as shown, determine the linear acceleration $a$ of the center of the roll and the angular acceleration $\alpha$ of the roll. The coefficient of friction between the paper and the table is 0.20.

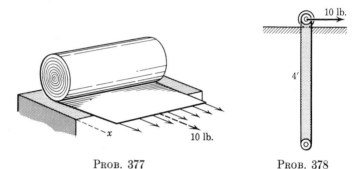

PROB. 377                   PROB. 378

**378.** The uniform link weighs 20 lb. and is initially at rest in the vertical position before the 10 lb. force is applied as shown. Neglect friction in the bearing of the light guide roller, and compute the linear acceleration $a$ of the center of the roller and the angular acceleration $\alpha$ of the bar an instant after the 10 lb. force is applied.        *Ans.*   $a = 64.5$ ft./sec.$^2$, $\alpha = 24.2$ rad./sec.$^2$

**379.** A long uniform cable of length $L$ and weight $W$ is wrapped at a constant radius around a spool of negligible weight. One end of the cable is fixed as shown, and the spool is released from rest with the distance $x$ essentially zero. Show that the acceleration of the center of the spool is equal to $g/2$ at the start of the motion.

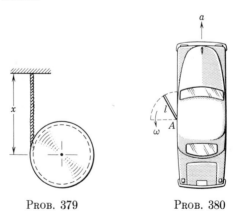

PROB. 379                   PROB. 380

**380.** A car starts from rest with one of its doors slightly ajar and moves forward with a constant acceleration $a$. If the door is hinged about its rear vertical edge, determine its angular velocity $\omega$ when it reaches the 90 deg. position.

The door may be considered as a uniform rectangular plate hinged about its vertical edge at $A$ as shown.          *Ans.*   $\omega = \sqrt{3a/l}$

**381.** End $A$ of the uniform 16.1 lb. link is pinned freely to the collar which is given an acceleration $a = 4$ ft./sec.$^2$ along the fixed horizontal shaft. If the link has a clockwise angular velocity $\omega = 2$ rad./sec. as it swings past the vertical, determine the components of the force on the bar at $A$ at this instant.

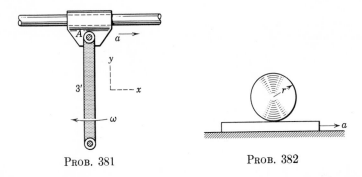

PROB. 381          PROB. 382

**382.** The platform which supports the circular cylinder is given an acceleration $a = 2g$ to the right. Compute the angular acceleration $\alpha$ of the cylinder if the coefficient of friction is (*a*) 0.8 and (*b*) 0.5.

*Ans.*   $(a)\ \alpha = \dfrac{4g}{3r},\ (b)\ \alpha = g/r$

**383.** The solid cylinder weighs 16.1 lb. and rolls without slipping down the circular guide, starting from the rest position shown. Determine the normal reaction $N$ under the cylinder as it passes the bottom position. (See Prob. 118.)

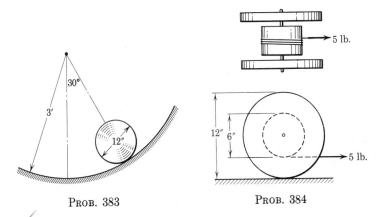

PROB. 383          PROB. 384

**384.** Each of the solid circular disk wheels weighs 10 lb., and the inner solid cylinder weighs 15 lb. The disks and cylinder are mounted on the small central shaft independently of one another with negligible friction in their bearings. If a horizontal 5 lb. force is applied to a cord wrapped around the cylinder as shown, find the angular acceleration $\alpha$ of the disk wheels. The coefficient of friction between the wheels and the level plane is 0.20.

*Ans.* $\alpha = 7.16$ rad./sec.²

**385.** A large steel roller bearing has the dimensions shown. The outer race $A$ is fixed and the inner race $B$ is turned by the action of friction between it and

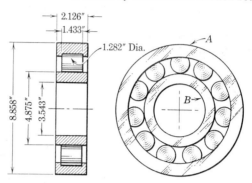

PROB. 385

the shaft on which it is fitted. Find the value of this frictional torque $M$ applied to the inner race necessary to accelerate the bearing to an operating speed of 3000 rev./min. in 2 sec. Assume that the rollers do not slip.

*Ans.* $M = 15.0$ lb. in.

**386.** The truck, initially at rest with a solid cylindrical roll of paper in the position shown, moves forward with a constant acceleration $a$. Find the dis-

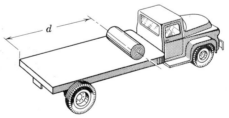

PROB. 386

tance $s$ which the truck goes before the paper rolls off the edge of its horizontal bed. Friction is sufficient to prevent slipping.

*Ans.* $s = \dfrac{3d}{2}$

**387.** A wheel of radius $r$ and radius of gyration $k$ is spinning with an angular velocity $\omega_0$ while being held a small distance above the horizontal surface. If the wheel is released, determine the distance $s$ which its center moves before slipping of the wheel on the plane ceases. The coefficient of friction is $f$.

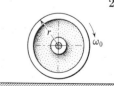

PROB. 387

**388.** A uniform bar of length $l$ and weight $W$ is secured to a circular hoop of radius $l$ as shown. The weight of the hoop is negligible. If the bar and hoop are released from rest in the position illustrated, determine the initial values of the friction force $F$ and normal force $N$ under the hoop if friction is sufficient to prevent slipping. What is the minimum coefficient of friction $f$ to prevent slipping? *Ans.* $F = \frac{3}{8}W$, $N = \frac{13}{16}W$, $f = \frac{6}{13}$

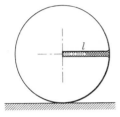 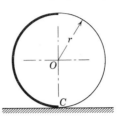

PROB. 388      PROB. 389

**389.** A bar of weight $W$ is formed into a semicircular arc and forms one half of a circular hoop. The other half of the hoop to which it is fastened has negligible weight. If the unbalanced hoop is released from rest in the position shown and rolls without slipping, determine the initial acceleration $a$ of the center $O$ and the corresponding value of the normal reaction $N$ under the hoop. (Is it permissible to use $\Sigma M_C = I_C \alpha$ in this case?)

**390.** The uniform 16.1 lb. link $AB$ is released from rest in the position shown. Determine the reactions at $A$ and $B$ as the link begins to slide if friction in the guides is negligible. *Ans.* $A = 5.2$ lb., $B = 7.1$ lb.

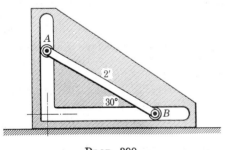 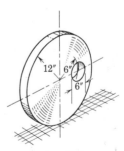

PROB. 390      PROB. 392

$\Sigma M_a = I\alpha + m\bar{a}d$

**391.** Determine the forces on the piston and crank pins for the connecting rod of Sample Prob. 369 when the crank angle is 90 deg. instead of 60 deg. Take the gas pressure on the piston at this position to be 80 lb./in.² *Ans.* $A = 3020$ lb., $B = 3840$ lb.

**\* 392.** The circular disk has a net weight of 20 lb. after the 6 in. diameter hole is cut out of it. If the disk is released from rest on a horizontal surface in the position shown, find the momentary angular acceleration $\alpha$ of the disk. The coefficient of friction is 0.10. *Ans.* $\alpha = 0.708$ rad./sec.²

\* **393.** The large concrete slab shown in its edge view is being tilted slowly into position by the winch at $A$. In the position shown the cable at $B$ is horizontal, and $\theta$ is 30 deg. If the cable breaks at the winch in this position, determine the initial acceleration $a$ of the bottom $C$ of the slab which is free to move on rollers.

$$Ans. \quad a = \frac{3\sqrt{3}}{8}g$$

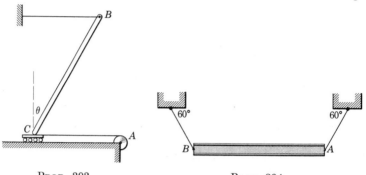

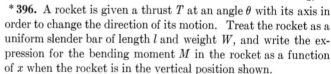

PROB. 393                          PROB. 394

\* **394.** The uniform steel beam weighs 480 lb. and is supported at its ends by the two cables shown. If the fitting which secures the cable to the beam at $A$ breaks, determine the momentary value of the tension $T$ in the remaining cable an instant after the break occurs.        $Ans. \quad T = 128$ lb.

\* **395.** If the roll of paper in Prob. 386 is placed on the truck bed with its axis turned an angle $\theta$ from the position shown, find the angular acceleration $\alpha$ of the roll if its radius is $r$ and if the truck has an acceleration $a$. Assume no slipping.        $Ans. \quad \alpha = \dfrac{2a \cos \theta}{3r}$

\* **396.** A rocket is given a thrust $T$ at an angle $\theta$ with its axis in order to change the direction of its motion. Treat the rocket as a uniform slender bar of length $l$ and weight $W$, and write the expression for the bending moment $M$ in the rocket as a function of $x$ when the rocket is in the vertical position shown.

$$Ans. \quad M = \left(\frac{l-x}{l}\right)^2 xT \sin \theta$$

\* **397.** The solid half-cylinder has an angular velocity $\omega = 4$ rad./sec. at the instant shown as it pivots about point $C$. Find the acceleration $a$ of the center $O$ of the half-cylinder in this position if it moves under the action of its own weight. Also determine the minimum coefficient of friction $f$ to prevent slipping for the position shown.

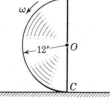

PROB. 396      $Ans. \quad a = 10.24$ ft./sec.$^2$, $f = 0.308$        PROB. 397

*398. If the wheel described in Prob. 375 has an angular velocity of $\omega = $ 10 rad./sec. as $G$ passes the position shown, calculate the friction force $F$ which acts on the wheel at this instant. Friction is sufficient to prevent slipping.

Ans.  $F = 6.40$ lb.

**38. D'Alembert's Principle.** In the preceding articles of this chapter the basic relationship between force, mass, and acceleration has been applied to particle and rigid-body motion. In this analysis the resultants of the applied force system were determined for each type of motion encountered, and the equivalence between the external forces and their resultants was used in the solution of each problem. This approach is straightforward and treats dynamics in a direct manner by always relating the external forces to the accelerations, described from fixed reference axes.

An alternative viewpoint for the solution of problems involving the relationship between forces and accelerations is contained in D'Alembert's principle which was enunciated in 1743 by D'Alembert in his *Traité de dynamique*. In brief the principle permits the solution of a dynamics problem by the methods of statics. If the basic equation of motion of a particle is rewritten as $\Sigma F - ma = 0$, it takes the form of an equation of force equilibrium where the sum of a number of force terms equals zero. Thus, if a fictitious force equal to $ma$ were applied to the accelerating particle in the direction opposite to the acceleration, the particle could then be considered to be in equilibrium under the action of the real forces $\Sigma F$ and the fictitious force $ma$. This fictitious force is often called an *inertia force*, and the artificial state of equilibrium is known as *dynamic equilibrium*. The resultant of the actual forces is called the *effective force*, and the equal and opposite fictitious inertia force is known as the *reversed effective force*. The apparent transformation of a problem in dynamics to one in statics is known as *D'Alembert's principle*.

In extending D'Alembert's principle to rigid-body motion it is merely necessary to add a fictitious inertia force $m\bar{a}$ through the center of mass in the direction opposite to the acceleration $\bar{a}$ of the mass center and an inertia couple $\bar{I}\alpha$ in the direction opposite to the angular acceleration $\alpha$. These additions to the free-body diagram together with the real forces constitute a system which obeys the force and moment equilibrium equations.

Although opinion differs, D'Alembert's principle as treated in this book is considered to be mainly of historical interest. It was enunciated during a time when understanding and experience with dynamics were extremely limited and was an attempt to explain dynamics in terms of the principles of statics which at that time were more fully understood. This excuse for using an artificial situation to describe a real one no longer exists, as there is today a wealth of knowledge and experience with the phenomena of dynamics to support strongly the direct approach of thinking in terms of dynamics rather than in terms of statics. It is somewhat difficult to justify the long persistence in the acceptance of statics as a way of understanding dynamics particularly in view of the continued search for the understanding and description of physical phenomena in their undisguised form.

# WORK AND ENERGY

**39. General.** In Chapter 4 the basic equation of motion relating force, mass, and acceleration was applied to particle and rigid-body motion. In all cases attention was focused on the instantaneous relationship between the forces and the corresponding accelerations. In some problems the accelerations were integrated to obtain changes in velocities. There are many problems where the change in velocity may be determined directly from the integral of the equation of motion without first having to establish the instantaneous relationships between force, mass, and acceleration. The work-energy method developed in this chapter is a consequence of the first integral of the equation of motion with respect to displacement. The integral with respect to time is discussed in Chapter 6.

The equation of motion for a particle of mass $m$ moving in the $x$-direction is $\Sigma F_x = m\, d^2x/dt^2$. Multiplication by $dx$ gives

$$\Sigma F_x\, dx = m\, dx\, \frac{d}{dt}\left(\frac{dx}{dt}\right) = m\, \frac{dx}{dt}\, d\left(\frac{dx}{dt}\right) = \frac{1}{2}\, m\, d\left(\frac{dx}{dt}\right)^2.$$

The first integral with respect to displacement is, then,

$$\int \Sigma F_x\, dx = \frac{1}{2}\, m\left(\frac{dx}{dt}\right)^2 + \text{constant}.$$

The left-hand side of the equation is the *work* done on $m$ during the interval involved and can be evaluated if $\Sigma F_x$ is a known function of $x$. The right-hand side is the corresponding change in the *kinetic energy* of $m$. Before applying the first integral of the equation of motion to problems it will be well to discuss the concepts of work and kinetic energy in some detail and to generalize the integral so that it may be applied to curvilinear motion and to a system composed of connected particles.

**40. Work.** The concept of work was defined in Chapter 7 of *Part I* where virtual or assumed movements were considered in establishing equilibrium configurations. In the present chapter real and

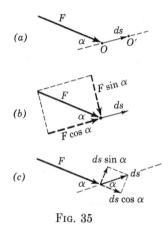

Fig. 35

finite displacements will be considered, but the definition of work remains unchanged. The *work* done by a force $F$ during the movement $ds$ of its point of application $O$, Fig. 35a, is

$$dU = F \, ds \cos \alpha.$$

This definition may be viewed either as the force component $F \cos \alpha$ in the direction of the displacement times the displacement, Fig. 35b, or as the force times the displacement component $ds \cos \alpha$ in the direction of the force, Fig. 35c. With this definition it is seen that the component of the force at right angles to the displacement does no work. The work done by the force is positive when the working component $F \cos \alpha$ has the same sense as the displacement and negative when in the opposite sense. Work is a scalar quantity with the dimensions of [distance] × [force]. Work and moment are dimensionally the same, and in order to distinguish between them work may be expressed as foot pounds (ft. lb.) and moment as pound feet (lb. ft.). The fundamental difference between work and moment is that work is a scalar involving the product of force and distance both measured in the same direction, whereas moment is a vector and is the product of force and distance measured at right angles to the force.

During a finite movement the work done by the force is

$$U = \int F \cos \alpha \, ds.$$

FIG. 36

This expression can be integrated if the relation between $F$ and $s$ and between $\cos \alpha$ and $s$ is known.

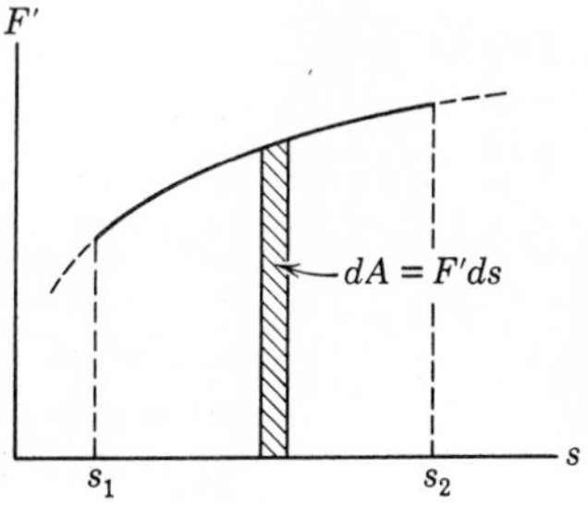

Experimental data often enable a graph to be constructed of the working component $F' = F \cos \alpha$ and the displacement $s$ of its point of application as schematically represented in Fig. 36. The differential area $dA$ under the curve during the movement $ds$ is the work done by $F'$ during that interval, and the net or total work done between any two displacements $s_1$ and $s_2$ is the area under the curve between these limits.

In the case of an elastic spring of stiffness $k$ and negligible weight the force $F$ supported by the spring at any deformation $x$, either compression or extension, is $F = kx$. Thus the work done on a spring during a compression or extension from its undeformed position, Fig. 37, is

FIG. 37

$$\int F \, dx = \int_{x_1}^{x_2} kx \, dx = \tfrac{1}{2}kx_2{}^2 - \tfrac{1}{2}kx_1{}^2$$

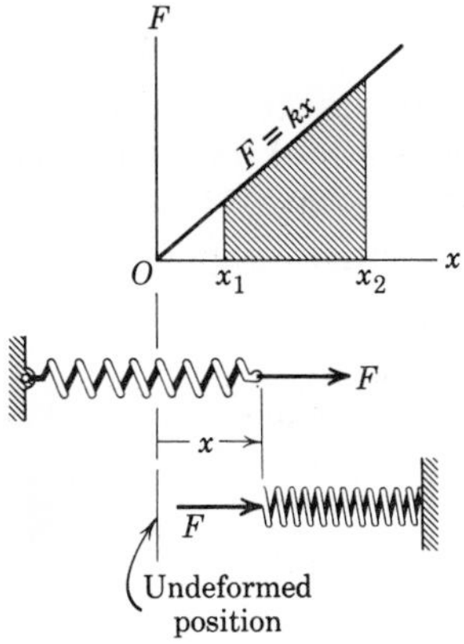

which represents the trapezoidal area on the $F$–$x$ diagram. It is noted that positive work is done on the spring when it is being extended or compressed. In the reverse process during a release from its tension or compression, negative work is done on the spring which means that the spring does positive work on the body against which it is allowed to act.

The work done by a couple $M$ acting on a body, Fig. 38, during a rotation $d\theta$ of the body in the plane of the couple is $dU = M \, d\theta$. This expression is easily obtained by representing the couple by two forces and evaluating the work done by each force during the rotation $d\theta$. The total work done by $M$ during a finite angular displacement $\theta$ is

$$U = \int M \, d\theta.$$

The angle $\theta$ is expressed in radian measure, and work is positive when the rotation is in the sense of the couple and negative when in the sense opposite to the couple. A couple does no work during a movement which is entirely one of translation since the angular displacement is zero. In the event that the body ro-tates in a plane other than the plane of the couple the work done equals the magnitude of the couple vector times the magnitude of the rotation vector multiplied by the cosine of the angle between the vectors.

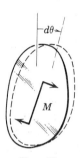

When a body slides on a fixed surface, the work done by the friction force acting on the body is negative since the friction force acts in the direction opposite to the displacement. In the case of a wheel which rolls on a fixed surface without slipping, a static friction force acts and does no work since the point of application

Fig. 38

does not slip. If the wheel slips as it rolls, kinetic friction is generated and negative work is done on the wheel.

The total work done by any system of forces and couples acting on a body during any movement is the algebraic sum of the works done by each force and couple considered separately.

**41. Kinetic Energy of a Particle.** The first integral of the equation of motion as given in Art. 39 will now be rederived for the motion of a particle of mass $m$ along any curved path, Fig. 39. The resultant of all forces acting on $m$ is $F$. Only the tangential component of $F$ does work on $m$ during motion along the path. During a displacement $ds$ the work done on $m$ is

$$dU = F \cos \alpha \, ds.$$

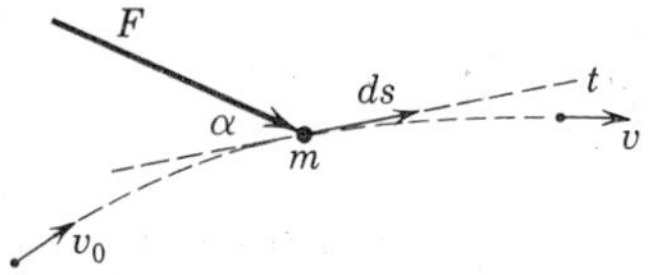

Fig. 39

From the equation of motion in the tangential direction, $F \cos \alpha = ma_t$, the work may be expressed as

$$dU = ma_t \, ds.$$

But $a_t \, ds = v \, dv$, so that

$$dU = mv \, dv.$$

The net work done on $m$ during an interval of its motion for which the velocity changes from $v_0$ to $v$ is

$$\Delta U = \int dU = \int_{v_0}^{v} mv \, dv = \tfrac{1}{2}mv^2 - \tfrac{1}{2}mv_0{}^2.$$

The term $\tfrac{1}{2}mv^2$ is the work done in bringing the particle from rest to a velocity $v$ and is known as the *kinetic energy* $T$ of the particle. Hence the definition

$$T = \tfrac{1}{2}mv^2. \tag{47}$$

The net work done on $m$ in changing its velocity from $v_0$ to $v$ therefore equals the *change* $T - T_0$ in its kinetic energy, or

$$\Delta U = \Delta T. \tag{48}$$

Equation 48 is known as the *work-energy equation* and always involves the *change* in kinetic energy as a result of the net work done during the corresponding interval of motion.

If a particle moving with a velocity $v$ is allowed to act on some body and is brought to rest during this action, the loss of its kinetic energy equals the work done on the other body by the contact force. Thus kinetic energy represents the capacity to do work by reason of acquired velocity.

Kinetic energy is a *scalar* quantity which depends only on the mass and the magnitude of the velocity. Since the velocity $v$ is squared, kinetic energy is always a positive quantity. The units of kinetic energy are the same as those of work, as may be seen from the dimensional equation

$$[\tfrac{1}{2}mv^2] = [FL^{-1}T^2][LT^{-1}]^2 = [LF].$$

When a body is subjected to a system of forces the resultant of which acts through the center of mass, the body may be treated as a particle as was seen in Chapter 4. Thus the work-energy equation as developed for a particle may be applied to such a body.

When two or more particles (or translating bodies considered as particles) are joined together by connections which are frictionless and incapable of elastic deformation, the forces in the connections occur in pairs of equal and opposite forces, and the points of application of these forces necessarily have identical movements. Hence the net work done by these internal forces is zero during any movement of the system. Thus Eq. 48 is applicable to the *entire system*, where $\Delta U$ is the total or net work done on the system by *external* forces and $\Delta T$ is the change in the total kinetic energy of the system. The total kinetic energy is the algebraic sum of the kinetic energies of all elements of the system.

In Chapter 7 of *Part I* of *Mechanics* on virtual work it was seen that the method of work has a basic advantage over the force and moment-summation method for solving the equilibrium problem for a system of multiconnected bodies. The same advantage exists in the method of work and energy for the dynamics of interconnected bodies since again consideration of internal forces is not necessary.

Application of the work-energy method calls for an isolation of the body or system under consideration. For a single body a *free-body diagram* showing all externally applied forces should be drawn. For a system of connected bodies without springs an *active-force diagram* which shows only those external forces which do work (active forces) on the system may be drawn.

### SAMPLE PROBLEMS

**399.** Determine the velocity $v$ of the 100 lb. crate when it reaches the bottom of the chute if it is given an initial velocity of 15 ft./sec. down the chute at $A$. The coefficient of friction is 0.30.

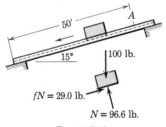

Prob. 399

*Solution.* The free-body diagram of the crate is drawn and includes the normal and friction forces calculated in the usual manner. The work done by the component of the weight down the plane is positive, whereas that done by the friction force is negative. The total or net work done during the interval is, then,

$$\Delta U = (100 \sin 15° - 29.0)50 = -155 \text{ ft. lb.}$$

The change in kinetic energy is

$$\Delta T = \frac{1}{2} \frac{100}{32.2} (v^2 - 15^2).$$

The work-energy equation gives

$$[\Delta U = \Delta T] \qquad -155 = \frac{1}{2} \frac{100}{32.2} (v^2 - 225),$$

$$v^2 = 125, \qquad v = 11.2 \text{ ft./sec.} \qquad Ans.$$

**400.** In the system shown the weights of the cable and pulleys and the friction in the pulley bearings are negligible. Determine the velocity $v$ of the 2000 lb. weight after it has moved 10 ft. from the rest position from which the system was released.

*Solution.* The only external forces which do work on the entire system are the weights of the two bodies. With these two forces indicated the sketch may be used as the active-force diagram.

The 10 ft. displacement of the 2000 lb. weight is clearly up, whereas that of the 1500 lb. weight is 20 ft. down. Also the velocity of the 1500 lb. weight is twice that of the 2000 lb. weight. The work-energy equation for the system is applied and gives

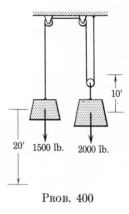

PROB. 400

$$[\Delta U = \Delta T] \quad -2000 \times 10 + 1500 \times 20 = \frac{1}{2}\frac{2000}{32.2}(v^2 - 0) + \frac{1}{2}\frac{1500}{32.2}(4v^2 - 0),$$

$$v = 8.97 \text{ ft./sec.} \qquad\qquad Ans.$$

**401.** The 20 lb. slider starts from rest at $A$ with an initial tensile force of 5 lb. in the attached spring and moves in the smooth horizontal slot under the action of a constant 50 lb. force in the cable. If the modulus of the spring is 5 lb./ft., determine the velocity $v$ of the block as it passes the position $B$.

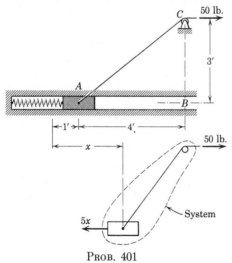

PROB. 401

*Solution.* It will be assumed that the stiffness of the spring is small enough to allow the block to reach position $B$. The active-force diagram for the system composed of the block and the cable is shown for a general position. The spring force and the 50 lb. tension are the only forces external to this system which do work on the system. The force of the guide on the block, the weight of the block, and the reaction of the pulley on the cable do no work on the system and are not included on the active-force diagram.

The displacement $x$ of the block is measured from the undeformed position of the spring which is a distance $F/k = \frac{5}{5} = 1$ ft. to the left of $A$. The work done on the system by the spring force during the movement from $A$ to $B$ is negative and is

$$-\int_1^5 5x \, dx = -\tfrac{1}{2} \times 5(5^2 - 1^2) = -60 \text{ ft. lb.}$$

If the displacement $x$ had been measured from the starting position of the block, the spring force would be $5(x + 1)$, and the limits of integration would be 0 and 4.

The work done on the system by the constant 50 lb. force in the cable is the force times the net horizontal movement of the cable over pulley $C$ which is $\sqrt{4^2 + 3^2} - 3 = 2$ ft. Thus the work done is $50 \times 2 = 100$ ft. lb., and the work-energy equation applied to the system gives

$$[\Delta U = \Delta T] \qquad -60 + 100 = \frac{1}{2}\frac{20}{32.2}(v^2 - 0), \qquad v = 11.35 \text{ ft./sec.} \quad Ans.$$

The advantage of the choice of system should be noted. If the block only had constituted the system, the horizontal component of the 50 lb. cable tension acting on the block would have to be integrated over the 4 ft. displacement. This step would require considerably more effort than was needed in the solution as presented.

### PROBLEMS

**402.** A projectile weighing 8 lb. is fired through a stack of asbestos sheets 6 ft. thick. If the projectile approaches the asbestos with a velocity of 1800 ft./sec. and emerges with a velocity of 900 ft./sec., determine the average penetration resistance $R$ over the 6 ft.  $Ans.$  $R = 50,300$ lb.

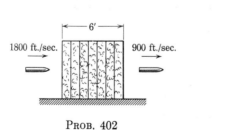

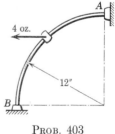

PROB. 402                                PROB. 403

**403.** A small 2 oz. bead starts from rest at $A$ and slides freely in the vertical plane along the fixed wire under the action of the constant 4 oz. horizontal force. Find the velocity $v$ of the bead as it hits the stop at $B$.

$Ans.$  $v = 13.90$ ft./sec.

**404.** A car is traveling at 30 mi./hr. down a 5 per cent grade when the brakes on all four wheels lock. If the kinetic coefficient of friction between the tires and the road is 0.70, find the distance $s$ which the car skids in coming to a stop.

*Ans.* $s = 46.3$ ft.

**405.** The skid marks left by all four wheels of a car on a level road are measured by a police officer to be 65 ft. in length. The driver of the car claims that he was not exceeding the speed limit of 50 mi./hr. before he applied the brakes. Furthermore the driver released the brakes before coming to a stop and was observed to continue at the speed of 20 mi./hr. after his skid. From experience with the road conditions prevailing the coefficient of kinetic friction is known to be at least 0.8. Can it be shown that the driver was guilty of speeding?

**406.** Find the total energy $E$ absorbed (negative work) by the brakes of a 1200 ton passenger train in bringing it to a stop from a velocity of 60 mi./hr. in a distance of 2 mi. down a 1 per cent grade.

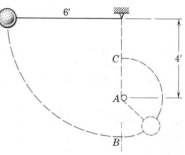

*Ans.* $E = 542 \times 10^6$ ft. lb.

**407.** The weight is released from rest with the cord in the horizontal position shown. When the bottom position is reached, the cord strikes the small fixed bar shown in section at $A$, and the weight follows the dotted path. Calculate the velocity of the weight at $B$ and $C$.

PROB. 407

**408.** The pressure $p$ in a .30-caliber rifle (diameter of bore is 0.30 in.) for a certain bullet weighing 0.030 lb. is plotted in terms of the position of the bullet

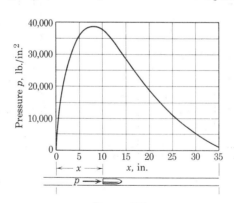

PROB. 408

in the 35 in. barrel. Determine the muzzle velocity $v$ of the bullet. Neglect the effect of friction in the barrel compared with the force of the gases on the bullet.

*Ans.* $v = 3040$ ft./sec.

**409.** The slider weighs 30 lb. and is constrained to slide on the fixed circular bar. If the slider is elevated from rest at $A$ to position $B$ by a constant 50 lb. force in the cable and if friction is negligible, determine the velocity $v$ of the slider as it reaches $B$.

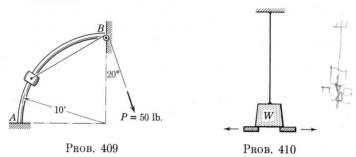

| Prob. 409 | Prob. 410 |

**410.** The weight $W$ is attached to an elastic cable, and the lower supports are raised slightly until the cable tension and elongation are zero. If the supports are suddenly removed, find the maximum tension $T$ in the cable.

*Ans.* $T = 2W$

**411.** The frame is moving horizontally with a constant velocity of 4 ft./sec., and the pendulum is hanging in the vertical position. If the frame is suddenly brought to a stop, determine the maximum amplitude $\theta$ of the angular oscillations imparted to the pendulum. *Ans.* $\theta = 33° 27'$

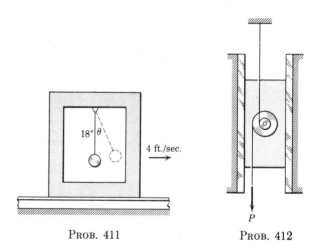

| Prob. 411 | Prob. 412 |

**412.** Determine the velocity $v$ of the 32.2 lb. freely sliding block after it has moved 4 ft. from rest under the action of the constant force $P = 35$ lb. The light cables are wrapped securely around the integral pulley of negligible weight whose diameters are in the ratio of 2:1. Friction in the pulley bearing is negligible.

**413.** The two sliders weigh 8 lb. each, are connected by a light, rigid link and move with negligible friction in their guides. If the sliders are released from rest in the position shown, find the velocity $v$ of the upper one as it crosses the center line of the vertical slot.  *Ans.*  $v = 4.15$ ft./sec.

**414.** In tests on the resistance of a certain material to penetration the sharp-pointed 2 oz. projectile shown is fired at the specimen with a velocity of 500 ft./sec. Prediction of penetration depth $x$ is based on the assumption that the resistance $R$

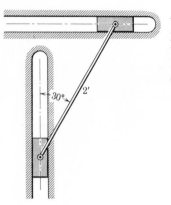

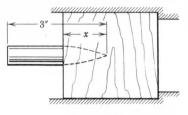

PROB. 413                    PROB. 414

offered by the material to the projectile depends directly on the projectile surface area embedded in the specimen. This area is proportional to $x^2$, so that $R = kx^2$ is written. If tests indicate an average penetration of 1.25 in., determine $k$.

**415.** The pulleys around which the cables pass have negligible weight and friction. Determine the velocity $v$ of the 50 lb. sliding weight after it has moved 10 ft. from rest under the action of the constant 15 lb. tension.  *Ans.*  $v = 10.88$ ft./sec.

**416.** A small rocket-propelled test vehicle with a total weight of 160 lb. starts from rest at $A$ and moves with negligible friction along the track in the vertical plane as shown. If the

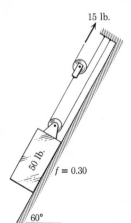

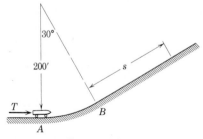

PROB. 415                    PROB. 416

propelling rocket exerts a constant thrust $T$ of 250 lb. from $A$ to point $B$ where it is shut off, determine the distance $s$ which the vehicle rolls up the incline before stopping. The loss of weight due to the gases expelled by the rocket is small and may be neglected.

**417.** Show that the work-energy equation for the motion of a particle in the $x$-direction holds for an experiment conducted in a coordinate system moving with a constant velocity in the $x$-direction where all measurements are made relative to the coordinate system.

**418.** A bullet of mass $m$ is fired with a velocity $v$ from a rifle at rest relative to the ground. With the rifle attached to an airplane flying with a speed $u$ an identical bullet is fired in the direction of $u$. The kinetic energy of the bullet fired from the ground is $\frac{1}{2}mv^2$, and that of the bullet fired from the airplane is $\frac{1}{2}m(u + v)^2 = \frac{1}{2}mu^2 + \frac{1}{2}mv^2 + muv$. Explain the significance of the $muv$ term. Assume the velocity of the airplane remains constant during the firing.

**419.** The plunger weighs 30 lb. and is released from rest in the position shown for which the spring is compressed a distance of $\frac{1}{4}$ in. Determine the maximum velocity $v$ reached by the plunger and the modulus $k$ of the spring if the plunger drops a maximum of $\frac{1}{2}$ in. from its released position.

*Ans.*   $k = 60$ lb./in., $v = 6.95$ in./sec.

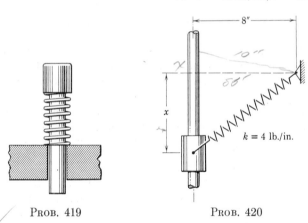

PROB. 419          PROB. 420

**420.** The 4 lb. collar slides freely on the fixed vertical shaft and is released from rest in the position at $x = 0$, for which the spring is compressed 2 in. Determine the velocity $v$ of the collar when $x = 12$ in.

**421.** The nest of two springs is used to bring the 16.1 lb. plunger $A$ to a stop from a speed of 9 ft./sec. and reverse its direction. The inner spring increases

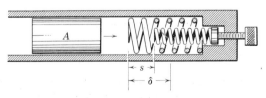

PROB. 421

the deceleration, and its adjustable position is used to control the exact point at which the plunger reverses its direction. If this point is to correspond to a maximum deflection of δ = 6 in. for the outer spring, determine the adjustment of the inner spring by specifying the distance s. The outer spring has a stiffness of 12 lb./in., and that of the inner spring is 8 lb./in.  *Ans.*  s = 3.40 in.

**422.** The 10 lb. plunger is released from rest in the position shown, where the right-hand spring is compressed 3 in. Determine the maximum velocity v reached by the plunger. Friction in the guide is negligible.  *Ans.*  v = 9.22 ft./sec.

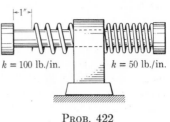

$k = 100$ lb./in.    $k = 50$ lb./in.

PROB. 422

**423.** Calculate the velocity v with which an object would strike the earth if released from rest above the north pole at an altitude equal to the radius R of the earth and if atmospheric resistance were absent. The radius of the earth is 3960 mi.

**424.** The chain is released from rest on the smooth surface in the position shown. Find the velocity v of the chain as the last link leaves the edge. Compare the work-energy solution with the solution of this same problem (Prob. 222) by the method of the previous chapter.

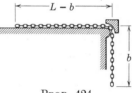

$$Ans. \quad v = \sqrt{gL \left(1 - \frac{b^2}{L^2}\right)}$$

PROB. 424

**425.** If the surface upon which the chain in Prob. 424 slides is not smooth and if it starts from rest with a sufficient number of links hanging over the edge to barely initiate motion, determine the velocity v of the chain as the last link leaves the edge. The coefficient of friction is f. Neglect friction at the edge.

**426.** The system is released from rest with x = 0. Determine the velocity v

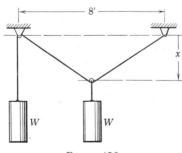

PROB. 426

of the center weight when x = 3 ft. and the maximum displacement x of the center weight.  *Ans.*  v = 5.14 ft./sec., x = 5.33 ft.

*427. Find the velocity $v$ of the slider in Sample Prob. 401 as it passes $B$ if friction in the guide is not negligible and the coefficient of friction is 0.30.

*Ans.*   $v = 6.84$ ft./sec.

*428. The piston and ram of the steam hammer weigh 400 lb. The absolute pressure $p$ acting on the piston is constant at 200 lb./in.$^2$ for the first 4 in. of the stroke beginning at the top, for which $x = 2$ in. The pressure $p$ then varies according to $pV = $ constant, where $V$ is the total volume of the cylinder above the piston, for the remaining 10 in. of the 14 in. stroke. Determine the velocity $v$ of impact of the ram with the work at the bottom of the stroke. The atmospheric pressure of 14.7 lb./in.$^2$ acts on the lower side of the piston.

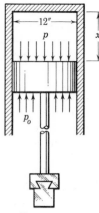

*Ans.*   $v = 52.5$ ft./sec.          Prob. 428

## 42. Work-Energy in Plane Motion.

It was shown in the previous article that the work-energy equation, $\Delta U = \Delta T$, may be applied to a system of joined particles whose internal connections are without friction and are incapable of absorbing energy (no internal springs). The term $\Delta U$ is the net work done on the system by all *external* active forces, and $\Delta T$ is the change in the total kinetic energy of the system. This principle holds for any rigid body or system of rigid bodies since a rigid body may be considered as a composite of joined particles whose connections meet the stated requirements. The principle $\Delta U = \Delta T$ does *not* hold for a deformable body since the particles of such a body are not rigidly connected, and some of the external work done will be absorbed in the internal "springs."

Before the principle of work and energy can be applied to rigid bodies it is necessary to know the expressions for the kinetic energy $T$ of a rigid body having any one of the three types of plane motion. These expressions are derived as follows:

*Translation.* The translating body of mass $m$ in Fig. 40$a$ has a velocity $v$. The kinetic energy of any particle of mass $m_i$ is $\frac{1}{2}m_iv^2$, and the kinetic energy of the entire body is

$$T = \Sigma\tfrac{1}{2}m_iv^2 = \tfrac{1}{2}v^2\Sigma m_i,$$

or

$$T = \tfrac{1}{2}mv^2. \tag{49}$$

*Fixed-Axis Rotation.* The body in Fig. 40$b$ is rotating about a fixed axis through $O$ with an angular velocity $\omega$. The linear velocity of any particle of mass $m_i$ is $r\omega$, and the kinetic energy of this particle is

$\frac{1}{2}m_i(r\omega)^2$. The kinetic energy of the entire rotating body is the sum of the kinetic energies of all its particles and is

$$T = \Sigma \frac{1}{2}m_i r^2 \omega^2 = \frac{1}{2}\omega^2 \Sigma m_i r^2,$$

or

$$T = \frac{1}{2}I_0\omega^2. \tag{50}$$

The term $I_O$ is the moment of inertia about the fixed axis of rotation. The similarity between the expressions for kinetic energy of rotation and translation should be noted. Moment of inertia and angular velocity replace mass and linear velocity, respectively. The reader may verify easily that the dimensions of both expressions are identical.

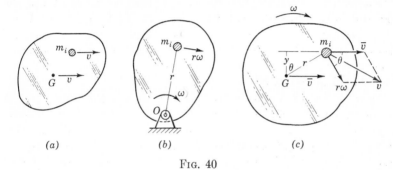

FIG. 40

*Plane Motion.* The body in Fig. 40c has any plane motion, and, at the instant considered, the velocity of its mass center $G$ is $\bar{v}$ and the angular velocity of the body is $\omega$. The velocity $v$ of any particle is conveniently expressed in terms of $\bar{v}$ and the velocity $r\omega$ of the particle relative to $G$ as shown. The square of the particle velocity is obtained by the law of cosines and is

$$v^2 = \bar{v}^2 + r^2\omega^2 + 2\bar{v}r\omega \cos\theta.$$

The kinetic energy of the representative particle of mass $m_i$ is $\frac{1}{2}m_i v^2$, and that for the entire body is

$$T = \Sigma \frac{1}{2}m_i \bar{v}^2 + \Sigma \frac{1}{2}m_i r^2 \omega^2 + \Sigma(\frac{1}{2}m_i)(2\bar{v}r\omega \cos\theta),$$

$$= \frac{1}{2}\bar{v}^2 \Sigma m_i + \frac{1}{2}\omega^2 \Sigma m_i r^2 + \bar{v}\omega \Sigma m_i y.$$

The last summation is zero since the $y$-coordinate to the center of gravity is zero, and the second summation is merely the moment of inertia $\bar{I}$ about the center of gravity $G$. Thus the kinetic energy for any rigid body having plane motion is

$$T = \frac{1}{2}m\bar{v}^2 + \frac{1}{2}\bar{I}\omega^2. \tag{51}$$

This expression clearly shows the separate contribution to the total kinetic energy due to the translational velocity of the mass center and the rotational velocity about the mass center.

The kinetic energy of plane motion may be expressed also in terms of the rotational velocity about the instant center $C$ of zero velocity. Since $C$ momentarily has zero velocity, the proof for Eq. 50 holds equally well for this point. Thus the kinetic energy of plane motion may be expressed by

$$T = \tfrac{1}{2}I_C\omega^2 \qquad (52)$$

in place of Eq. 51.

The total kinetic energy $T$ of a system of bodies having plane motion is the sum of the kinetic energies of all its parts calculated by Eqs. 49, 50, and 51 or 52 for the particular kinds of motion involved. When the work-energy principle $\Delta U = \Delta T$ is applied to such a system, $\Delta T$ is the change in the *total* kinetic energy of the system and $\Delta U$ is the net work done by *all* active forces which are applied *externally* to the system during the interval involved.

In applying the work-energy principle to a single rigid body in plane motion either a free-body diagram or an active-force diagram may be drawn. When applying the work-energy principle to a *connected system of rigid bodies*, an *active-force diagram of the entire system* should be drawn to isolate the system and disclose all external forces which do work on the system.

### SAMPLE PROBLEMS

**429.** Determine the velocity $v$ of the center of the circular disk after it has rolled a distance $s$ down the incline from rest. Friction is sufficient to prevent slipping.

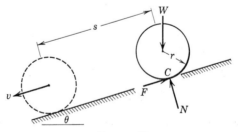

PROB. 429

*Solution.* Of the three forces shown on the free-body diagram of the disk only the weight does work. The friction force does no work if the wheel does not slip.

Thus

$$\Delta U = Ws \sin \theta,$$

$$\Delta T = \frac{1}{2}\frac{W}{g}v^2 + \frac{1}{2}\left(\frac{1}{2}\frac{W}{g}r^2\right)\omega^2 = \frac{3}{4}\frac{W}{g}v^2.$$

The work-energy equation is

$$[\Delta U = \Delta T] \qquad Ws \sin \theta = \frac{3}{4}\frac{W}{g}v^2, \qquad v = \sqrt{\frac{4gs \sin \theta}{3}}. \qquad Ans.$$

The kinetic energy may also be expressed by

$$\frac{1}{2}I_c\omega^2 = \frac{1}{2}\left(\frac{1}{2}\frac{W}{g}r^2 + \frac{W}{g}r^2\right)\omega^2 = \frac{3}{4}\frac{W}{g}v^2.$$

**430.** The 30 lb. link with center of gravity at $G$ has a centroidal radius of gyration of 0.8 ft. and moves in the vertical plane under the action of its own weight. The ends of the link are confined to move in the horizontal and vertical slots. If end $B$ is given a horizontal velocity of 10 ft./sec. when the link passes the dotted vertical position, compute the linear velocity $v$ of end $A$ as the link reaches the horizontal position by analyzing the initial and final conditions directly. Also determine the expression for the angular velocity $\omega$ of the link at any instant when its angle with the horizontal is $\theta$.

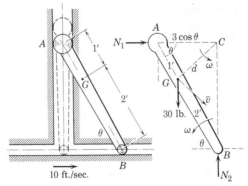

PROB. 430

*Solution.* The free-body diagram shows that the 30 lb. weight is the only force which does work on the body. Between the vertical and horizontal positions of the link point $G$ drops through a vertical distance of 2 ft. so that $\Delta U = 30 \times 2 = 60$ ft. lb.

In the vertical position end $A$ is the instant center of zero velocity, so that the kinetic energy for the initial position is $T_1 = \frac{1}{2}I_A\omega_1^2$. In the final position end $B$ is the instant center of zero velocity, and the kinetic energy is $T_2 =$

$\frac{1}{2}I_B\omega_2^2$. (The kinetic energy may also be computed from $T = \frac{1}{2}m\bar{v}^2 + \frac{1}{2}\bar{I}\omega^2$ by relating $\bar{v}$ and $\omega$.) Thus

$$T_1 = \frac{1}{2}\frac{30}{g}(0.8^2 + 1^2)\left(\frac{10}{3}\right)^2 = 8.49 \text{ ft. lb.}$$

and

$$T_2 = \frac{1}{2}\frac{30}{g}(0.8^2 + 2^2)\left(\frac{v}{3}\right)^2 = 0.240v^2 \text{ ft. lb.}$$

Application of the work-energy principle to the entire interval gives

$[\Delta U = \Delta T]$ $\qquad 60 = 0.240v^2 - 8.49, \qquad v = 16.89 \text{ ft./sec.}$ *Ans.*

For the general position $\theta$ the center of gravity $G$ has dropped a distance of $2 - 2\sin\theta$, so that the work done is $\Delta U = 60(1 - \sin\theta)$ ft. lb. The kinetic energy at this position is $T = \frac{1}{2}m\bar{v}^2 + \frac{1}{2}\bar{I}\omega^2$ where $\omega$ is the angular velocity of the body. If the instant center $C$ of zero velocity is used, $\bar{v} = \omega d$ where $\omega$ is also the angular velocity of line $GC$ which rotates instantaneously with the body about $C$. Thus

$$T = \tfrac{1}{2}m\omega^2 d^2 + \tfrac{1}{2}m\bar{k}^2\omega^2 = \tfrac{1}{2}m(d^2 + \bar{k}^2)\omega^2 = \tfrac{1}{2}I_C\omega^2.$$

From the law of cosines $d^2 = 1^2 + 3^2\cos^2\theta - 6\cos^2\theta = 1 + 3\cos^2\theta$, and

$$T = \frac{1}{2}\frac{30}{32.2}(1 + 3\cos^2\theta + 0.8^2)\omega^2 = \frac{15}{32.2}(1.64 + 3\cos^2\theta)\omega^2.$$

Finally the work-energy principle for the interval between the vertical position and the inclined position gives

$[\Delta U = \Delta T]$ $\qquad 60(1 - \sin\theta) = \dfrac{15}{32.2}(1.64 + 3\cos^2\theta)\omega^2 - 8.49$

from which

$$\omega^2 = \frac{32.2(68.49 - 60\sin\theta)}{15(1.64 + 3\cos^2\theta)}. \qquad\qquad Ans.$$

The answer to the first part of the problem may be checked by computing $\omega$ for $\theta = 0$ and obtaining the velocity of $B$ from $v = 3\omega$.

**431.** Specify the necessary modulus $k$ of the spring which will allow the gear sector to rotate a maximum of $\frac{1}{8}$ turn when released from rest in the position shown. Also find the velocity $v$ of the 6 lb. plunger when the spring is compressed 1 in. during this motion. The gear sector weighs 10 lb. and may be treated as a semicircular disk. Also, friction in the parts is negligible.

*Solution.* The sector and attached plunger are taken as the system to be isolated, and the active-force diagram, showing all external forces which act on the system and do work, is drawn. The 10 lb. and 6 lb. weights and the spring force are the only such active forces.

For a rotation of $\frac{1}{8}$ of a turn $\theta = \pi/4$, and the compression of the spring is $x = (6\pi/4) - 2 = 2.71$ in. Also $\bar{r} = 4r/(3\pi) = 2.55$ in. The vertical movement of $G$ for $\theta = \pi/4$ is

$$(2 + x) - (\bar{r} - \bar{r}\cos\theta) = 4.71 - 2.55(1 - 0.707) = 3.96 \text{ in.}$$

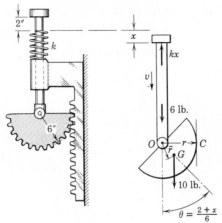

PROB. 431

The work-energy principle for $\Delta T = 0$ is

$[\Delta U = 0]$           $10 \times 3.96 + 6 \times 4.71 - \frac{1}{2}k(2.71)^2 = 0,$

$k = 18.48$ lb./in.                    *Ans.*

For a spring compression of 1 in. the angular movement of the sector is

$$\theta = \frac{2 + 1}{6} = 0.5 \text{ rad.} \qquad \text{or} \qquad \theta = 28° 39',$$

and the vertical movement of $G$ is

$$(2 + 1) - 2.55(1 - 0.878) = 2.69 \text{ in.}$$

Thus the net work done during the 1 in. compression of the spring is

$$\Delta U = 10 \times 2.69 + 6 \times 3 - \frac{1}{2} \times 18.48 \times 1^2 = 35.7 \text{ in. lb.}$$

The kinetic energy of the disk may be computed from the expression $\frac{1}{2}I_C\omega^2$, where

$$I_C = \bar{I} + m\overline{GC}^2 = I_O - m\bar{r}^2 + m\overline{GC}^2 = I_O + m(\overline{GC}^2 - \bar{r}^2).$$

The law of cosines applied to the triangle $OGC$ gives

$$\overline{GC}^2 - \bar{r}^2 = r^2 - 2r\bar{r} \cos\left(\frac{\pi}{2} - \theta\right) = 21.3 \text{ in.}^2,$$

and the moment of inertia about $O$ is

$$I_O = \frac{1}{2}\left(\frac{1}{2} \times 2mr^2\right) = \frac{1}{2}mr^2 = \frac{10 \times 6^2}{2 \times 32.2 \times 12} = 0.466 \text{ lb. in. sec.}^2$$

Therefore the kinetic energy of the disk is

$$\frac{1}{2}I_C\omega^2 = \frac{1}{2}\left(0.466 + \frac{10}{32.2 \times 12} \times 21.3\right)\frac{v^2}{6^2} = 0.01414v^2 \text{ in. lb.}$$

Finally, the kinetic energy of the plunger is accounted for, and the work-energy equation gives

$$[\Delta U = \Delta T] \qquad 35.7 = 0.01414v^2 + \frac{1}{2}\frac{6}{32.2 \times 12}v^2,$$

$$v = 40.4 \text{ in./sec.} \qquad\qquad Ans.$$

The kinetic energy of the gear sector may be determined also from the relation $\frac{1}{2}m\bar{v}^2 + \frac{1}{2}\bar{I}\omega^2$. In this method it is necessary to relate $\bar{v}$ and $\omega$ to the velocity $v$ of the plunger, and the labor is comparable to that of obtaining $I_C$ as was done in the present solution. Unless strict adherence to principles is observed the casual reader may be tempted to evaluate the kinetic energy of a full rolling disk and take half of it for the given sector. Such calculation is erroneous since the kinetic energies of the particles of each half of the disk are not the same by reason of their different velocities.

### PROBLEMS

**432.** The suspended log shown is used as a battering ram. At what angle $\theta$ should the log be released from rest in order to strike the object to be smashed with a velocity of 20 ft./sec.? $\qquad$ *Ans.* $\theta = 41° 16'$

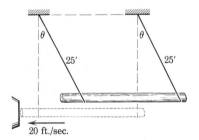

25'          25'

20 ft./sec.

PROB. 432

**433.** Find the torque $M$ applied to the 40 lb. circular disk necessary to give its center a velocity of 4 ft./sec. in a distance of 10 ft. up the incline from rest. The wheel does not slip. $\qquad$ *Ans.* $M = 5.47$ lb. ft.

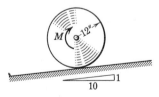

PROB. 433

**434.** The steel girder $AB$ is being raised into a vertical position by tension in the cable $C$ from a power winch. If this cable snaps when the supporting cable $AD$ is horizontal, determine the velocity $v$ of end $A$ when it reaches $A'$. Friction at $B$ may be neglected.                     *Ans.*   $v = 27.8$ ft./sec.

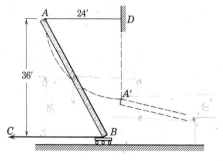

PROB. 434

**435.** The hoop of negligible wall thickness has a radius of 6 in. and rolls without slipping. If its center is given an initial velocity of 5 ft./sec. up the incline from point $A$, find its velocity $v$ when point $B$ is passed on the way down.

*Ans.*   $v = 7.55$ ft./sec.

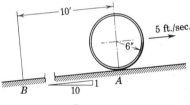

PROB. 435

**436.** The wheel has a centroidal radius of gyration of 7 in. and weighs 45 lb. A constant 5 lb. force is applied to the light cable wrapped around the inner

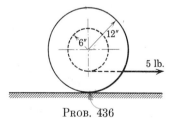

PROB. 436

hub. Determine the velocity $v$ of the center of the wheel after it has rolled 8 ft. to the right from rest without slipping.                     *Ans.*   $v = 4.62$ ft./sec.

**437.** The gear and attached drum have a combined weight of 150 lb. and a radius of gyration of 10.5 in. The weight of the motor pinion is small and may be neglected. The 400 lb. load acquires an upward velocity of 15 ft./sec. after rising 20 ft. from rest with constant acceleration. Determine the torque $M$ on the motor pinion.

*Ans.* $M = 52.5$ lb. ft.

**438.** The hoisting drum weighs 150 lb. and has a radius of gyration of 8 in. If the 100 lb. weight acquires a velocity of 10 ft./sec. after falling 20 ft. from rest, find the constant frictional moment $M_f$ acting on the drum bearing. The small sheave has negligible weight and is perfectly free to rotate about its bearing.

**439.** Each of the two symmetrical toggle links weighs 10 lb. and has a centroidal radius of gyration of 4 in. The slider at $B$ weighs 5 lb. and moves freely in the vertical guide. The spring modulus is 4 lb./in. If a constant torque $M$ of 250 lb. in. is applied to link $OA$ through its shaft

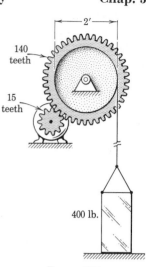

PROB. 437

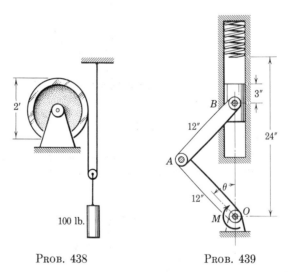

PROB. 438          PROB. 439

at $O$ starting from the rest position at $\theta = 45$ deg., determine the angular velocity $\omega$ of $OA$ at the instant when $\theta = 0$.     *Ans.* $\omega = 7.36$ rad./sec.

**440.** The circular cylinder of weight $W$ and radius $r$ is released from rest in the position shown and rolls without slipping on the circular surface. Determine the reaction $N$ between the surface and the cylinder when the bottom position is reached.

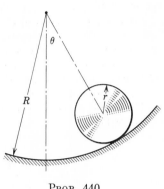

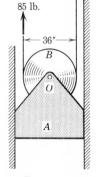

PROB. 440                    PROB. 441

**441.** The 100 lb. load $A$ and the attached 50 lb. sheave $B$ have an upward velocity of 10 ft./sec. after rising 15 ft. from rest under the action of the constant 85 lb. cable tension. Determine the frictional moment $M_f$ in the bearing $O$ if the radius of gyration of the sheave is 12 in. and the cable does not slip on the sheave. Friction along the vertical guides is negligible.

Ans.   $M_f = 3.25$ lb. ft.

**442.** The platform $A$ weighs 20 lb., and each of the links weighs 4 lb. and may be considered a slender rod. If a constant moment $M$ of 24 lb. ft. is applied to the link as shown and if the platform starts from rest in its lowest position with $\theta$ essentially zero, determine the angular velocity $\omega$ of the links when they reach (a) the vertical position at $\theta = 90$ deg. and (b) the horizontal position at $\theta = 180$ deg.

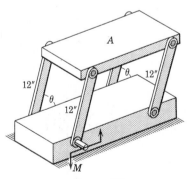

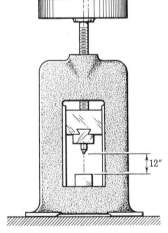

PROB. 442                    PROB. 443

**443.** A type of press frequently used in the hot working of nonferrous metals is shown in the figure. The flywheel and attached screw together weigh 600 lb. and have a radius of gyration about the vertical center line of 16 in. The screw has a double thread of 2 in. lead, and the forming head and die weigh 80 lb.

If the flywheel has a speed of 100 rev./min. in the position shown, determine the rotational speed $N$ just before the die strikes the work. Neglect friction.
*Ans.* $N = 117.1$ rev./min.

**444.** If the frame $F$ of the car must be jacked up to a height of $x = 14.5$ in. to release the compression in the springs, determine the least value of $x$ resulting from a sudden removal of the jack if there are no shock absorbers. The constant of each spring is 409 lb./in., and the line $AC$ may be assumed to remain vertical throughout the movement. The weight of the frame $F$ and that part of the attached body supported by $F$ is 1500 lb.     *Ans.* $x = 4.68$ in.

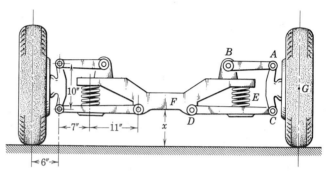

PROB. 444

**445.** What initial clockwise angular velocity $\omega$ must the uniform 10 lb. bar have as it crosses the vertical position ($\theta = 0$) in order that it just reach the horizontal ($\theta = 90$ deg.)? The spring has a modulus of 4 lb./ft. and is unstretched when $\theta = 0$.     *Ans.* $\omega = 6.43$ rad./sec.

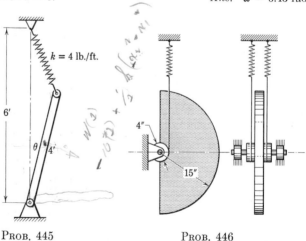

PROB. 445          PROB. 446

**446.** The semicircular disk weighs 30 lb. It is supported in the equilibrium position shown by the two cables which are wrapped around its hubs and which lead to the identical springs. Each spring has a modulus of 15 lb./in. If the disk is rotated through 90 deg. so that its center of gravity is in the lowest position and then released from rest, determine the angular velocity ω of the disk as it passes the equilibrium position. Neglect the mass of the hubs and the shaft.

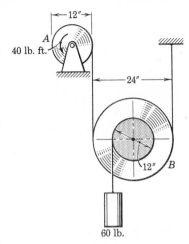

**447.** The 60 lb. weight is descending with a velocity of 4 ft./sec. when a constant counterclockwise torque of 40 lb. ft. is applied to the solid cylindrical drum A, which weighs 20 lb. If the centroidal radius of gyration of the integral 40 lb. pulley B is 10 in., find the number of revolutions n through which A turns before the system comes to rest.

*Ans.* n = 0.569 rev.

**448.** The uniform bar of length l and weight W is secured to a circular hoop of radius l as shown. The weight of the hoop is negligible. If the bar and hoop

PROB. 447

are released from rest in the position illustrated, determine the angular velocity ω of the hoop as the bar passes the horizontal position. Friction is sufficient to prevent slipping.

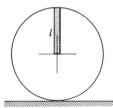

PROB. 448

PROB. 449

**449.** The bar ACB weighs 10 lb. with center of gravity at C and has a centroidal radius of gyration of 6 in. The bar is screwed to the face of the wheel as shown. The wheel weighs 20 lb. with center of gravity at O and has a centroidal radius of gyration of 0.8 ft. If the wheel and bar are released from rest in the position shown and the wheel rolls without slipping, determine the angular velocity ω of the wheel when the center C of the bar is directly below O.

*Ans.* ω = 2.32 rad./sec.

**450.** The two identical steel frames with the dimensions shown are fabricated from the same bar stock and are hinged at the midpoints A and B of their sides. If the frame is resting in the position shown on a horizontal surface with negligible friction, determine the velocity $v$ with which each of the upper ends of the frame hits the horizontal surface if the cord at $C$ is cut.

$$Ans. \quad v = \sqrt{12gb \frac{c + 2b}{3c + 4b}} \cos \frac{\theta}{2}$$

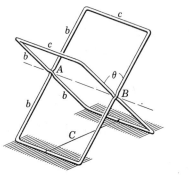

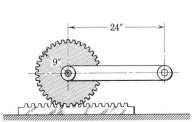

PROB. 450          PROB. 451

**451.** The gear and attached bar are released from rest with the bar in the horizontal position shown. Determine the angular velocity $\omega$ of the bar and gear when the bar reaches the vertical position. The gear weighs 24 lb. and has a centroidal radius of gyration of 6 in. The bar weighs 18 lb. and may be considered a uniform slender rod.

**452.** Crawler-type tractors with endless treads are used mainly for low-velocity earth-moving machinery. In the case of the military tank, however, appreciable velocities are attained. Determine that portion $M$ of the constant total torque applied to the front driving sprocket $A$ necessary to give the tread alone its motion corresponding to a velocity $v$ of the tank in a distance $s$ from rest. Neglect the thickness of the tread compared with the dimensions $d$ and $L$. The tread has a weight $\mu$ per unit of its length. $\quad Ans. \quad M = \dfrac{\mu v^2 d}{gs} \left( L + \dfrac{\pi d}{2} \right)$

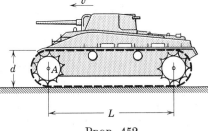

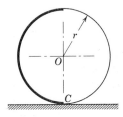

PROB. 452          PROB. 453

**453.** One half of the circular hoop consists of the curved bar of weight $W$, and the other half has negligible weight. If the hoop is released from rest in the position shown and rolls without slipping, determine its angular velocity $\omega$ after rolling through 90 deg.

$$Ans. \quad \omega = \sqrt{\frac{2g}{(\pi - 2)r}}$$

**454.** The half-cylinder is released from rest in the position shown and rocks on the horizontal surface without slipping. Determine the angular velocity $\omega$ of the cylinder as it passes the equilibrium position $\theta = 0$.

$$Ans. \quad \omega = 4\sqrt{\frac{g}{r}\left(\frac{1 - \cos\theta}{9\pi - 16}\right)}$$

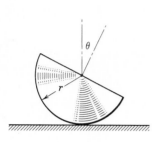

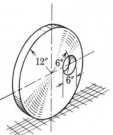

PROB. 454          PROB. 455

**455.** If the disk is released from rest in the position shown and rolls without slipping, find its angular velocity $\omega$ as the hole passes the top position.

**456.** A constant torque $M = 40$ lb. ft. is applied to the axle of the 50 lb. solid circular cylinder to roll it from rest at position $A$ to position $B$. Friction is sufficient to prevent slipping. Determine the angular velocity $\omega$ of the disk when it reaches $B$.      *Ans.* $\omega = 8.48$ rad./sec.

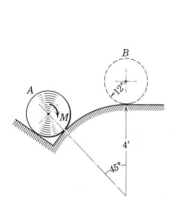

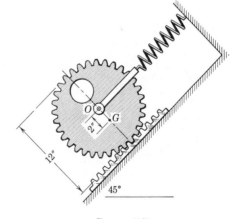

PROB. 456          PROB. 457

\* **457.** The unbalanced gear oscillates on the inclined rack because of the action of the spring. Determine the modulus $k$ of the spring which will allow the gear to rotate a maximum of $\frac{1}{2}$ turn from the position shown, where it is released from rest with no force in the spring. Also find the angular velocity $\omega$

of the gear when it has revolved ¼ turn. The gear weighs 40 lb. with center of gravity at $G$ and has a radius of gyration about $O$ of 4.10 in.

*Ans.*    $k = 2.36$ lb./in., $\omega = 4.22$ rad./sec.

\* **458.** The ring of mass $m$ and radius $r$ is mounted on light spokes (not shown) and rotates about its shaft ($y$-axis) with an angular velocity $\omega$. Simultaneously its shaft, which is hinged at $O$, rotates about the $x$-axis with an angular velocity $\Omega$. Determine the kinetic energy $T$ of the ring by integrating the energy for an element over the entire periphery and show that this expression equals the sum of the energies $\frac{1}{2}I_y\omega^2 + \frac{1}{2}I_x\Omega^2$. Can this result be generalized for any type of rotor symmetrical about either axis of rotation? Does the result hold for an incomplete hoop?

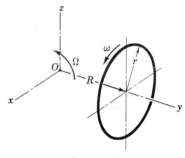

PROB. 458

*Ans.*    Holds for symmetrical but not for unsymmetrical rotor

\* **459.** In the differential gears the shaft and gear $A$ are fixed and do not rotate. If a constant torque of 2 lb. in. is applied to gear $B$ through its shaft, determine the angular speed $N$ of $B$ after it has turned through 4 rev. from rest. Each of the four identical bevel gears has a weight of 5 lb. and a centroidal radius of gyration of 2 in. (*Hint:* Use the results cited in the statement of Prob. 458 and neglect the thickness of each gear in the direction of its axis compared with its diameter.)      *Ans.*   $N = 248$ rev./min.

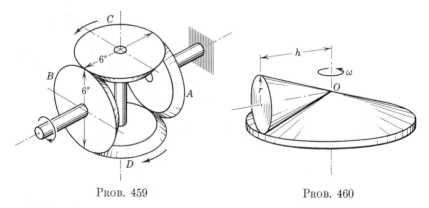

PROB. 459                  PROB. 460

\* **460.** Derive the expression for the kinetic energy $T$ of a solid right circular cone of mass $m$ rolling on a fixed conical surface so that the axis of the rolling cone remains in a horizontal plane and rotates about the vertical axis through the vertex $O$ with an angular velocity $\omega$.      *Ans.*   $T = \dfrac{9}{20} mh^2\omega^2 \left(1 + \dfrac{r^2}{6h^2}\right)$

**43. Energy Equation and Conservation of Energy.** The *energy* of a body may be defined as the capacity of the body to do work by reason of its motion or configuration. Mechanical energy includes kinetic and potential energies, and nonmechanical energy includes thermal, chemical, electrical, and atomic energies.

*Kinetic energy* $T$ is energy due to motion (velocity) and has been described in the preceding two articles.

*Potential energy* $V$ (see Art. 61 of *Mechanics, Part I*) is conveniently expressed in terms of the potential energy of position $V_g$ of a body in a field of force and the potential energy $V_e$ of a body due to its elastic state of deformation.

*Potential energy of position* $V_g$ is the work done against the field of force in changing the position of the body in that field. The most common force field is the gravitational field of the earth which may be considered of constant intensity near the surface of the earth. Thus the potential energy $V_g$ of a body of weight $W$ which is elevated a distance $h$ above an arbitrary datum plane is $+Wh$ relative to this datum plane. Conversely, if the body is a distance $h$ below the plane, the potential energy of position is $-Wh$. The expression for $V_g$, then, accounts for the work done by the force of gravity. When $V_g$ depends only on the position of a body in the field of force and not upon the path followed in reaching that position, the force field is said to be *conservative*. In a conservative field the net work done on a body during any movement which returns the body to its original position and state of motion is zero.

*Elastic potential energy* $V_e$, also known as *strain energy*, is energy stored in a body during an elastic deformation. For a simple spring of stiffness $k$ which is compressed or extended an amount $x$ the elastic energy is $V_e = \frac{1}{2}kx^2$ and equals the work done on the spring in producing the deformation. Elastic energy represents work done by a *conservative* force as long as the force equals $kx$ and in addition does not exceed the elastic limitation of the material. All the energy stored is potentially available since the spring or body will do work equal to $V_e$ on any body against which it is allowed to act during the relief of its extension or compression.

The total mechanical potential energy of a system is $V = V_e + V_g$, and the total mechanical energy is $E = T + V$. The work-energy principle, expressed by Eq. 48, may now be modified to read

$$\Delta U = \Delta T + \Delta V_e + \Delta V_g = \Delta E. \qquad (53)$$

If this alternate form of the work-energy principle is used, it must be clearly understood that $\Delta U$ is the work done on the system by all external active forces *except* the weights of the members. The work done by these gravitational forces is included in the term $V_g$. Also with this formulation of the energy principle a spring with its strain energy $V_e$ may be considered a part of the system.

A body or system of bodies subjected to forces either external or internal which depend only on the position and configuration of the system and its particles is said to be a *conservative system*. If, during any interval, no work is done on such a conservative system by external forces (other than gravity or other potential forces), then no part of the energy of the system is lost. Therefore, the principle of conservation of energy requires that the total mechanical energy of a conservative system remain unchanged. Hence, $T + V =$ constant or

$$\Delta T + \Delta V = 0. \qquad (54)$$

Equation 54 is known as the *law of conservation of dynamical energy* and is one of the basic principles of mechanics. This law is a limiting principle and holds only in the ideal case of no kinetic friction. A kinetic friction force always does negative work which is dissipated from the system in the form of heat loss.

A kinetic friction force is *nonconservative* since its value does not depend on the position of the body upon which it acts but on relative movement of the contacting surfaces and the direction of the movement. A system subjected to kinetic friction forces is *nonconservative*, and the sum of its potential and kinetic energies decreases with continued motion of the system. Although all mechanical systems are actually nonconservative, still, for those where the kinetic friction forces are small, analysis based on a conservative system is justified.

Many systems which involve mechanical energy also involve non-mechanical energy.

*Thermal energy Q* is energy due to the heat content of a body. This energy is indicated by the temperature of a body, which is actually a measure of the kinetic energy of the molecules. The common engineering unit of heat energy is the British thermal unit (B.t.u.), which is equivalent to 778 ft. lb. of mechanical energy.

*Chemical energy C* is energy due to atomic arrangement and may be considered a form of potential energy. The combustion of fuel, for instance, is accompanied by atomic rearrangement and liberation of thermal energy. Chemical energy is usually expressed in B.t.u.'s of equivalent heat energy.

*Electrical energy $E_e$* is the energy associated with electrical charges. Electrical energy is related to mechanical energy by the work done by electrical forces which accompany the flow of electric charges.

*Atomic energy A* is energy released because of the rearrangement of the structure of the atom and is the most recent form of energy to be used by man. Atomic energy may be considered also a form of potential energy.

When a change in energy and a transfer of energy between mechanical and nonmechanical forms take place in a system during any interval, it is convenient to account for the total energy $E$ of the system and changes in energy by the equation

$$E_1 + E_{in} - E_{out} = E_2.$$

This simple balance states that the total energy $E_1$ of the system at the beginning of the interval plus any energy put into the system (includes positive work done on the system) minus any energy taken out of the system (includes negative work done on the system) must equal the final energy $E_2$ of the system at the end of the interval.

It is important to recognize that energy is a relative quantity. Thus the potential energy $V_g$ depends on the arbitrary selection of a datum plane for zero potential energy. Also kinetic energy $T$ is arbitrarily (but conveniently) expressed relative to the condition at zero velocity. Hence any physical measurement of energy describes in reality a *change* in energy. Since the energy equation may be written in terms of the energy change $E_2 - E_1$, it follows that all reference to any arbitrary datum used for the expression of energy will cancel.

### SAMPLE PROBLEM

**461.** The two-wheeled skip $A$ has a total weight of 600 lb. and is pulled up the incline by the action of the descending 350 lb. counterweight $B$. Each of the two wheels of the skip weighs 100 lb. and has a radius of gyration of 12 in. The drum $C$ upon which the cable is wound weighs 100 lb., and its radius of gyration is 10 in. The counterweight slide is greased and gives a coefficient of friction of 0.20. If the skip has a velocity of 3 ft./sec. up the incline in the position shown, find the maximum compression $x$ of the spring bumper. Assume that tipping of the cart as it strikes the spring is negligible and that the wheels do not slip on the track.

*Solution.* The skip, cables, drum, counterweight, and spring will be considered together as the isolated system. Other than the weights of the members (potential forces) the only external active force on the system as a whole is the friction force acting up the plane on the counterweight, and its magnitude is $F = 0.2 \times 350 \times 0.5 = 35$ lb. Thus the net work done on the system during the downward movement of $2(6 + x)$ ft. of the counterweight is

$$\Delta U = -35 \times 2(6 + x) = -70(6 + x) \text{ ft. lb.}$$

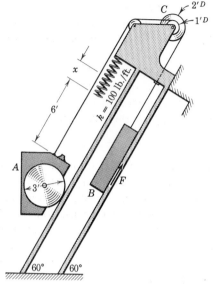

PROB. 461

The change in potential energy of position of the system is the weight of the skip times its vertical rise minus the weight of the counterweight times its vertical drop or

$$\Delta V_g = 600(6 + x)\frac{\sqrt{3}}{2} - 350 \times 2(6 + x)\frac{\sqrt{3}}{2} = -50\sqrt{3}\,(6 + x)\text{ ft. lb.}$$

The change in elastic potential energy is the strain energy of the spring

$$\Delta V_e = \tfrac{1}{2}kx^2 - 0 = 50x^2 \text{ ft. lb.}$$

The change in kinetic energy of the system is the zero kinetic energy at the final position of maximum spring compression minus the initial kinetic energy or $\Delta T = -T$. The initial kinetic energy of each part is

$$T_{\text{skip}} = \frac{1}{2}\frac{600}{32.2} \times 3^2 + 2 \times \frac{1}{2}\frac{100}{32.2} \times 1^2 \times \left(\frac{3}{1.5}\right)^2 = 96.3 \text{ ft. lb.,}$$

$$T_{\text{drum}} = \frac{1}{2}\frac{100}{32.2} \times \left(\frac{10}{12}\right)^2 \times \left(\frac{3}{0.5}\right)^2 = 38.8 \text{ ft. lb.,}$$

$$T_{\text{ctwt.}} = \frac{1}{2}\frac{350}{32.2} \times (2 \times 3)^2 = 195.6 \text{ ft. lb.}$$

Thus

$$\Delta T = -96.3 - 38.8 - 195.6 = -331 \text{ ft. lb.}$$

The work-energy principle, Eq. 53, gives

$$[\Delta U = \Delta T + \Delta V_e + \Delta V_g] \qquad -70(6 + x) = -331 + 50x^2 - 50\sqrt{3}\,(6 + x).$$

Solution of the quadratic gives

$$x = 3.11 \text{ ft.} \qquad\qquad Ans.$$

The second root of the equation is $x = -2.77$ ft., which is of no interest since the skip must move 6 ft. before it strikes the spring, and $x$ is, therefore, positive.

The difference between the solution given here and that which would follow the method of the previous article is that the work done by the weights of the members is included in the $\Delta V_g$ term instead of the $\Delta U$ term.

If friction were absent, the net work done on the system as a whole would be zero. The total energy would remain constant, and $\Delta T + \Delta V_e + \Delta V_g = \Delta E = 0$.

## PROBLEMS

In the following problems account for the work done by the weights of the various bodies in the potential energy term $\Delta V_g$ and not in the work term $\Delta U$.

**462.** The small 3 lb. weight $A$ is released from rest in the position shown and slides without friction along the smooth fixed rod. If the free length of the spring is 20 in., find the velocity $v$ with which the weight strikes the support at $B$.      *Ans.*   $v = 22.4$ ft./sec.

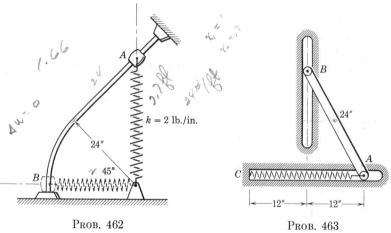

PROB. 462             PROB. 463

**463.** The uniform slender bar $AB$ has a weight of 20 lb. and is released from rest in the position shown. The spring, which can support compression as well as tension, has a stiffness of 2 lb./in. and has a free length of 16 in. measured from the support at $C$. If friction is negligible, determine the velocity $v$ of end $A$ as the bar passes the vertical.      *Ans.*   $v = 42.8$ in./sec.

**464.** A large 6-cylinder internal-combustion engine is cranked at 100 rev./min. by a small auxiliary starting engine before the ignition is turned on. During the suction stroke each of the 6 cylinders admits $0.420 \times 10^{-3}$ lb. of fuel which has an energy content of 20,000 B.t.u./lb. When the engine fires and its speed increases, the overriding starter clutch is automatically disengaged. The kinetic energy of the 450 lb. flywheel with radius of gyration of 16 in. is large compared with the kinetic energy of the other moving parts. Determine the speed $N$ of the engine 2 rev. after the ignition is turned on, assuming that each of the 6 cylinders fires once during the 2 rev. (4-cycle engine). Because of the heat loss only 25 per cent of the fuel energy is converted into mechanical energy.

*Ans.* $N = 286$ rev./min.

**465.** The end of a coil of flexible rope of total length $L$ and weight $\mu$ per unit length is run over a small pulley with negligible weight and bearing friction and brought down to a position very slightly below the coil. The small unbalance causes the rope to accelerate from rest and uncoil the remainder of the rope. Find the velocity $v$ of the rope as the coiled end leaves the platform. Assume energy is conserved.

*Ans.* $v = (L - 2h)\sqrt{\dfrac{g}{L}}$    PROB. 465

**466.** The pulley has a weight of 40 lb. and a radius of gyration of 10 in., and the chain weighs 4 lb./ft. If the pulley is released from rest in the position shown, determine its angular velocity $\omega$ when the lower end of the chain has dropped 3 ft.

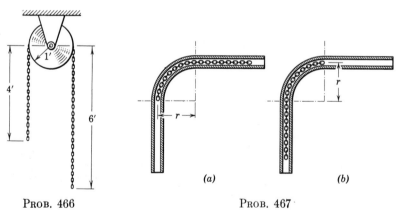

*(a)*              *(b)*

PROB. 466              PROB. 467

**467.** A chain of length $l$ and weight $\mu$ per unit length is released from rest in the fixed tube at position $a$. Determine the velocity $v$ of the chain when it reaches position $b$ if it slides with negligible friction.

*Ans.* $v = \sqrt{gl\left(1 - \dfrac{\pi r}{2l}\right)\left(1 - [4 - \pi]\dfrac{r}{2l}\right)}$

**468.** The figure shows the cross section of a segmented industrial door which weighs 100 lb. per foot of length measured in the vertical plane of the figure. In the open position $\theta = 0$, and the corresponding value of $x$ is 0.575 ft. which is computed so that the door will just close the 10 ft. opening with $\theta = 2\pi$. In the $\theta = 0$ position the torsion spring on the axle of the drum is uncoiled and offers no resisting torque. Specify the modulus $k$ of the spring in inch pounds per revolution which will permit the door to be released from rest in the $\theta = 0$ position and just reach the bottom without any impact. In what way does the moment of inertia of the drum influence the action of the door?

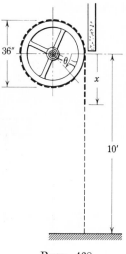

**469.** The figure shows the cross section $AB$ of a 360 lb. garage door which is a rectangular 8 ft. by 16 ft. panel of uniform thickness. The door is supported by four struts, two on each side, and hinged at $O$. The weight of the struts may be neglected. The action of the door is controlled by two duplicate spring and cable assemblies, one on each side of the door, as illustrated. When in the

PROB. 468

open position, $AB$ is horizontal, and each spring is unextended. If the door is given a slight unbalance from the open position, determine the value of each spring constant $k$ which will limit the angular velocity of the door to 1.5 rad./sec. when edge $B$ reaches the floor.          *Ans.*   $k = 73.3$ lb./ft.

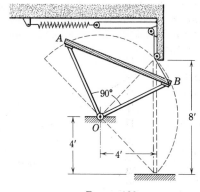

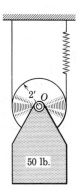

PROB. 469                    PROB. 470

**470.** The system is released from rest with the spring initially stretched 4 in. Determine the velocity $v$ of the center $O$ of the pulley after it has dropped 1 in. The spring has a stiffness of $k = 36$ lb./ft. The pulley weighs 30 lb. and has a centroidal radius of gyration of 18 in.

**471.** The system is released from rest in the position shown. The 10 lb. weight passes through the hole in the bracket but the 8 lb. rider does not. Determine the maximum distance $s$ which the 10 lb. weight descends from the starting position. (What happens to the kinetic energy of the rider?)

*Ans.* $s = 6.53$ ft.

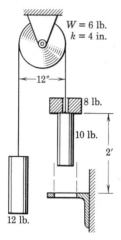

$W = 6$ lb.
$k = 4$ in.

←12″→

8 lb.

10 lb.

2′

12 lb.

PROB. 471

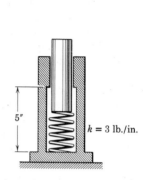

5″

$k = 3$ lb./in.

PROB. 472

**472.** The 5 lb. plunger is released from rest in the position shown, where the light spring is compressed to one half of its free length of 6 in. Determine the maximum velocity $v$ reached by the plunger.          *Ans.* $v = 20.3$ in./sec.

**473.** The link $AB$ has a weight of 10 lb. and may be treated as a uniform slender rod. The 15 lb. wheel is a circular disk with sufficient friction on the horizontal surface to prevent slipping. The link is released from rest in the position shown, and end $A$ slides down the smooth rod. Neglect friction in the moving parts and determine (a) the angular velocity $\omega$ of the link as $A$ strikes the spring with $AB$ in the horizontal position and (b) the maximum deflection $x$ of the spring.

*Ans.* (a) $\omega = 4.91$ rad./sec.,
(b) $x = 4$ in.

**474.** The gravitational potential $V$ in the vicinity of a fixed mass $m_0$ is the work which must be done on a unit mass in changing its position in the gravitational field of $m_0$. It is often convenient to consider, arbitrarily, that the potential is zero when the unit mass is at an infinite distance from $m_0$. Determine the potential $V$ at a distance $r$ from $m_0$. The gravitational constant is $\gamma$, and the mass $m_0$ may be considered concentrated at a point.

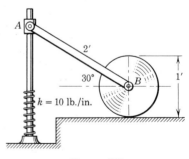

$A$

2′

30°     $B$     1′

$k = 10$ lb./in.

PROB. 473

*Ans.* $V = -\dfrac{\gamma m_0}{r}$

**475.** At the surface of the earth a body is subject to a gravitational force $W$. Determine the potential energy $V_g$ relative to the earth's surface when this body is elevated to an altitude $h$ which is not negligible compared with the radius $R$ of the earth. If the earth had no atmosphere, with what velocity $v$ would an object strike the earth if released at a distance from the earth many times greater than the radius of the earth?

**476.** In the equilibrium position shown each of the two springs with a modulus of 4 lb./in. is under a tension of 48 lb. If the frame is deflected and released from rest in the position where $AB$ and $CD$ make an angle of 30 deg. with the vertical, determine the angular velocity $\omega$ of $AB$ as it passes the vertical position. Each of the three links is a uniform bar weighing 10 lb.

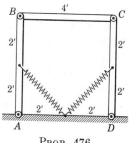

PROB. 476

*Ans.* $\omega = 1.225$ rad./sec.

**477.** The figure shows the cross section of a uniform 200 lb. ventilator door hinged about its upper horizontal edge at $O$. The door is controlled by the spring-loaded cable which passes over the small pulley at $A$. The spring has a stiffness of 15 lb. per foot of stretch and is undeformed when $\theta = 0$. If the door is released from rest in the horizontal position, determine the maximum angular velocity $\omega$ reached by the door. *Ans.* $\omega = 3.11$ rad./sec.

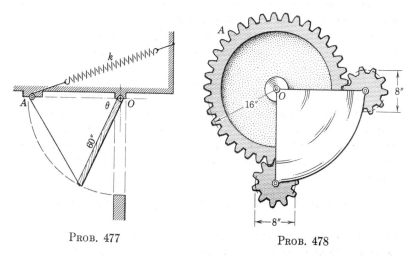

PROB. 477

PROB. 478

**\*478.** Gear $A$ is fixed and does not rotate. Each of the smaller gears has a weight of 6 lb. and a radius of gyration of 3 in. and is freely mounted in a bearing on the sector. The sector is a uniform quarter-circular plate which weighs 10 lb. and is freely pivoted about $O$. Determine the maximum angular velocity $\omega$ reached by the small gears if the assembly is released from rest in the position shown. *Ans.* $\omega = 13.13$ rad./sec.

*479. Determine the constant force $P$ required to give the center of the pulley a velocity of 4 ft./sec. in an upward movement of the center of 3 ft. from the rest position shown. The pulley weighs 30 lb. with a radius of gyration of 10 in., and the cable has a total length of 15 ft. with a weight of 2 lb./ft.       *Ans.* $P = 38.6$ lb.

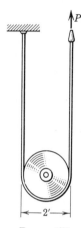

**44. Acceleration from Work Energy; Virtual Work.** In the three previous articles the work-energy relations were used to solve problems where the work done by the active forces applied to a system during finite displacements resulted in changes in the kinetic and potential energies of the system. A major advantage of this method is that analysis may be made of an entire system without having to dismember it. The work-energy equation has two additional uses which are important and which embody the same advantages of analysis of a system as a whole. The equation may be used to establish the instantaneous accelerations of the members of a system of interconnected bodies as a result of the active forces applied.

PROB. 479

Or the equation may be modified to establish the configuration of such a system when it is subjected to prescribed accelerations or where there are several different possible modes of motion.

If the work-energy relation, Eq. 53, is evaluated for an infinitesimal change in the displacements in place of a finite change, it may be written as

$$dU = dT + dV$$

for a conservative mechanical system. The term $dU$ represents the total work done by all active forces on the system during an infinitesimal change in the displacements. If the subscript $i$ is used to denote a representative body of the system, the differential change in kinetic energy $T$ becomes

$$dT = d(\Sigma \tfrac{1}{2} m_i \bar{v}_i^2 + \Sigma \tfrac{1}{2} \bar{I}_i \omega_i^2) = \Sigma m_i \bar{v}_i \, d\bar{v}_i + \Sigma \bar{I}_i \omega_i \, d\omega_i$$

where $d\bar{v}_i$ and $d\omega_i$ are the respective changes in the magnitudes of the velocities and where the summation is taken over all bodies of the system. But for each body $m_i \bar{v}_i \, d\bar{v}_i = m_i \bar{a}_i \, d\bar{s}_i$ and $\bar{I}_i \omega_i \, d\omega_i = \bar{I}_i \alpha_i \, d\theta_i$, where $d\bar{s}_i$ represents the infinitesimal linear displacement of the center of mass and where $d\theta_i$ represents the infinitesimal angular displacement of the body. It should be noted that $\bar{a}_i$ is the component of the acceleration of the center of mass in the direction of the displacement

$d\bar{s}_i$ since $v\,dv = a_t\,ds$ and, similarly, $\alpha_i$ is the angular acceleration about the rotation axis. Consequently for the entire system

$$dT = \Sigma m_i \bar{a}_i\,d\bar{s}_i + \Sigma \bar{I}_i \alpha_i\,d\theta_i.$$

This change may also be written as

$$dT = \Sigma R_i\,d\bar{s}_i + \Sigma M_i\,d\theta_i$$

where $R_i$ and $M_i$ are the components of the resultant force and resultant couple in the directions of $d\bar{s}_i$ and $d\theta_i$, respectively, acting on each body. The components normal to the displacements do no work. Thus these last two equations show that the differential change in the kinetic energy equals the differential work done on the body by the resultant force and resultant couple.

The term $dV$ represents the differential change in the total gravitational potential energy $V_g$ and the total elastic potential energy $V_e$ and has the form

$$dV = d(\Sigma W_i h_i + \Sigma \tfrac{1}{2} k_i x_i^2) = \Sigma W_i\,dh_i + \Sigma k_i x_i\,dx_i$$

where $h_i$ represents the vertical distance of the center of mass of the representative body of weight $W_i$ above any convenient datum plane and where $x_i$ stands for the deformation, tensile or compressive, of a representative elastic member of the system (spring) whose stiffness is $k_i$.

The complete expression for $dU$ may now be written as

$$dU = \Sigma m_i \bar{a}_i\,d\bar{s}_i + \Sigma \bar{I}_i \alpha_i\,d\theta_i + \Sigma W_i\,dh_i + \Sigma k_i x_i\,dx_i. \qquad (55)$$

In applying Eq. 55 to a system of *one degree of freedom*, which is any system whose configuration or position is uniquely determined by the value of a single coordinate, the terms $m_i \bar{a}_i\,d\bar{s}_i$ and $\bar{I}_i \alpha_i\,d\theta_i$ will be positive if the accelerations are in the same direction as the respective displacements and negative if in the opposite direction. If it is more convenient to specify the position of the center of mass of a body in terms of its distance $h_i$ below rather than above some arbitrary datum plane, then the sign of the $W_i\,dh_i$ term must be reversed. Equation 55 has the advantage of relating the accelerations to the active forces directly which eliminates the need for dismembering the system and then eliminating the internal forces and reactive forces by simultaneous solution of the force-mass-acceleration equations written for each member of the system.

In Eq. 55 the differential motions are differential changes in the real or actual displacements which occur. For mechanical systems whose configuration is an unknown function of a prescribed motion and for systems where there are more than one degree of freedom, it becomes necessary to introduce the concept of *virtual work* when applying the work-energy relationship. The concepts of virtual work and virtual displacement were introduced and used for the solution of equilibrium configurations for static systems of interconnected bodies in Chapter 7 of *Mechanics, Part I*. A virtual displacement is any assumed and arbitrary displacement, linear or angular, away from the natural or actual position. For a system of connected bodies the virtual displacements must be consistent with the constraints of the system. For example, when one end of a link is hinged about a fixed pivot, the virtual displacement of the other end must be normal to the line joining the two ends. Or, if two links are freely pinned together, any virtual displacement of the joint considered as a point on one link must be identical with the virtual displacement of the joint considered as a point on the other link. Such requirements for displacements consistent with the constraints are purely kinematical, i.e., have to do with the geometry of possible motions, and provide what are known as the *equations of constraint*. If a set of virtual displacements containing the equations of constraint and therefore consistent with the constraints is given to a mechanical system, the proper relationship between the coordinates which specify the configuration of the system will be established by applying the work-energy equation expressed by Eq. 55. This equation must be applied as many times as there are degrees of freedom of the system. For each application only one of the coordinate variables is allowed to change at a time, and the others are held constant. It is customary to use the differential symbol $d$ to refer to differential changes in the real displacements, whereas the symbol $\delta$ is used to signify differential changes which are assumed or virtual changes. Thus Eq. 55 is rewritten as

$$\delta U = \Sigma m_i \bar{a}_i \, \delta \bar{s}_i + \Sigma \bar{I}_i \alpha_i \, \delta \theta_i + \Sigma W_i \, \delta h_i + \Sigma k_i x_i \, \delta x_i. \quad (55a)$$

The term $m_i \bar{a}_i$ represents the component of the resultant force on each body in the direction of the virtual displacement $\delta s_i$ of the mass center of the body, and, hence, $m_i \bar{a}_i \, \delta \bar{s}_i$ is the work done by the resultant force on the body during the virtual displacement. Similar reasoning holds for the $\bar{I}_i \alpha_i$ term. Equation 55a provides a very general and powerful method for the solution of complex problems involving conservative mechanical systems. The sample problems which follow illustrate solutions for a single degree of freedom only.

## SAMPLE PROBLEMS

**480.** The movable rack $A$ weighs 6 lb., and the 4 lb. gear may be treated as a solid circular disk of 3 in. radius. In the position shown the spring, which has a stiffness of 8 lb./in., is stretched a distance of 2 in. For the instant represented determine the acceleration $a$ of rack $A$ under the action of the 20 lb. force. The plane of the figure is vertical.

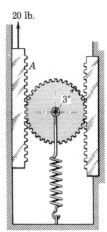

20 lb.

*Solution.* The figure represents the active-force diagram for the entire mechanical system which is conservative. During an infinitesimal upward displacement of $dx$ ft. for rack $A$ the work done on the system is $dU = 20\ dx$, and this equals the sum of the corresponding changes in the total energy of the system. These changes in energy which appear in Eq. 55 are expressed as follows:

$$[dT = \Sigma m_i \bar{a}_i\, ds_i + \Sigma \bar{I}_i \alpha_i\, d\theta_i] \qquad dT_{\text{rack}} = \frac{6}{g}\,a\,dx,$$

$$dT_{\text{gear}} = \frac{4}{g}\frac{a}{2}\frac{dx}{2} + \frac{1}{2}\frac{4}{g}\left(\frac{3}{12}\right)^2 \left(\frac{a}{6/12}\right)\left(\frac{dx}{6/12}\right) = \frac{3}{2}\frac{a}{g}\,dx.$$

PROB. 480

The total change in kinetic energy is, then, $dT = (15a/2g)dx$. The change in the potential energies of the system is

$$[dV = \Sigma W_i\, dh_i + \Sigma k_i x_i\, dx_i] \qquad dV = 6\,dx + 4\frac{dx}{2} + 8\times 2\frac{dx}{2} = 16\,dx.$$

Substitution of these values into Eq. 55 gives

$$20\,dx = \frac{15}{2}\frac{a}{g}\,dx + 16\,dx, \qquad a = \tfrac{8}{15}g = 17.16 \text{ ft./sec.}^2 \qquad Ans.$$

**481.** The two weights $W$ revolve about the vertical axis with an angular velocity $\omega$. Collar $A$ is fixed and collar $B$ is free to slide on the shaft. The spring of stiffness $k$ has an uncompressed length $b$. Determine the angle $\theta$ between the hinged links as a function of $\omega$. The weight of the links is small compared with $W$ and may be neglected.

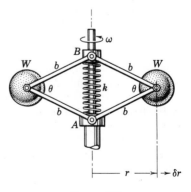

PROB. 481

*Solution.* The steady-state configuration may be determined by giving the system a virtual displacement. The virtual change in kinetic energy $T$ due to the virtual change $\delta r$ in radial distance is

$$[\delta T = \Sigma m_i \bar{a}_i\, \delta s_i] \qquad \delta T = -2\frac{W}{g}\,r\omega^2\,\delta r$$

where the minus sign accounts for the fact that the resultant force $(W/g)r\omega^2$ for each weight is directed oppositely to $+\delta r$. But

$$\delta r = \delta \left( b \cos \frac{\theta}{2} \right) = -\frac{b}{2} \sin \frac{\theta}{2} \, \delta\theta, \quad \text{so } \delta T = \frac{W}{g} b^2\omega^2 \cos \frac{\theta}{2} \sin \frac{\theta}{2} \, \delta\theta.$$

The change in potential energy is

$$[\delta V = \Sigma W_i \, \delta h_i + kx \, \delta x]$$

$$\delta V = 2W \, \delta \left( b \sin \frac{\theta}{2} \right) + kb \left( 1 - 2\sin \frac{\theta}{2} \right) \delta \left[ b \left( 1 - 2\sin \frac{\theta}{2} \right) \right]$$

$$= Wb \cos \frac{\theta}{2} \, \delta\theta + kb^2 \left( 1 - 2\sin \frac{\theta}{2} \right) \left( -\cos \frac{\theta}{2} \, \delta\theta \right)$$

where the datum plane for zero potential energy of position is taken through the fixed collar $A$. Substitution of the virtual changes into Eq. 55a gives

$$0 = \frac{W}{g} b^2\omega^2 \cos \frac{\theta}{2} \sin \frac{\theta}{2} \, \delta\theta + Wb \cos \frac{\theta}{2} \, \delta\theta - kb^2 \left( 1 - 2\sin \frac{\theta}{2} \right) \cos \frac{\theta}{2} \, \delta\theta$$

$$= b \cos \frac{\theta}{2} \left[ \frac{W}{g} b\omega^2 \sin \frac{\theta}{2} + W - kb \left( 1 - 2\sin \frac{\theta}{2} \right) \right] \delta\theta.$$

The solution $\cos(\theta/2) = 0$ is of no practical interest. When the expression in the bracket is set equal to zero, the solution for $\sin(\theta/2)$ gives

$$\theta = 2 \sin^{-1} \left( \frac{1 - \dfrac{W}{kb}}{2 + \dfrac{W\omega^2}{kg}} \right). \qquad Ans.$$

The expression for $\sin(\theta/2)$ requires certain limitations on the relationship between $k$, $b$, $W$, and $\omega$ in order that $\sin(\theta/2)$ be positive and less than unity.

## PROBLEMS

Solve the following problems by the work-energy equation using infinitesimal displacements.

**482.** Neglect friction and determine the acceleration $a$ of the 100 lb. load $A$ as a result of the 85 lb. force in the cable. The pulley weighs 50 lb. and has a centroidal radius of gyration of 12 in. *Ans.* $a = 3.74$ ft./sec.$^2$

**483.** The platform $A$ weighs 20 lb., and each of the links weighs 4 lb. and may be considered a slender rod. If a constant moment $M = 24$ lb. ft. is applied to the link as shown, determine the angular acceleration $\alpha$ of the links for any value of $\theta$.

*Ans.* $\alpha = 5.08(6 - 7\cos\theta)$ rad./sec.$^2$

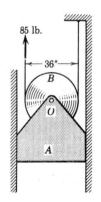

85 lb.

36"

B

O

A

PROB. 482

**484.** A constant force $F$ is applied to one end of the two identical and uniform links as shown, and a constant acceleration $a$ results. Determine the steady-state angle $\theta$ between the links if friction is absent.

$$Ans. \quad \theta = 2 \tan^{-1} \frac{2a}{g}$$

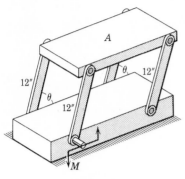

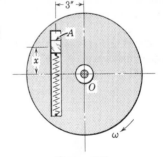

PROB. 483            PROB. 484

**485.** A small railway work car of total weight $W$ is propelled by its motor which supplies a torque $M$ to the light pinion of radius $r_1$. The pinion, in turn, drives a gear of radius $r_2$ which is integral with the wheel. The centroidal moment of inertia of the rear axle and wheel assembly is $I$, and that of the front axle and wheel assembly is also $I$. Determine the torque $M$ required to give the car an acceleration $a$ up the grade if the wheels do not slip.

$$Ans. \quad M = \frac{r_1}{r_2} \left( \frac{W}{g} aR + 2I \frac{a}{R} + WR \sin \theta \right)$$

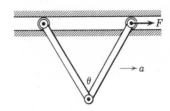

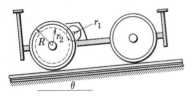

PROB. 485            PROB. 486

**486.** The slotted disk revolves in a horizontal plane about its center $O$. The position of the smooth 1 lb. slider $A$ in the slot is controlled by the spring and the angular velocity $\omega$ of the disk. If the spring has a stiffness of 2 lb./in. and is unstretched when $x = 1$ in., determine $x$ for a constant disk speed of 230 rev./min.         $Ans. \quad x = 4.02$ in.

**487.** The device shown is in the horizontal plane and has the configuration indicated when at rest with no force in the spring. If the acceleration of $A$ is increased gradually to the value $a$, each sector assumes a new angular position about the pivots marked $O$. Design the spring by specifying its modulus $k$

so that the central rack moves 1 in. to the left relative to the frame under a constant acceleration of $a = 2g$. Each sector unit weighs 3 lb. with center of gravity at $G$, and the central rack weighs 2 lb.          *Ans.*  $k = 3.56$ lb./in.

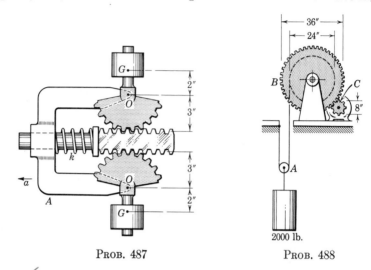

PROB. 487

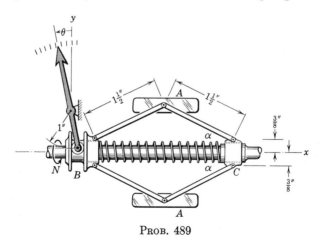

PROB. 488

**488.** Determine the torque $M$ which must be supplied by the motor of the hoisting mechanism to the light pinion $C$ to give the 2000 lb. weight an upward acceleration of 4 ft./sec.² The weight of the pulley at $A$ is negligible. The drum and gear unit $B$ weighs 400 lb. and has a radius of gyration of 15 in. about its center.          *Ans.*  $M = 284$ lb. ft.

**489.** A tachometer of the centrifugal type measures engine speed by the horizontal movement of the collar $B$ on the rotating shaft. This movement is caused by the centrifugal action of the small 8 oz. rotating weights marked $A$.

PROB. 489

Collar $C$ is fixed to the shaft. Determine the speed $N$ of rotation for a reading of $\theta = 20$ deg. The spring has a constant of 4 lb./in. and is uncompressed at the position for which both $\alpha$ and $\theta$ are zero. The weights of the links may be neglected.

         *Ans.* $N = 217$ rev./min.

**490.** The uniform arm $OA$ weighs 8 lb., and the gear $D$ weighs 10 lb. with a radius of gyration of 2.4 in. about its center. If the large gear is fixed and if the arm and small gear are free to rotate in a vertical plane about their respective bearings, find the angular acceleration $\alpha$ of $OA$ just after the arm is released from rest in the position shown.

         *Ans.* $\alpha = 27.7$ rad./sec.$^2$

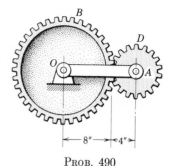

PROB. 490

**45. Power and Efficiency.** The capacity of a machine is measured by the time rate at which it can do work or deliver energy. The total work or energy output is not a measure of this capacity since a motor, no matter how small, can deliver any amount of energy if given sufficient time. On the other hand a large and powerful machine is required to deliver a large amount of energy in a short period of time. Thus the capacity of a machine is rated by its *power*, which is defined as the *time rate of doing work.*

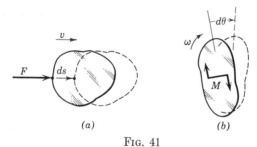

(a)                 (b)

FIG. 41

The work done by a force $F$, Fig. 41a, during a displacement $ds$ of its point of application in the direction of the force is $dU = F\,ds$, and the time rate at which the force does work is the power

$$P = \frac{dU}{dt} = Fv, \qquad (56)$$

where $v$ is the velocity of the point of application of the force. Likewise, the work done by a couple $M$, Fig. 41b, during an angular displacement $d\theta$ in the direction of the couple is $dU = M\,d\theta$, and the time rate at which the couple does work is the power

$$P = \frac{dU}{dt} = M\omega, \tag{57}$$

where $\omega$ is the angular velocity of the body. If the force $F$ is not in the direction of the displacement $ds$, the power developed will be equal to the component of $F$ in the direction of the velocity times the velocity. Likewise, if the couple and angular displacement vectors are not in the same direction, the cosine of the angle between them will be a factor. It should be emphasized that Eqs. 56 and 57 are instantaneous expressions for power and represent the time rate at which work is being done at the instant considered.

The unit of mechanical power in common use is the *horsepower* (h.p.), and the common electrical unit of power is the *watt* or *kilowatt* (1000 watts). The definitions of these units and their equivalences are

$$1 \text{ h.p.} = 550 \text{ ft. lb./sec.} = 33,000 \text{ ft. lb./min.},$$

$$1 \text{ watt} = 10^7 \text{ ergs/sec.} = 0.737 \text{ ft. lb./sec.},$$

$$1 \text{ h.p.} = 746 \text{ watts} = 0.746 \text{ k.w.}$$

The work done in one hour at the rate of one horsepower is one *horsepower hour* (h.p. hr.), and, similarly, the electrical energy used in one hour at the rate of one kilowatt is one *kilowatt hour* (k.w. hr.). Thus

$$1 \text{ h.p. hr.} = 1,980,000 \text{ ft. lb.},$$

$$1 \text{ k.w. hr.} = 2,654,000 \text{ ft. lb.}$$

The *efficiency* $e$ of a machine is the ratio of the energy output of the machine during a certain interval to the energy supplied to the machine during the same interval. This definition assumes that the machine operates uniformly so that there is no accumulation or depletion of energy within it. Efficiency is always less than unity since every device operates with some loss of energy and since energy cannot be created within the machine. In mechanical devices which involve moving parts there will always be a loss of energy due to the negative work of kinetic friction forces. This work is converted to heat energy which in turn is dissipated to the surroundings. Frictional losses may be minimized by lubrication but may never be eliminated entirely. The ratio of the work done *by* a machine to the work done *on* the machine during equal intervals of time is the *mechanical efficiency* $e_m$. The mechanical efficiency at any instant of time may be expressed in terms of mechanical power $P$ by

$$e_m = \frac{P_{\text{output}}}{P_{\text{input}}}.$$

The mechanical efficiencies of accurately made and properly lubricated machines are often 90 per cent or more.

In addition to energy loss by mechanical friction there may also be electrical and thermal energy loss in which case the *electrical efficiency* $e_e$ and *thermal efficiency* $e_t$ are also involved. The *overall efficiency* $e$ of a machine is the product of its several efficiencies. Thus

$$e = e_m e_e e_t.$$

A device used for measuring the power output of a machine is called a dynamometer. A dynamometer may be either of the *absorption* type, where the energy developed by the machine is absorbed and usually converted into heat, or of the *transmission* type, where the energy is passed on unchanged. In Fig. 42 is shown a simple brake dynamometer of the absorption type for measuring the power output of an electric motor. The power of the motor is absorbed in the work of friction between the brake blocks and the pulley. From the statical equilibrium of the brake, the total frictional moment acting on the pulley is seen to be $M_f = Rb$, if the moment due to the weight of the brake is neglected. The reaction

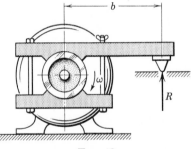

Fig. 42

$R$ is easily measured by a weighing scale, and the power at any constant angular speed $\omega$ is $P = M_f\omega = Rb\omega$. If a measurement is taken during an acceleration $\alpha$ of the motor, part of the power will be used in increasing the rotational kinetic energy. If the moment of inertia of the rotating elements is $I$, the equation of rotation is

$$M = M_f + I\alpha,$$

where $M$ is the driving torque applied by the electrical field. The capacity or power developed by the motor under these circumstances is, then,

$$P = M\omega = M_f\omega + I\alpha\omega.$$

Measurements of power output are generally made at various operating speeds, and a plot of the results will disclose the optimum speed for maximum power.

**491.** A car of weight $W$ has an acceleration $a$ up an incline $\theta$. Determine the power $P$ delivered by the engine to the rear wheels when the car reaches a velocity $v$. The horizontal force required to tow the car on a level road at the velocity $v$ with engine disengaged is $R$.

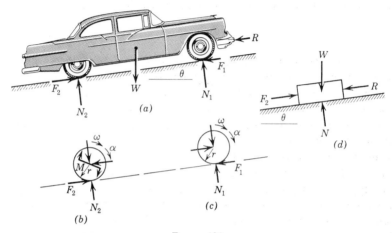

Prob. 491

*Solution.* The free-body diagram of the car is shown in the $a$-part of the illustration. The negative work done on the car by friction forces in the wheel bearings and by windage is accounted for by considering a retarding force $R$ to act on the car which does negative work at a rate equal to that done by friction in the wheel bearings and by windage. This force is equal to the experimentally determined "road resistance."

The normal forces $N_1$ and $N_2$ act on each respective pair of wheels as do the friction forces $F_1$ and $F_2$. The forces $F_1$ and $F_2$ are the friction forces between the tires and the road which would act if there were no internal mechanical friction in the bearings. From the free-body diagram of the front wheels in the $c$-part of the figure the direction of $F_1$ is chosen to provide the necessary clockwise moment about the wheel bearing in the direction of $\alpha$. From the free-body diagram of the rear wheels in the $b$-part of the illustration the friction force is in the direction to prevent the wheel from slipping under the applied torque $M$ of the drive shaft.

The power delivered to the rear wheels by the engine is $P = M\omega$. The torque $M$ may be expressed in terms of known quantities from the equations of motion for the wheels separately and the car as a whole. Thus for the front and rear pair of wheels

$$[\Sigma \bar{M} = \bar{I}\alpha] \qquad\qquad F_1 r = I_1 \alpha; \qquad M - F_2 r = I_2 \alpha,$$

where $I_1$ and $I_2$ are the centroidal moments of inertia for the front and rear pair of wheels, respectively. For the complete car

$$[\Sigma F = ma] \qquad\qquad F_2 - F_1 - W \sin\theta - R = \frac{W}{g} a.$$

From these expressions the rear-axle driving torque $M$ is

$$M = \left( W \sin\theta + R + \frac{W}{g} a \right) r + (I_1 + I_2)\alpha,$$

and, therefore, the power supplied to the rear wheels by the engine is

$$P = M\omega = \left( W \sin\theta + R + \frac{W}{g} a \right) v + (I_1 + I_2)\alpha\omega. \qquad Ans.$$

The term $Wv \sin\theta$ is the power required to increase the potential energy of the car at the given rate; $Rv$ is the power used in overcoming friction and windage; and $Wav/g$ is the power required to increase the translational kinetic energy at the given rate. This third term is merely

$$\frac{d}{dt}\left( \frac{1}{2} mv^2 \right) = mv\frac{dv}{dt} = \frac{W}{g} av.$$

The last terms $(I_1 + I_2)\alpha\omega$ represent the power used in increasing the rotational energy of the wheels and may be obtained from

$$\frac{d}{dt}\left( \frac{1}{2} I_1\omega^2 + \frac{1}{2} I_2\omega^2 \right) = (I_1 + I_2)\omega\frac{d\omega}{dt} = (I_1 + I_2)\alpha\omega.$$

Inasmuch as the rotational energy of the wheels is a small fraction of the total kinetic energy of the car, these last two terms may be neglected. This approximation amounts to neglecting $F_1$ in the case of the front wheels and the difference between $M$ and $F_2 r$ for the rear wheels.

With neglect of the rotational energy of the wheels, the car may be simulated by a block, shown in the $d$-part of the figure, sliding up the incline under the action of $F_2$, $W$, and $R$. The power is then computed from the rate at which $F_2$ would do work and is

$$P = F_2 v = \left( W \sin\theta + R + \frac{W}{g} a \right) v.$$

It should be noted that, in the actual car, neither one of the frictional forces $F_1$ or $F_2$ does work if slipping of the wheels does not occur.

**492.** A test of power and efficiency for a gasoline engine is made by connecting the engine to an electrical dynamometer which operates as a generator. The frame or stator $A$ of the dynamometer is mounted independently of its rotor in bearings which are coaxial with those of the rotor. In this way a direct measurement of the torque on the rotor developed by the generation of electric current may be made. The electrical energy generated is converted into heat by passing the current through electrical resistors. In the particular test involved the speed ratio shown is 3:1, and the engine is run at 2250 rev./min. The force $R$ measured during the test is 22 lb. and that due to the unbalanced weight of the stator alone with the motor disconnected is 4 lb. A gasoline consumption of 17.5 lb./hr. is also measured. If the gasoline liberates 20,000 B.t.u. of heat energy per pound when burned, determine the power output $P$ of the engine and its overall efficiency $e$. Neglect any energy loss in the dynamometer.

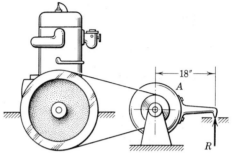

PROB. 492

*Solution.* The power developed is obtained from the rate at which the moment on the generator shaft does work. This moment is

$$M = \tfrac{18}{12}\Delta R = \tfrac{3}{2}(22 - 4) = 27 \text{ lb. ft.}$$

The power output is, then,

$$[P = M\omega] \qquad P = 27 \times 3 \times 2250 \times 2\pi = 1{,}145{,}000 \text{ ft. lb./min.}$$

or

$$P = \frac{1{,}145{,}000}{33{,}000} = 34.7 \text{ h.p.} \qquad\qquad Ans.$$

The overall efficiency $e$ is

$$\left[ e = \frac{P_{\text{output}}}{P_{\text{input}}} \right] \qquad e = \frac{1{,}145{,}000 \times 60}{17.5 \times 20{,}000 \times 778} = 02.52. \qquad Ans.$$

## PROBLEMS

**493.** Derive a formula for the horsepower transmitted by a shaft which revolves at a constant speed of $N$ rev./min. under a torque of $M$ lb. ft.

**494.** The dump truck carries 6 yd.³ of earth with a density of 110 lb./ft.³, and the elevating mechanism rotates the dump about the pivot $A$ at the constant rate of 4 deg./sec. The center of gravity of the load is at $G$, and the weight of the empty dump is negligible compared with its load. Find the greatest power $P$ required during the tilting of the load.  *Ans.*  $P = 11.30$ h.p.

Prob. 494

**495.** The total weight of a rubber-tired tractor is 30,000 lb.  Determine the speed $v$ in mi./hr. at which the tractor can haul a four-wheeled trailer weighing 40,000 lb. up a 15 per cent grade if the engine develops 200 h.p.

*Ans.*  $v = 7.22$ mi./hr.

**496.** The dynamometer shown is balanced on the knife edge at $O$.  The brake band is tightened while the engine is running until the arm balances with the 50 lb. weight in the position shown corresponding to a measured speed $N$ of 1640 rev./min. Determine the power output at this speed for the engine which drives the flywheel. With the 50 lb. weight removed and the brake band loose the arm is in static balance about $O$.

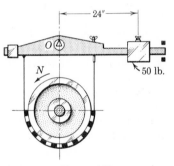

Prob. 496

*Ans.*  $P = 31.2$ h.p.

**497.** The brakes of a 3000 lb. car bring it to a stop with a constant deceleration from a velocity of 30 mi./hr. in a distance of 88 ft. measured down a 20 per cent grade. Determine the maximum power $P$ absorbed by the brakes.

**498.** In a test of a centrifugal sump pump a power input to the motor of 4.65 k.w. was measured at a speed of 1720 rev./min.  The pump discharged fresh water at the rate of 72 ft.$^3$/min. with a total lift of 30 ft.  Determine the overall efficiency $e$ of the pump.  *Ans.*  $e = 0.655$

**499.** A jet-propelled airplane weighs 12,500 lb. empty and is fueled with 10,000 lb. of kerosene with a heat energy content of 19,800 B.t.u./lb.  The turbojet engine develops a constant forward thrust of 4000 lb., and fuel is consumed at the rate of 1.03 lb./hr. for each pound of thrust.  If the maximum velocity in level flight is 650 mi./hr., determine the useful power $P$ developed by the engine in driving the airplane against air resistance.  Also find the overall efficiency $e$ of conversion of heat energy to useful work in propelling the airplane at this speed.

**500.** The *propulsive coefficient* $C$ for a ship is the ratio of the power required to overcome the resistance to motion through the water at a certain speed to the corresponding total power delivered by the engines to the propellers. The resistance to motion through the water is very nearly proportional to the square of the speed. For a certain ship a force of 40,000 lb. is required in a horizontal cable to tow the ship at 3 knots (1 knot = 1.689 ft./sec.), and, when the ship is under its own power at 10 knots, the engines deliver 28,000 h.p. to the propellers through the shaft (*shaft horsepower*). Determine $C$ for the speed of 10 knots.       *Ans.*   $C = 0.487$

**501.** A 400 lb. flywheel with a centroidal radius of gyration of 15 in. is brought up to a speed of 300 rev./min. from rest in 30 sec. with constant acceleration. The electric motor which powers the flywheel is connected to it by a V-belt drive with a 2:1 speed reduction so that the motor speed is always twice that of the flywheel. Calculate the power output of the motor at the instant when the flywheel reaches 200 rev./min., and find the corresponding output torque $M$ of the motor shaft. *Ans.*   $P = 0.774$ h.p., $M = 121.9$ lb. in.

**502.** A Diesel locomotive burns oil with an energy content of 19,000 B.t.u./lb. and pulls a 1000 ton train of cars up a 2 per cent grade with a constant velocity of 30 mi./hr. The frictional resistance to motion is 12 lb./ton. If the locomotive burns fuel at the rate of 2200 lb./hr., determine the power $P$ developed by the locomotive at the drawbar and the overall efficiency $e$ of conversion of heat energy to useful work in moving the entire train, including the 500,000 lb. locomotive.

**503.** The figure shows a typical "indicator diagram" for a 1-cylinder, 2-cycle reciprocating engine. The card is a graphical record taken directly on the engine of the pressure on the piston versus the piston travel during one complete cycle (one revolution of the crank). For the actual diagram 1 in. on the vertical scale corresponds to 200 lb./in.² gage pressure, and

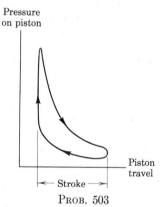

Pressure on piston

Stroke

Piston travel

PROB. 503

1 in. on the horizontal scale corresponds to 4 in. of actual piston travel. The area $A$ within the loop on the card is measured with a planimeter and is found to be 0.910 in.² Determine the power input $P$ to the engine (*indicated power*) if the piston diameter is 6 in., the stroke is also 6 in., and the engine turns at 1750 rev./min.       *Ans.*   $P = 91.0$ h.p.

**504.** The electric motor shown is delivering 4 h.p. at 1725 rev./min. Determine the angle $\delta$ through which the motor deflects under load if the constant of each of the four spring mounts is 40 lb./in. What direction is the motor running?

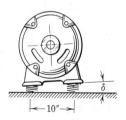

10″

PROB. 504

**505.** If the power output $P$ of a car of weight $W$

# Problems

remains constant during a certain interval, find the distance $s$ required to increase its speed within this interval from $v_1$ to $v_2$ on a level road. Neglect frictional resistance and rotational energy of the wheels.

$$Ans. \quad s = \frac{W}{3Pg}(v_2^3 - v_1^3)$$

**506.** A heavy cable of total length $L$ and weight $\mu$ per unit length is hoisted by the drum around which it is wrapped. The drum has negligible weight and is driven clockwise by a motor through a gear reduction drive. Determine the power output $P$ of the motor at the instant represented when the vertical section of the cable has an upward acceleration $a$ and the drum has an angular velocity $\omega$. Neglect the mass of the gears and the effect of a partial turn of cable around the drum.

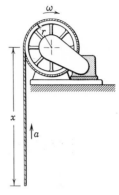

**507.** At the bottom of a grade a 4000 lb. car has a velocity of 30 mi./hr. The engine produces a constant torque on the wheels so that the friction force between the wheels and the road is 900 lb. Frictional resistance to motion is constant at 100 lb. The grade becomes steeper according to $\sin \theta = s/1000$, where $\theta$ is the angle of the grade with the horizontal and $s$ is the distance traveled in feet measured from the bottom of the grade. Determine the maximum power $P$ developed by the engine

PROB. 506

and the distance $s$ to the position where the car stalls. Neglect the rotational energy of the wheels.  $Ans.$  $P_{max} = 93.0$ h.p., $s = 516$ ft.

**508.** Slider $A$ of weight $W$ is placed in a smooth tube and released from rest in a position for which the spring of stiffness $k$ is compressed a total amount $x_0$. Find maximum power $P$ developed by the spring in moving the slider and the displacement $x$ at which this condition occurs.

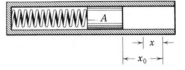

$$Ans. \quad P = \frac{k}{2}\sqrt{\frac{kg}{W}}x_0^2, \quad x = x_0/\sqrt{2}$$

PROB. 508

*  **509.** The drawbar pull $F$ exerted by a steam turbine locomotive on a 1500 ton train of cars running on level track decreases uniformly with the velocity $v$ as shown. Construct a curve showing the power delivered by the locomotive to the train versus the velocity and find the maximum power $P$ developed and the velocity $v$ at which this occurs.

$Ans.$  $P = 6000$ h.p., $v = 75$ mi./hr.

*  **510.** In the speed range between 30 and 60 mi./hr. the Diesel engine of a 15 ton truck develops a constant power output of 200 h.p. Resistance to motion is constant at 400 lb. Determine the time $t$ required for the truck to change its speed from 30 to 60 mi./hr. Neglect the rotational kinetic energy of the wheels.  $Ans.$  $t = 32.7$ sec.

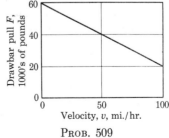

Velocity, $v$, mi./hr.

PROB. 509

# 6

# IMPULSE AND MOMENTUM

**46. Linear Impulse and Momentum.** The work-energy method discussed in Chapter 5 is a consequence of the first integral of the equation of motion with respect to displacement. This approach leads to the solution of problems where changes in velocity may be calculated directly from the work done by the forces on the system where the forces are expressed in terms of the displacements. For problems where the forces are expressed in terms of the time a first integral of the equation of motion with time is implied. This approach leads to the quantities of impulse and momentum.

The equation of motion of a particle of mass $m$ in the $x$-direction is

$$\Sigma F_x = ma_x = m\frac{dv_x}{dt},$$

where $\Sigma F_x$ is the sum of the $x$-components of all forces acting on $m$, and $a_x$ and $v_x$ are the $x$-components of the acceleration and velocity, respectively. Since the mass $m$ of the single particle is a constant, this equation may be written in either of the two forms

$$\Sigma F_x = \frac{d}{dt}(mv_x) \qquad \text{or} \qquad \Sigma F_x\,dt = d(mv_x). \qquad (58)$$

The product of mass and linear velocity is defined as *linear momentum*, and thus the first of Eqs. 58 states that the resultant force in any one direction on a particle of mass $m$ equals the time rate of change of its linear momentum in that direction.  This formulation is an alternate way of stating Newton's second law of motion.  The product of force and time is defined as *linear impulse*, and thus the second of Eqs. 58 states that the linear impulse of $\Sigma F_x$ on $m$ during time $dt$ equals the change in linear momentum.  The dimensions of both linear impulse and linear momentum are [force] $\times$ [time], (lb. sec.).  The relations expressed by Eqs. 58 may also be written for the $y$- and $z$-directions, and these equations are, then, the scalar components of a single vector relation which may be stated as

$$\Sigma F = \frac{d}{dt} (mv) \qquad \text{or} \qquad \Sigma F \, dt = d(mv).$$

In the vector formulation $\Sigma F$ is the resultant of all forces on $m$, and $mv$ is the resultant linear momentum of $m$.  Linear impulse and linear momentum are both vector quantities which have the directions of $\Sigma F$ and $v$, respectively.  Thus the direction of $\Sigma F$ coincides with the direction of the *change* in linear momentum which is also the direction of the acceleration.

The action of $\Sigma F_x$ during a finite interval of time $t$ is given by integration of the second of Eqs. 58.  The integral is

$$\int_0^t \Sigma F_x \, dt = mv_x - mv_{0_x}, \tag{59}$$

where $v_x$ is the velocity in the positive $x$-direction at time $t$ and $v_{0_x}$ is the velocity in the positive $x$-direction at time $t = 0$.  The integral on the left side of the equation is the linear impulse of $\Sigma F_x$ during the time $t$, and the right side of the equation is the corresponding change in the linear momentum.  When the functional relation between $\Sigma F_x$ and $t$ is unknown but experimental data for the variation of $\Sigma F_x$ with $t$ are available, the total impulse may be found by approximating the area under the curve of $\Sigma F_x$ versus $t$.  If $\Sigma F_x$ is constant, the expression becomes

$$\Sigma F_x t = mv_x - mv_{0_x}.$$

It was shown in Chapter 4 that the resultant of all forces acting on a translating rigid body passes through the center of mass and that such motion may be analyzed as though the body were a particle.  Thus the foregoing principles of impulse and momentum developed for the motion of a particle may be applied equally well to a translating rigid body.

Consider now any general system of particles. These particles need not be joined but may be considered to have any motions whatsoever. If $F_{1_x}, F_{2_x}, F_{3_x}, \cdots$ represent the $x$-components of all forces applied to a representative particle of mass $m_i$ from sources *external* to the system, and if $f_{1_x}, f_{2_x}, f_{3_x}, \cdots$ represent the $x$-components of all internally applied forces on $m_i$, the first of Eqs. 58 may be written

$$ F_{1_x} + F_{2_x} + F_{3_x} + \cdots + f_{1_x} + f_{2_x} + f_{3_x} + \cdots = \frac{d}{dt}(m_i v_{i_x}), $$

where $v_{i_x}$ is the $x$-component of the velocity of $m_i$. Similar expressions may be written for each particle of the system. By adding all these equations and remembering that the sum of the internal actions and reactions is zero, the sum of external forces in the $x$-direction becomes

$$ \Sigma F_x = \Sigma \frac{d}{dt}(m_i v_{i_x}) = \frac{d}{dt}\Sigma(m_i v_{i_x}). $$

The expression $\Sigma(m_i v_{i_x})$ is the sum of the linear momenta of all particles in the $x$-direction and is defined as the linear momentum $G_x$ of the system in the $x$-direction. This momentum may be expressed in terms of the motion of the mass center. The principle of moments is

$$ m\bar{x} = \Sigma(m_i x_i), $$

where $x_i$ is the $x$-coordinate of $m_i$, $m$ is the total mass of the system, and $\bar{x}$ is the $x$-coordinate to the mass center. If attention is focused on the total system, its mass may be considered as constant, and differentiation with respect to time gives

$$ m\bar{v}_x = \Sigma(m_i v_{i_x}) = G_x. $$

Thus the linear momentum of any given system equals the total mass of the system multiplied by the velocity of the center of mass.

The symbol $G_x$ and its interpretation may now be used in the equation for $\Sigma F_x$. With similar expressions for the $y$- and $z$-directions there result

$$ \Sigma F_x = \frac{dG_x}{dt}, $$

$$ \Sigma F_y = \frac{dG_y}{dt}, \tag{60} $$

$$ \Sigma F_z = \frac{dG_z}{dt}. $$

Equations 60 are the scalar components of the single vector equation

$$\Sigma F = \frac{dG}{dt}, \tag{61}$$

where $G = m\bar{v}$. Equation 61 states that the resultant of the external forces acting on any given system of particles equals the magnitude and direction of the time rate of change of the linear momentum of the system. This formulation is an extremely important concept in mechanics, and is an alternate way of expressing the equation of motion of the mass center of any system as stated previously in Chapter 3 by Eq. 32.

A rigid body is a special case of the more general system of particles, and the principles developed here may be used to describe the relation between the resultant force on the body and the time rate of change of linear momentum $m\bar{v}$ of the mass center of the body regardless of its motion. The linear momentum vector $G = m\bar{v}$ has the direction of $\bar{v}$ but does not pass through the mass center except in the special case of a translating rigid body.

Application of the principles of impulse and momentum requires the use of a *free-body diagram* where *all external forces* acting on the body or system are accounted for. In the method of work and energy it is necessary to consider only those forces which do work, whereas with the method of impulse and momentum *all* forces with components in the direction of motion exert impulses whether they do work or not.

The generality of Eq. 61, derived for any given system of particles, is not needed when dealing with a translating rigid body. This generality will be found useful in discussing problems which involve mass flow in articles which follow.

### SAMPLE PROBLEM

**511.** The 100 lb. weight is pulled up the incline from rest by the action of the force $P$, which varies with the time according to the accompanying graph. Determine the velocity $v$ of the weight 8 sec. after $P$ begins to act. The coefficient of friction is 0.30.

*Solution.* The free-body diagram of the block is drawn and discloses three forces which have components in the direction of motion. There is zero resultant force on the 100 lb. weight until $P$ overcomes the limiting frictional force of $0.30 \times 100 \cos 10° = 29.5$ lb. and reaches the value of

$$P = 29.5 + 100 \sin 10° = 46.9 \text{ lb.}$$

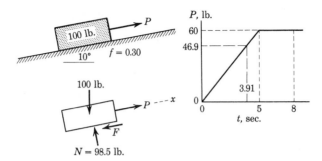

when $t = (46.9/60)5 = 3.91$ sec. For the remaining 4.09 sec. the net force in the direction of motion is

$$\Sigma F_x = P - 46.9.$$

The impulse during the 4.09 sec. is

$$\int_{3.91}^{8} P \, dt - 46.9 \times 4.09 = 46.4 \text{ lb. sec.,}$$

where the integral is discontinuous and may be obtained from the area under the curve to the right of $t = 3.91$ sec. The impulse-momentum principle gives

$$\left[ \int \Sigma F_x \, dt = \Delta(mv_x) \right] \qquad 46.4 = \frac{100}{32.2}(v - 0),$$

$$v = 14.94 \text{ ft./sec.} \qquad Ans.$$

## PROBLEMS

**512.** A jet-propelled airplane weighing 8 tons is flying at a constant speed of 500 mi./hr. when the pilot ignites two rocket-assist units, each of which develops a forward thrust of 1000 lb. for 12 sec. If the velocity of the airplane is 530 mi./hr. at the end of the 12 sec., find the time average of the increase $\Delta R$ in air resistance. The weight of the rocket fuel is negligible compared with the weight of the airplane.          *Ans.* $\Delta R = 178$ lb.

**513.** Determine the constant drawbar pull $P$ required to increase the velocity of a 1500 ton train of freight cars from 30 mi./hr. to 50 mi./hr. up a 1 per cent grade in 3 min. Train resistance is 10 lb./ton.          *Ans.* $P = 60,200$ lb.

**514.** A particle of mass $m$ starts from rest and moves in a horizontal straight line under the action of a constant force $P$. Resistance to motion is proportional to the square of the velocity and is $R = kv^2$. Determine the total impulse $I$ on the particle from the time it starts until it reaches its maximum velocity.

*Ans.* $I = m\sqrt{P/k}$

**515.** A 2 lb. body which has a velocity of 10 ft./sec. to the left is struck with an impact force $F$ acting to the right on the body as represented in the graph. Approximate the loading by the dotted triangle and determine the final velocity $v$ of the object.     *Ans.*   $v = 38.3$ ft./sec. to the right

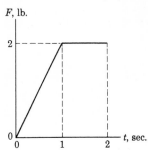

PROB. 515                PROB. 516

**516.** A 3.22 lb. body is moving in a horizontal straight line with a velocity of 15 ft./sec. when a horizontal force $F$ is applied to it at right angles to the initial direction of motion. If $F$ varies according to the given relation, remains constant in direction, and is the only force acting on the body in its plane of motion, find the velocity of the body when $t = 2$ sec.

**517.** An 8000 lb. rocket sled is propelled by six rocket motors each with an impulse rating of 30,000 lb. sec. The rockets are fired at ¼ sec. intervals starting from rest, and the duration of each rocket is 1.5 sec. If the velocity of the sled is 600 ft./sec. in 3 sec. from the start, compute the time average $R$ of the total resistance to motion. Neglect the loss of weight due to exhaust gases compared with the total weight of the sled. *Ans.*   $R = 10,330$ lb.

**518.** The motion of the 15 lb. weight in the vertical slot is controlled by the two cable tensions shown. Friction in the guides is negligible. If the weight

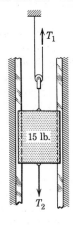

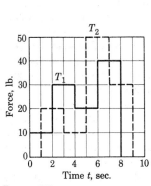

PROB. 518

has a downward velocity of 4 ft./sec. at time $t = 0$, determine its velocity $v$ when 10 sec. have elapsed.

**519.** Careful measurements made during the impact of the metal cylinder against the spring-supported plate disclose a semielliptical relation between the contact force $F$ and the time $t$ as shown. Determine the rebound velocity $v$ of the cylinder if it weighs 8 oz. and strikes the plate with an initial velocity of 20 ft./sec.          *Ans.* $v = 11.0$ ft./sec.

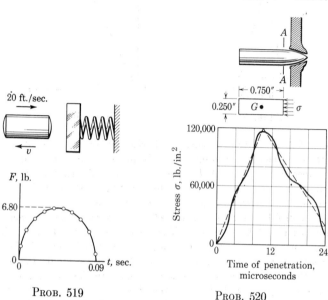

PROB. 519          PROB. 520

**520.** In a test on the penetration of armor plate by a projectile the longitudinal stress $\sigma$ in the projectile has been measured around section $A$–$A$ by means of electrical resistance-wire strain gages. The experimental relation between the time during penetration and the compressive stress $\sigma$ induced across section $A$–$A$ is shown in the graph where the time is plotted in microseconds ($10^{-6}$ sec.). At the instant of 24 microseconds penetration find the velocity $v$ of the center of mass $G$ of that part of the projectile to the left of section $A$–$A$ if this portion has a weight of 0.0110 lb. and if the projectile reaches the plate with a velocity of 2000 ft./sec. Approximate the impulse with the dotted line shown.

**521.** The drawbar pull exerted by a locomotive on a 1000 ton train of cars going up a 1 per cent grade increases linearly with the time from 40,000 lb. to 50,000 lb. in 30 sec. If the velocity of the train was 30 mi./hr. at the beginning of the interval, find the velocity $v$ after 30 sec. Train resistance is constant at 10 lb./ton.          *Ans.* $v = 34.9$ mi./hr.

**522.** The rocket thrust $T$ and total resistance $R$ for a 4000 lb. rocket sled vary with the time $t$, measured from the start of the motion, as shown on the graph. The rocket motors are ignited for 2 sec. only. If the loss in mass is negligible, determine the velocity $v$ of the sled after 3 sec. of motion.

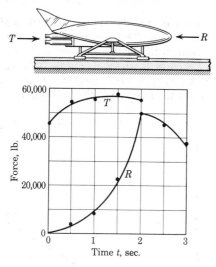

PROB. 522

**523.** An 8 oz. body vibrates along the $x$-axis under the action of an alternating force in the $x$-direction whose amplitude decreases with the time as shown in the accompanying graph and as given by

$$F_x = 2e^{-t} \cos 2\pi t,$$

where $F_x$ is in pounds and $t$ is in seconds. If the body is moving with a velocity of 4 ft./sec. in the negative $x$-direction at time $t = 0$, find its velocity $v$ at time $t = 2\frac{1}{2}$ sec. *Ans.* $v_x = -0.56$ ft./sec.

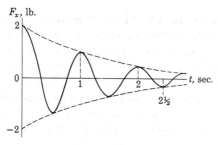

PROB. 523

**524.** If the resistance $R$ to the motion of a train of weight $W$ increases with velocity according to $R = R_0 + Kv$, where $R_0$ is the initial resistance to be overcome in starting the train and $K$ is a constant, find the time $t$ required for the train to reach a velocity $v$ from rest on a horizontal track under the action of a constant tractive force $F$.

$$\text{Ans.}\quad t = \frac{W}{Kg}\log\frac{F - R_0}{F - R_0 - Kv}$$

**525.** Electrons of mass $m$ are introduced into an electric field with a velocity $u$ at the 45 deg. angle as shown. The electric field or voltage gradient $E$ has components which pulsate with the time according to $E_x = E_0 \sin pt$ and $E_y = E_0 \cos pt$. If an electron is admitted into the field at time $t = 0$, determine its velocity $v$ after $\frac{1}{4}$ cycle has elapsed ($t = \pi/2p$). The force on the electron in the direction of the field equals the field times the charge $e$ on the electron.

$$\text{Ans.}\quad v = \sqrt{u^2 + 2\left(\frac{eE_0}{mp}\right)^2}$$

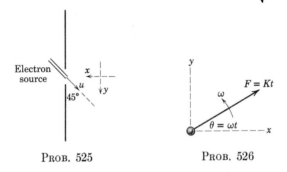

PROB. 525                PROB. 526

**526.** A charged particle of mass $m$ starts from rest at time $t = 0$. It is subjected to a force $F$ due to a rotating field of force whose intensity increases linearly with time $F = Kt$ and whose direction with the $x$-axis is $\theta = \omega t$ with $\omega$ a constant. Determine the magnitude of the velocity $v$ acquired by the particle during one half of a revolution of the force field starting from time $t = 0$ and determine the angle $\beta$ made by $v$ with the positive $x$-axis at this instant.

$$\text{Ans.}\quad v = \frac{K}{m\omega^2}\sqrt{\pi^2 + 4}\,,\ \beta = \tan^{-1}(-\pi/2)$$

**47. Diversion of Steady Fluid Streams.** The principle of impulse and momentum finds important application in the analysis of the dynamics of fluids. In particular, consider the diversion of a steady stream of fluid by a fixed section of pipe or a vane as represented in Fig. 43. The fluid enters with a velocity $v_1$ through a cross-sectional area $A_1$ normal to the flow and leaves with a velocity $v_2$ through a cross-sectional area $A_2$ normal to the flow. With steady flow there is no accumulation or depletion of fluid in the system. The free-body diagram of the section of fixed pipe and the fluid within it is shown in the $a$-part of the figure where $\Sigma F$ is the resultant of all external forces acting on the system isolated. This resultant will include the weight of the pipe and fluid, if appreciable, and all external supporting forces applied to the pipe section. Also included are the forces due to the

static pressure (gage) across the entrance and exit sections exerted
on the fluid within the system by the fluid external to the system.
For fluid flow across an open vane the pressure in the stream is atmospheric, in which case there is no force due to static pressure which
contributes to $\Sigma F$.

The force $\Sigma F$ may be determined by a direct application of Eq.
61 which states that the resultant force on any given mass system
equals the time rate of change of the momentum of the system. Since
there is no change in momentum of the pipe, the time rate of change

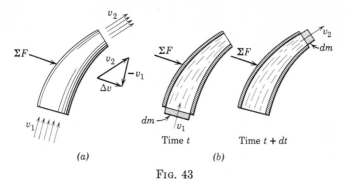

Time $t$        Time $t + dt$

(a)                    (b)

FIG. 43

of momentum is the vector difference between the rate at which
momentum leaves the system and the rate at which momentum enters
the system. If $m'$ stands for the mass rate of flow, Eq. 61 gives

$$\Sigma F = m' \, \Delta v \qquad (62)$$

where $\Delta v = v_2 \to v_1$. Since this is a vector equation, $\Sigma F$ will have
the same direction as $\Delta v$. Equation 62 may be applied directly as a
vector equation, or it may be used in terms of its $x$- and $y$-components.

The impulse-momentum equation for steady fluid flow may also be
obtained by an incremental analysis. Figure 43b illustrates the system at time $t$ and also at time $t + dt$. The system consists of the
fixed pipe, the fluid within it, and the fluid of mass $dm$ which will
enter the pipe in time $dt$. After the interval $dt$ the same system occupies
the position shown in the right-hand view of Fig. 43b, where a mass
of fluid equal to $dm$ has emerged from the section. The momentum
of the fluid within the pipe between the two ends at time $t$ is identical
with that between the same two ends at time $t + dt$, and therefore
the difference between the momenta of the system at the two times
is $v_2 \, dm \to v_1 \, dm$ or $\Delta v \, dm$. Since this change occurs in time $dt$, the
time rate of change of momentum is $\Delta v \, dm/dt$ or $m' \, \Delta v$ which equals
the resultant force $\Sigma F$ on the system as given by Eq. 62.

When the entrance and exit areas for the fluid flow are not the same, it is necessary to apply the equation of continuity which merely accounts for the constancy of mass flow. If $\rho$ is the mass density, then $\rho_1 A_1 v_1 = \rho_2 A_2 v_2$. If the fluid is a liquid, the density will be essentially constant.

Equation 62 is independent of the properties of the fluid and may be used to analyze any type of steady mass flow whether it be liquid, gas, or particles of mass such as sand.

One of the most important applications of the momentum equation for fluid flow occurs when the diverting body is in motion, such as a pump vane or turbine blade. The sample problem which follows will illustrate this condition.

### SAMPLE PROBLEM

**527.** The smooth vane shown diverts the open stream of fluid of cross-sectional area $A$, mass density $\rho$, and velocity $v$. (a) Determine the force components $R$ and $F$ required to hold the vane in a fixed position. (b) Find the forces when the vane is given a constant velocity $u$ less than $v$ and in the direction of $v$. (c) Determine the optimum speed $u$ for the generation of maximum power by the action of the fluid on the moving vane.

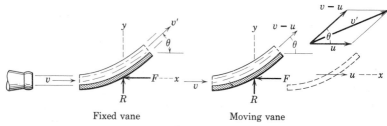

Fixed vane                    Moving vane

PROB. 527

*Solution.* *Part (a).* The free-body diagram of the vane together with the fluid portion undergoing the momentum change is shown. The momentum equation may be applied to the isolated system for the change in motion in both the $x$- and $y$-directions. With the vane stationary the magnitude of the exit velocity $v'$ equals that of the entering velocity $v$ with fluid friction neglected. The changes in the velocity components are, then,

$$\Delta v_x = v' \cos \theta - v = -v(1 - \cos \theta) \qquad \text{and} \qquad \Delta v_y = v' \sin \theta - 0 = v \sin \theta.$$

The mass rate of flow is $m' = \rho A v$, and substitution into Eq. 62 gives

$[\Sigma F_x = m' \Delta v_x] \quad -F = \rho A v[-v(1 - \cos \theta)], \qquad F = \rho A v^2 (1 - \cos \theta), \quad Ans.$

$[\Sigma F_y = m' \Delta v_y] \quad R = \rho A v[v \sin \theta], \qquad R = \rho A v^2 \sin \theta. \qquad Ans.$

*Part (b).* In the case of the moving vane the final velocity of the fluid upon exit is the vector sum of the velocity $u$ of the vane plus the velocity of the fluid relative to the vane. This combination is shown in the velocity diagram to the right of the figure for the exit conditions. The relative velocity is that which would be measured by an observer moving with the vane. This observer would measure $v - u$ feet of fluid passing over the vane per second, and the direction of this relative velocity is tangent to the vane at exit. The combination of these two velocity components gives the final absolute fluid velocity $v'$ as shown. The $x$-component of $v'$ is the sum of the components of its two parts, so $v_x' = (v - u) \cos \theta + u$. The change in $x$-velocity of the stream is

$$\Delta v_x = (v - u) \cos \theta + (u - v) = -(v - u)(1 - \cos \theta).$$

The $y$-component of $v'$ is $(v - u) \sin \theta$, so that the change in the $y$-velocity of the stream is $\Delta v_y = (v - u) \sin \theta$.

The mass rate of flow $m'$ is the mass undergoing momentum change per unit of time. This rate is the mass flowing over the vane per unit time and *not* the rate of issuance from the nozzle. Thus

$$m' = \rho A(v - u).$$

The impulse-momentum principle applied to the positive coordinate direction gives

$[\Sigma F_x = m' \, \Delta v_x] \qquad -F = \rho A(v - u)[-(v - u)(1 - \cos \theta)],$

$$F = \rho A(v - u)^2(1 - \cos \theta), \qquad\qquad Ans.$$

$[\Sigma F_y = m' \, \Delta v_y] \qquad R = \rho A(v - u)^2 \sin \theta. \qquad\qquad Ans.$

*Part (c).* Since $R$ is normal to the velocity of the vane, it does no work. The work done by the force $F$ shown is negative, but the power developed by the force (equal and opposite to $F$) exerted by the fluid on the moving vane is

$[P = Fu] \qquad\qquad P = \rho A(v - u)^2 u(1 - \cos \theta).$

The velocity of the vane for maximum power for the one blade in the stream is specified by

$\left[\dfrac{dP}{du} = 0\right] \qquad\qquad \rho A(1 - \cos \theta)(v^2 - 4uv + 3u^2) = 0,$

$$(v - 3u)(v - u) = 0, \qquad u = \frac{v}{3}. \qquad\qquad Ans.$$

The second solution $u = v$ gives a minimum condition of zero power. An angle $\theta = 180$ deg. completely reverses the direction of the fluid and clearly produces both maximum force and maximum power for any value of $u$.

## PROBLEMS

**528.** When the air only of a sand-blasting gun is turned on, the force of the air on a flat surface normal to the stream and 6 in. from the nozzle is 2 lb. With the nozzle in the same position the force increases to 5 lb. when the sand is admitted to the stream. If sand is used at the rate of 10 lb./min., find the velocity $v$ of the particles of sand as they strike the surface.

$Ans.$   $v = 580$ ft./sec.

**529.** The tender of a locomotive traveling at the constant speed of 60 mi./hr. replenishes its supply of water by scooping it up from a trough between the rails at the rate of 6 ft.³/sec. Find the added resistance $R$ to motion due to the action of the scoop.      $Ans.$   $R = 1024$ lb.

**530.** The 180 deg. pipe return discharges salt water with a density of 64.4 lb./ft.³ into the atmosphere at a constant rate of 3 ft.³/sec. The static pressure in the water at section $A$ is 7 lb./in.² above atmospheric pressure. The flow area of the pipe at $A$ is 24 in.² and that at discharge is 11.8 in.² If each of the six flange bolts is tightened with a torque wrench so that it is under a tension of 200 lb., determine the average pressure $p$ on the gasket between the two flanges. The flange area in contact with the gasket is 10.4 in.²

$Ans.$   $p = 67.7$ lb./in.²

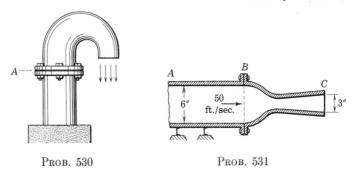

PROB. 530            PROB. 531

**531.** An air stream with a velocity of 50 ft./sec. is pumped through the stationary duct $A$ and exhausted through an experimental nozzle section. The average static pressure across the section $B$ is 150 lb./in.² gage, and the density of the air at this pressure and at the temperature prevailing is 0.820 lb./ft.³ The average static pressure across the exit section $C$ is measured to be 2 lb./in.² gage, and the corresponding air density is 0.0760 lb./ft.³ Determine the force $T$ exerted on the nozzle flange at $B$ by the bolts and the gasket to hold the nozzle in place.

**532.** In the case of multiple vanes where each vane which enters the jet is followed immediately by another, as in a turbine or water wheel, determine the maximum power $P$ which can be developed for a given blade angle and the corresponding optimum peripheral speed $u$ of the vanes in terms of the jet velocity $v$ for maximum power. Modify Sample Prob. 527 by assuming an infinite number of vanes so that the rate at which fluid leaves the nozzle equals the rate at which fluid passes over the vanes.    *Ans.*   $P = \frac{1}{4}\rho A v^3 (1 - \cos \theta),\ u = v/2$

**533.** A ball of weight $W$ is supported in a vertical jet of water with weight density $\mu$.  If the stream of water issuing from the nozzle has a diameter $d$ and velocity $u$, determine the height $h$ above the nozzle at which the ball is supported.  Assume that the jet remains intact and that there is no energy loss in the jet.

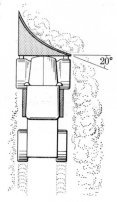

$$Ans. \quad h = \frac{1}{2g}\left(u^2 - \left[\frac{4Wg}{\pi\mu u d^2}\right]^2\right)$$

**534.** The snow plow operates on a level road at 10 mi./hr. and diverts 50 tons of snow per minute.  Determine the lateral force $R$ between the tires and the road and the tractive force $F$ required to drive the plow.  Due to compaction the snow leaves the blade with a velocity of 8 ft./sec. along and relative to the blade.

**535.** A stream of water flowing at the rate of 500 gal./min. from a 2 in. diameter nozzle is diverted by the fixed vane.  The vane is positioned so that ⅔ of the stream is diverted up and the remainder is deflected down and back as shown.  Determine the total force $F$ required to hold the vane in place. *144# upward to left*

PROB. 533

PROB. 534

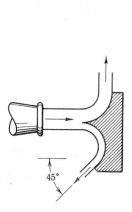

PROB. 535

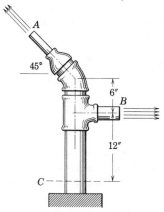

PROB. 536

**536.** Fresh water is supplied to the fixed pipe under a static pressure of 50 lb./in.² and issues from the nozzles $A$ and $B$ at velocities of 70 and 75 ft./sec., respectively.  The inside pipe diameters at $A$, $B$, and $C$ in that order are 1 in., 2 in., and 4 in.  Calculate the average tension $T$ and horizontal shear $Q$ in the pipe at section $C$.  Neglect the small weight of the pipe and water within it.

*Ans.*   $T = 682$ lb., $Q = 201$ lb.

**537.** The pipe bend shown has a cross-sectional area $A$ and is supported in its plane by the tension $T$ applied to its flanges by the adjacent connecting pipes (not shown). If the velocity of the liquid is $v$, its mass density $\rho$, and its static pressure $p$, determine $T$ and show that it is independent of the bend angle $\theta$.

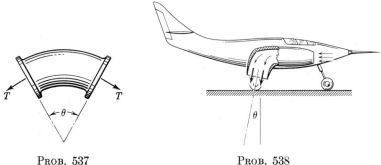

Prob. 537　　　　　　　　　　　　Prob. 538

**538.** The experimental aircraft has a total weight of 10,000 lb. and is designed for VTOL (vertical take-off and landing). Movable wing sections divert the engine jet stream downward to provide the component of vertical lift. Each of the two engines sucks in 83 lb. of air per second at a density of 0.0760 lb./ft.$^3$ and discharges the heated air with a velocity of 2000 ft./sec. The mass of fuel added to the exhaust stream is small and may be neglected. For the given conditions determine the angle $\theta$ which will initiate vertical take-off, and find the inlet area $A$ for each jet engine if the horizontal thrust on the airplane is zero.　　　　　　　　　　*Ans.*　$\theta = 14° 5'$, $A = 2.24$ ft.$^2$

**539.** A jet of fluid with velocity $v$, cross-sectional area $A$, and mass density $\rho$ impinges on a fixed slanted trough shown in section. Some of the fluid is diverted in each of the two directions. If the trough is smooth, the velocity of both diverted streams remains $v$, and the only force which can be exerted on the fluid is normal to the surface of the trough. By writing the impulse-momentum equations for the directions along and normal to the trough determine the force $F$ required to support the trough and the rate of flow $Q$ (volume per unit time) in each of the two directions.

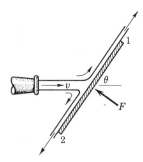

Prob. 539

*Ans.*　$F = \rho A v^2 \sin \theta$;
$$Q_1 = \frac{Q}{2} (1 + \cos \theta), \quad Q_2 = \frac{Q}{2} (1 - \cos \theta)$$

**540.** In a wind-tunnel test of a 4-bladed propeller the air approaches the test stand with a velocity of 200 mi./hr. and leaves the test stand with a velocity of 230 mi./hr. The density of the approaching air is 0.0760 lb./ft.$^3$, and the inside diameter of the tunnel is 10 ft. Compute the thrust $T$ on the propeller and the power output $P$ of the motor. Neglect rotational energy of the air, any temperature rise due to air friction, and any difference in static pressure between the approach and exit sections.

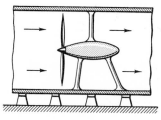

PROB. 540

**541.** The helicopter shown has a weight $W$ and hovers in midair by imparting downward momentum to a column of air defined by the slip-stream boundary shown. Find the downward velocity $v$ given to the air by the rotor at a section in the stream below the rotor where the pressure is atmospheric and the stream radius is $r$. Also find the power $P$ required by the engine. Neglect the rotational energy of the air, any temperature rise due to air friction, and any change in air density $\rho$.

$$Ans. \quad v = \frac{1}{r}\sqrt{\frac{W}{\pi\rho}}, \quad P = \frac{W}{2r}\sqrt{\frac{W}{\pi\rho}}$$

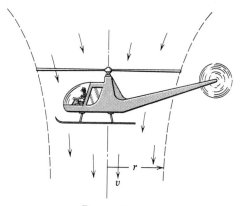

PROB. 541

\* **542.** The cross valve shown transfers water from the vertical pipe under a static pressure of 100 lb./in.² gage to the horizontal pipe at 25 lb./in.² gage. The constant flow rate through the vertical pipe is 260 gal./min. Determine the compression $C$ in the valve stem if it has a vertical lift of ⅛ in. above the closed position. The 25 lb./in.² pressure may be assumed to act over the upper exposed area of the valve. (*Hint:* Analyze a free body consisting of the valve and stem, and a section of water in the vertical pipe.)     *Ans.*   $C = 475$ lb.

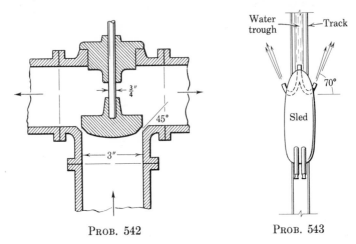

Prob. 542             Prob. 543

\* **543.** The water brake used to stop the 4000 lb. rocket sled consists of a scoop which contacts the fresh-water trough and curved ducts which return the water through an angle of 160 deg. on both sides of the sled. The cross-sectional area of the scoop and ducts is 32 in.² If the sled is coasting at 1600 ft./sec. when its scoop contacts the water, determine the time $t$ required for the sled to slow down to 40 ft./sec. Resistance to motion in addition to that offered by the water brake is given by $R = kv^2$ and is 50,000 lb. at 1600 ft./sec. Also compute the initial power $P$ absorbed by the water brake as it first contacts the water at 1600 ft./sec.    *Ans.*   $t = 3.54$ sec., $P = 6.22 \times 10^6$ h.p.

\* **544.** In the figure is shown an impulse turbine wheel for a hydroelectric

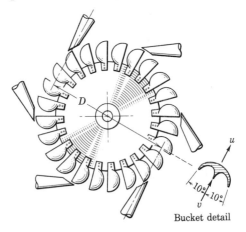

Bucket detail

Prob. 544

power plant which is to operate with a static head of water of 1000 ft. at each
of its 6 nozzles and is to rotate at the speed of 270 rev./min.  Each wheel and
generator unit is to develop an output power of 22,000 k.w.  The efficiency of
the generator may be taken to be 0.90, and an efficiency of 0.85 for the conversion of the kinetic energy of the water jets to energy delivered by the turbine
may be expected.  The mean peripheral speed of such a wheel for greatest efficiency will be about 0.47 times the jet velocity.  If each of the buckets is to
have the shape shown, determine the necessary jet diameter $d$ and wheel diameter $D$.  Assume that the water acts on the
bucket which is at the tangent point of each
jet stream

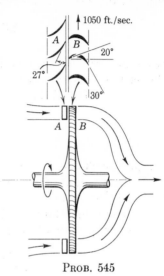

  *Ans.*   $d = 6.42$ in., $D = 8.45$ ft.
 *545.  In the figure is shown a detail of
the stationary nozzle diaphragm $A$ and the
rotating blades $B$ of a gas turbine.  The
products of combustion pass through the
fixed diaphragm blades at the 27 deg. angle
and impinge on the moving rotor blades.
The angles shown are selected so that the
velocity of the gas relative to the moving
blade at entrance is at the 20 deg. angle for
minimum turbulence, corresponding to a
mean blade velocity of 1050 ft./sec. at a
radius of 15 in.  If gas flows past the blades
at the rate of 30 lb./sec., determine the
theoretical power output $P$ of the turbine.
Neglect fluid and mechanical friction with
the resulting heat energy loss, and assume

PROB. 545

that all the gases are deflected along the surfaces of the blades with a velocity
relative to the blade of constant magnitude.          *Ans.*   $P = 1500$ h.p.

### 48. Motion with Variable Mass; Jet Propulsion.   Consider a
body, Fig. 44, which gains mass by virtue of its overtaking and swallow-
ing a stream of matter.  The mass of the body and its velocity at any

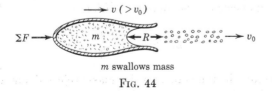

$m$ swallows mass

FIG. 44

instant are $m$ and $v$, respectively.  The stream of matter is assumed to
be moving in the same direction with a constant velocity $v_0$ less than
$v$ and moving without disturbance except after it enters $m$.  The force
exerted by $m$ on the particles of the stream to accelerate them from a

velocity $v_0$ to a greater velocity $v$ is designated by $R$ and is accompanied by an equal and opposite reaction on $m$. In addition to $R$ all other forces which are applied externally to $m$ are designated by $\Sigma F$, taken as positive in the direction of motion. The principle of motion of the mass center, Eq. 32, states that at any *instant* the resultant of all external forces on any mass system equals the mass at that instant times the acceleration of the center of mass. Thus the motion equation for $m$ at the instant represented is

$$\Sigma F - R = m\frac{dv}{dt}.$$

If the time rate of accumulation of mass in $m$ is designated by $m'$ and the relative velocity between the moving stream and $m$ is $\Delta v = v - v_0 = u$, then by Eq. 62 the force $R$ equals $m'u$. Hence

$$\Sigma F = m\frac{dv}{dt} + m'u. \tag{63}$$

Equation 63 may be considered the equation of motion of $m$, where $\Sigma F$ is the resultant of all forces on $m$ in the direction of $v$ exclusive of the force $R$ exerted on $m$ by the overtaken stream of matter.

The more important problem of a body which loses mass during motion is represented in Fig. 45. Mass within the body is ejected to

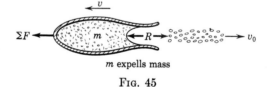

$m$ expells mass

Fig. 45

the rear with an absolute velocity $v_0$ by the force $R$ internally generated. Again, if $\Sigma F$ represents all other forces externally applied to $m$ in the direction of its velocity, the motion equation is

$$\Sigma F + R = m\frac{dv}{dt}.$$

If $m_0'$ represents the time rate at which mass is ejected, and the relative escape velocity of the ejected mass is $\Delta v = v_0 - (-v) = u$, then again by Eq. 62 the force $R$ is $m_0'u$. Hence

$$\Sigma F = m\frac{dv}{dt} - m_0'u. \tag{64}$$

Equation 64 may be considered the equation of motion of $m$, where $\Sigma F$ is the resultant of all forces on $m$ exclusive of the reaction $R$ of the ejected stream.  This reaction $R = m_0'u$ is known as the *jet reaction* or *momentum thrust* and forms the basis of jet propulsion.

Equations 63 and 64 were obtained by writing the force-mass-acceleration relation for the instantaneous motion of $m$ alone.  The equations may be obtained also by direct use of the impulse-momentum principle, Eq. 61, applied to the system composed of $m$ and a portion $m_0$ of the mass stream, as represented in Fig. 46 for the case of ejected

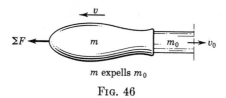

$m$ expells $m_0$

FIG. 46

mass.  In this formulation the jet reaction $R$ is a force *internal* to the system considered.  The dotted section which defines the extremity of $m_0$ is arbitrary as long as it is slightly removed from $m$ so that the velocity of the stream $m_0$ at this section is constant.  Thus the system is considered as having two parts at any instant, $m$ moving with a velocity $v$ and an arbitrary portion $m_0$ of ejected mass moving undisturbed away from $m$ with a constant velocity $v_0$.  Applying Eq. 61 to the entire system in the $v$-direction gives

$$\Sigma F = \frac{d}{dt}(mv - m_0v_0) = m\frac{dv}{dt} + v\frac{dm}{dt} - m_0\frac{dv_0}{dt} - v_0\frac{dm_0}{dt}.$$

The term $dv_0/dt$ is zero since $m_0$ moves undisturbed once free of $m$. Also the rate at which $m_0$ increases must equal the rate at which $m$ decreases, so that $dm_0/dt = -dm/dt$.  Thus

$$\Sigma F = m\frac{dv}{dt} + (v + v_0)\frac{dm}{dt}.$$

Introducing the relative velocity between $m$ and $m_0$ gives

$$\Sigma F = m\frac{dv}{dt} + u\frac{dm}{dt}. \tag{65}$$

Equations 63 and 64 are both contained in Eq. 65 as may be seen when the rate of decrease of mass $m_0' = -dm/dt$ or the rate of increase of mass $m' = dm/dt$ is substituted.

*Rocket Propulsion.* A rocket is a vehicle in which is stored all the matter to be ejected during its motion. The matter is ejected at high velocity by the expansion of gases from the combustion process, and both ingredients for combustion, fuel and oxidizer, are contained within the rocket. Figure 47 shows the free-body diagram of a rocket in vertical flight where the atmospheric resistance is $R$ and the variable weight is $W$. As shown the rocket is isolated from its exhaust stream. The jet reaction or momentum thrust $T$ becomes an external force which equals $-u\,dm/dt$ where $u$ is the velocity of the exhaust stream relative to the rocket and $m$ is the decreasing mass of the rocket. Application of $F = ma$ to the isolated rocket gives $T - (R + W) = m\,dv/dt$ which is the same as Eq. 65 since $\Sigma F$ equals $-(R + W)$ and excludes the jet reaction and since $T = -u\,dm/dt$. In addition when the exhaust pressure is greater (or less) than the pressure in the surrounding medium, a positive (or negative) thrust acting over the cross-sectional area of the exhaust stream as a result of this pressure difference will be present.

In most rockets the relative escape velocity $u$ and the mass rate of the expelled gas are essentially constant, and thus the momentum thrust will remain equally constant.

A rocket is the only known vehicle which will operate without a surrounding medium and, theoretically, is the only known means of achieving interplanetary travel.

Fɪɢ. 47

*Duct Propulsion.* A device in which the surrounding fluid, liquid or gas, is ducted through it and expelled at higher velocity by thermal or mechanical means is said to operate by duct propulsion. This system involves the motion of a vehicle which both swallows and expels mass. The forces acting on such a vehicle are shown in Fig. 48 for

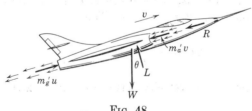

Fɪɢ. 48

the case of a *thermal-jet* airplane. If the pressures across the entering and exhaust sections are nearly atmpospheric, the net thrust $T$ is the difference between the exhaust momentum rate and the intake momentum rate. If $m_a'$ and $m_g'$ represent the mass rates of entering air and exhaust gas, respectively, and $R$ represents the resistance of the exterior surface of the airplane to motion through the surrounding atmosphere, the equation for accelerated flight is

$$m_g'u - m_a'v - R - W \sin \theta = m \frac{dv}{dt}.$$

The entering air is assumed to be at rest initially so that $v$ is its velocity relative to the airplane, and the velocity of the exhaust gas relative to the airplane is $u$.

If thermal power is used to accelerate the ducted fluid, as in the gas turbine of a turbojet engine, fuel at the mass rate $m_f'$ will be burned. The total exhaust mass rate is, then, $m_g' = m_a' + m_f'$. In most such engines, however, $m_f'$ is less than 2 per cent of $m_a'$, so that the net thrust is approximately

$$T = m_g'(u - v).$$

### SAMPLE PROBLEMS

**546.** The end of a chain of length $l$ and weight $\mu$ per unit length which is piled on a platform is lifted vertically with a constant velocity $v$ by a variable force $P$. Find $P$ as a function of the height $x$ of the end above the platform.

*Solution.* It will be assumed the chain is of the open-link type so that each link acquires its velocity $v$ abruptly from its rest condition.

The principle of impulse and momentum for a system of particles expressed by Eq. 61 will be applied to the entire chain considered as the system. The free-body diagram of the system shows the unknown force $P$, the total weight of all links $\mu l$, and the force $\mu(l - x)$ exerted by the platform on those links which are at rest upon it. The momentum of the system at any position is

$$G_x = \frac{\mu x}{g} v,$$

and the momentum equation gives

$$\left[ \Sigma F_x = \frac{dG_x}{dt} \right] \quad P + \mu(l - x) - \mu l = \frac{d}{dt} \left( \frac{\mu x}{g} v \right),$$

$$P = \mu \left( x + \frac{v^2}{g} \right). \quad Ans.$$

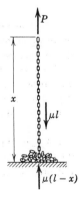

Prob. 546

The force $P$ is seen to be equal to the weight of the portion of the chain which is off the platform plus the added term which accounts for the time rate of increase of momentum of the chain.

Solution by Eq. 63 may also be made by considering the moving part $x$ of the chain as a body which gains mass. The force $\Sigma F$ is the resultant of all forces on the moving mass $\mu x/g$ of the chain except that exerted by the particles which are accumulated and is $\Sigma F = P - \mu x$. The velocity is constant so $dv/dt = 0$. The rate of adding mass is $m' = \mu v/g$. The relative velocity $u$ of the attaching particles is $v$. Thus

$$\left[\Sigma F = m\frac{dv}{dt} + m'u\right] \qquad\qquad P - \mu x = 0 + \frac{\mu v}{g}v,$$

$$P = \mu\left(x + \frac{v^2}{g}\right).$$

**547.** A jet-propelled airplane, similar to the one shown in Fig. 48, has a constant speed of 800 mi./hr. in horizontal flight. The turbojet engine consumes air through the intake scoop at the rate of 190 lb./sec. at this speed and uses fuel at the rate of 1.78 lb./sec. The gases are exhausted at a relative nozzle velocity of 2400 ft./sec. at atmospheric pressure. Determine the total drag $D$ (air resistance) on the exterior surface of the airplane and the useful power $P$ (thrust horsepower) of the engine at this speed.

*Solution.* The total thrust equals the drag for zero acceleration. Thus

$$[T = m_g'u - m_a'v] \qquad\qquad T = \frac{190 + 1.78}{32.2} \times 2400 - \frac{190}{32.2} \times 1173,$$

$$D = T = 14,300 - 6920 = 7380 \text{ lb.} \qquad\qquad Ans.$$

The useful power is

$$[P = Tv] \qquad\qquad P = \frac{7380 \times 1173}{550} = 15,750 \text{ h.p.} \qquad\qquad Ans.$$

## PROBLEMS

**548.** The rate $w'$ in pounds per second at which fuel is used in a certain rocket mounted vertically in a test stand is programed so that the momentum thrust balances the decreasing weight of the rocket for the duration of the test. If the initial total weight of rocket and fuel is $W_0$ and the exhaust velocity is $u$ regardless of the fuel rate, determine the manner in which $w'$ must vary with the time $t$ in seconds after firing. Find the expression for the total weight $W_f$ of fuel used in time $t$.

$$Ans. \quad w' = \frac{gW_0}{u}e^{-gt/u}, \quad W_f = W_0(1 - e^{-gt/u})$$

**549.** The dirt carrier dumps its load by ramming the dirt out of the rear of the truck. The ram moves at a constant rate of 2 ft./sec. relative to the carrier and provides a dumping rate of 3 yd.³/sec. The carrier and tractor, exclusive

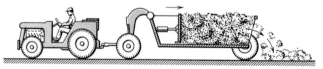

PROB. 549

of a 15 yd.³ load of dirt, have a combined weight of 60,000 lb. If the tractor moves forward from rest under a constant tractive force which exceeds all resistance to motion by 6000 lb., determine the acceleration $a$ of the tractor ($a$) as it starts from rest with the ram in motion when dumping begins and ($b$) when the last of the dirt is leaving the truck. The dirt weighs 2500 lb./yd.³

*Ans.* ($a$) $a = 1.98$ ft./sec.², ($b$) $a = 3.22$ ft./sec.²

**550.** A tank which weighs 100 lb. empty is propelled to the right by a force $F$ as shown and scoops up water from a stream flowing in the opposite direction at the velocity of 4 ft./sec. The entrance area of the scoop is 3 in.², and water

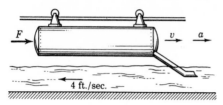

PROB. 550

enters the scoop at a rate equal to the velocity of the scoop relative to the stream. Find the weight $W$ of water in the tank at a certain instant for which $F = 25$ lb., $v = 5$ ft./sec., $a = 2$ ft./sec.² Neglect the small impact pressure at the scoop entrance necessary to elevate the water into the tank.

**551.** The 35,000 lb. missile is launched by two solid-propellant rocket boosters, one on each side of the body, which are jettisoned after burn-out. The relative exhaust velocity for each booster is 5000 ft./sec. directed as shown, and propellant is burned at the near-constant rate of 225 lb./sec. in each unit.

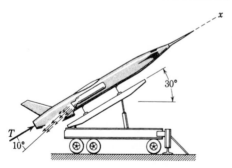

PROB. 551

Additional constant thrust $T$ of 10,000 lb. is supplied by the turbojet engine of the missile. Neglect the relatively small loss of mass during the 2 sec. burning time of the boosters, and compute the acceleration $a$ and velocity $v$ of the missile in the x-direction at the end of 2 sec. from rest. Neglect the relatively small atmospheric resistance at the start and any change in the launching angle.

*Ans.* $a = 56.4$ ft./sec.², $v = 112.8$ ft./sec.

**552.** Is it possible for the absolute velocity $v_0$ of the exhaust gases of a rocket to be in the same direction as the velocity $v$ of the rocket? Answer the same question for ducted jet propulsion.

**553.** A boat is propelled at a constant speed of 12 knots (1 knot equals 1.152 mi./hr.) by hydraulic jet propulsion. Salt water enters the intake scoops amidships as shown and is piped to the pump which exhausts it astern at the rate of 3550 gal./min. through a single pipe of 3.35 in. inside diameter. Also, the gaso-

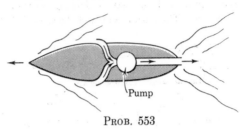

Pump

PROB. 553

line engine power plant delivers 260 h.p. to the pump. Determine the resistance $R$ to the motion of the ship through the water and find the percentage $e$ of the total output power of the engine which goes into driving the ship.

*Ans.* $R = 1711$ lb., $e = 24.3$ per cent

**554.** A small rocket of initial mass $m_0$ is fired vertically up near the surface of the earth ($g$ constant). If the air resistance is neglected, determine the manner in which the mass $m$ of the rocket must vary as a function of the time $t$ after launching in order that the rocket may have a constant vertical acceleration $a$ with a constant relative escape velocity $u$ of the gases.

**555.** The ram-jet unit shown is a thermal-jet engine in which the air is forced through the convergent section $AB$ and compressed because of the large velocity of the unit. Fuel is injected and burned at section $B$, and the expanded gases leave the nozzle $C$ with high velocity. Consider two such units, one on each tip of the two rotor blades of a helicopter which requires 100 thrust h.p. to hover at sea level. The 30 ft. diameter rotor revolves at the speed of 280 rev./min. because of the tangential thrust of the two ram jets. Determine the weight rate of air $w_a$ through each

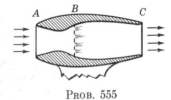

PROB. 555

jet if the relative exhaust velocity $u$ of the gases is 1450 ft./sec. at atmospheric pressure. Neglect the weight of the fuel burned. *Ans.* $w_a = 1.993$ lb./sec.

**556.** A chain of length $l$ and weight $\mu$ per unit length is held vertically above the platform scale shown and released from rest with the lower end just touching the scale. Determine the force $F$ read on the scale as a function of the distance $x$ through which the upper end has fallen. (*Comment:* The chain acquires a free-fall velocity of $\sqrt{2gx}$ since the links on the scale exert no force on those above which are still falling. Work the problem in two ways, first, by evaluating the time rate of change of momentum for the entire system and, second, by considering the force $F$ to be composed of the weight of links at rest on the scale and the force necessary to divert an equivalent stream of fluid.)

**557.** A rocket sled has an initial total mass $m_0$ including liquid rocket fuel of mass $m_f$. The rocket motors burn the fuel at a constant rate $m'$, and the exhaust velocity $u$ relative to the sled is constant. If the resistance to motion along the horizontal track is approximated by linear dependence on the velocity and is given by $R = kv$, determine the maximum velocity $v$ reached by the sled.

$$Ans. \quad v = \frac{m'u}{k}\left(1 - \left[1 - \frac{m_f}{m_0}\right]^{k/m'}\right)$$

**558.** A small rocket of initial mass $m_0$ is fired vertically up near the surface of the earth ($g$ constant), and the mass rate of exhaust $m'$ and the relative escape velocity $u$ are constant. Determine the velocity $v$ as a function of the time $t$ if the resistance of the air could be neglected and if the weight of the rocket case and machinery is negligible compared with the weight of fuel carried.

$$Ans. \quad v = u \log\left(\frac{m_0}{m_0 - m't}\right) - gt$$

PROB. 556

*** 559.** The *propulsive efficiency* $e$ for jet propulsion is defined as the ratio of the *thrust power* $Tv$ to the *propulsion power*. The propulsion power is the rate at which kinetic energy is developed by the engine and includes the thrust power and the rate at which kinetic energy is lost in the exhaust jet. Determine and plot the propulsive efficiency $e_r$ for a rocket and $e_j$ for a ducted jet in terms of the velocity ratio $\nu = v/u$. For the ducted jet neglect the fuel rate $m_f'$ compared with the total exhaust mass rate $m_g'$.

$$Ans. \quad e_r = \frac{2\nu}{1 + \nu^2}, \ e_j = \frac{2\nu}{1 + \nu}$$

*** 560.** The upper end of the loose-link chain of total length $L$ and of weight $\mu$ per unit length is released from rest at $2x = 0$. Determine the expression for the tension $T$ exerted on the chain at its supporting end $A$ in terms of $x$. Observe that the acceleration of the falling portion of the chain is $g$ and that mass is attached to the fixed portion at the rate of $(\mu/g)(dx/dt)$ with a velocity change of $2\,dx/dt$. Also determine the energy loss $\Delta E$ for the complete motion.

$$Ans. \quad T = 3\mu x, \ \Delta E = \mu L^2$$

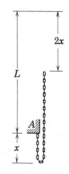

*** 561.** In the figure is shown a system used to arrest the motion of an airplane landing on a field of restricted length. The plane of weight $W$ rolling freely with a velocity $v_0$ engages a hook which pulls the ends of two heavy chains each of length $L$ and weight $\mu$ per unit length in the manner shown. A conservative calculation of the effectiveness of the device neglects the retardation of chain friction on the ground and any other resistance to the motion of the airplane. With these assumptions compute

PROB. 560

the velocity $v$ of the airplane at the instant that the last link of each chain is put in motion. Also determine the relation between displacement $x$ and the time $t$ after contact with the chain. Assume each link of the chain acquires its velocity $v$ suddenly upon contact with the moving links.

$$Ans. \quad v = \frac{v_0}{1 + (2\mu L/W)}, \quad x = \frac{W}{\mu}\left[\sqrt{1 + \frac{2v_0 t\mu}{W}} - 1\right]$$

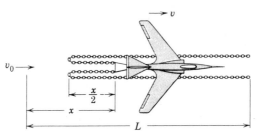

PROB. 561

**\*562.** One end of a pile of chain falls through a hole in its support as shown and pulls the remaining links after it in a steady flow. If the links which are initially at rest acquire the velocity of the chain suddenly and without frictional resistance or interference from the support or from adjacent links, find the velocity $v$ of the chain as a function of $x$ if $v = 0$ when $x = 0$. Also find the acceleration $a$ of the falling chain and the energy $\Delta E$ lost from the system as the last link leaves the platform. [*Hint:* Apply Eq. 63, and treat the product $xv$ as the variable when solving the differential equation. Also note at the appropriate step that $dx = v\,dt$.] The total length of the chain is $L$ and its weight per unit length is $\mu$.

$$Ans. \quad v = \sqrt{\frac{2gx}{3}}, \quad a = g/3, \quad \Delta E = \frac{\mu L^2}{6}$$

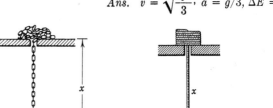

PROB. 562          PROB. 563

**\*563.** Replace the pile of chain in Prob. 562 by a coil of rope of unit weight $\mu$ and total length $L$ as shown, and determine the velocity of the falling section in terms of $x$ if it starts from rest at $x = 0$. Show that the acceleration is constant at $g/2$. The rope is considered to be perfectly flexible in bending but inextensible and constitutes a conservative system (no energy loss). Rope elements acquire their velocity in a continuous manner from zero to $v$ in a small transition section of the rope at the top of the coil. For comparison with the chain of Prob. 562 this transition section may be considered to be of negligible length without violating the requirement that there be no energy loss in the present problem. Also determine the force $R$ exerted by the platform on the coil in terms of $x$ and explain why $R$ becomes zero when $x = 2L/3$. Neglect the dimensions of the coil compared with $x$.

$$Ans. \quad v = \sqrt{gx}\,,\ R = \mu\left(L - \frac{3x}{2}\right)$$

**49. Angular Impulse and Momentum.** A particle of mass $m$ moving with velocity $v$, Fig. 49a, has a linear momentum $mv$. The *moment* of this linear-momentum vector about the point $O$ is $mvr$ and is defined as the *angular momentum* $H$ of the particle about the point.

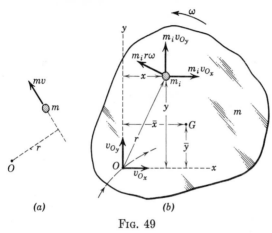

Fig. 49

The angular momentum is a vector which may be represented by the conventional right-hand rule for moments. The angular momentum of a rigid body, Fig. 49b, about an axis perpendicular to the plane of motion and passing through a point $O$ fixed in the moving body is the sum of the moments of the linear momenta of all its particles about the axis. Since the velocity of a representative particle of mass $m_i$ may be expressed in terms of the velocity components of $O$ plus the velocity of $m_i$ with respect to $O$, the linear momentum of $m_i$ will be the vector sum of the components shown in the figure. Thus the angular momentum of the particle about $O$ will be the sum of the moments of these linear momentum components about $O$. Summing up these terms for all particles gives for the total angular momentum of the body about point $O$ fixed in the body

$$H_O = \Sigma m_i r^2 \omega + \Sigma m_i v_{O_y} x - \Sigma m_i v_{O_x} y,$$

where the counterclockwise direction is arbitrarily taken as positive.

Introducing the definition of the moment of inertia about $O$ and the coordinates to the mass center gives

$$H_O = I_O\omega + \bar{x}mv_{O_y} - \bar{y}mv_{O_x}. \tag{66}$$

It should be observed that for clockwise rotation the signs of the last two terms in this equation would be reversed if $H_O$ is measured positive clockwise. Equation 66 finds its greatest use when the axis through $O$ is fixed (pure rotation), which gives

$$H_O = I_O\omega,$$

and also when the mass center $G$ is used as the reference point, in which case

$$\bar{H} = \bar{I}\omega.$$

The linear momentum of a body is the vector $G = m\bar{v}$ which has the direction of the velocity of the center of mass. Since angular momentum equals the moment of linear momentum, the position of the vector $m\bar{v}$ may be located for each of the three types of plane motion shown in Fig. 50. In the $a$-part of the figure for translation the mo-

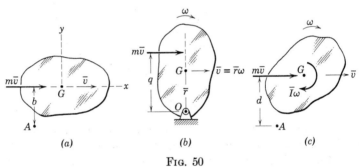

Fig. 50

mentum vector $m\bar{v}$ passes through $G$. This condition is easily seen since the resultant moment of the linear momenta of all particles about $G$ is

$$\Sigma m_i \bar{v}y = \bar{v}\Sigma m_i y = \bar{v}m\bar{y} = 0,$$

where $m_i$ is the mass of a representative particle. It follows that the angular momentum of a translating body about an axis through a moving or fixed point such as $A$ is $H_A = m\bar{v}b$.

For rotation about a fixed axis at $O$ in Fig. 50$b$ the moment of the linear momentum equals the angular momentum, so that

$$m\bar{v}q = I_O\omega, \quad \text{and} \quad q = \frac{I_O\omega}{m\bar{v}} = \frac{k_O^2}{\bar{r}}.$$

Thus the linear-momentum vector passes through the center of percussion relative to $O$. If the body rotates about a fixed axis through $G$, the linear momentum is zero, and the angular momentum is $\bar{I}\omega$, a free vector normal to the plane of rotation with all the properties of a couple. In this event the angular momentum is the same about all parallel axes, fixed or moving.

In the case of general plane motion, Fig. 50c, if the angular momentum of the body about the mass center $G$ is represented by $\bar{I}\omega$, which has the properties of a couple or free vector, the linear momentum $m\bar{v}$ must pass through $G$. The angular momentum of the body about some other axis, fixed or moving, through a point $A$ is $H_A = m\bar{v}d + \bar{I}\omega$. It may be noted that $m\bar{v}$ and $\bar{I}\omega$ may be replaced by a single vector $m\bar{v}$ with a different but parallel line of action if desired. This combination is identical to that for a force and a couple.

The relation between the angular momentum of a body and the applied moments is obtained from the rotational equation of motion. For rotation about the fixed axis through $O$, Fig. 50b, the sum of the moments of all forces about $O$ is $\Sigma M_O = I_O\alpha = I_O(d\omega/dt)$. Since the moment of inertia $I_O$ of the rigid body is constant, the motion equation may be written

$$\Sigma M_O = \frac{d}{dt}(I_O\omega). \tag{67}$$

In precisely the same manner the moment equation about the mass center for the case of any plane motion may be written

$$\Sigma\bar{M} = \frac{d}{dt}(\bar{I}\omega). \tag{68}$$

In words Eqs. 67 and 68 state that the resultant moment about the fixed axis of pure rotation or about an axis through the mass center in any plane motion equals the time rate of change of angular momentum about the respective axis.

Equations 67 and 68 hold during the entire time of motion, and each may be integrated to give

$$\int_0^t \Sigma M_O \, dt = I_O\omega - I_O\omega_0 \tag{69}$$

for rotation about the fixed axis through $O$ and

$$\int_0^t \Sigma\bar{M} \, dt = \bar{I}\omega - \bar{I}\omega_0 \tag{70}$$

for a reference axis through the mass center in plane motion. In each case the angular velocity changes from $\omega_0$ at time $t = 0$ to $\omega$ at time $t$. These equations state that the *total angular impulse equals the corresponding net change in angular momentum.*

The angular impulse-momentum equations are analogous to the linear impulse-momentum equations developed in Art. 46. Comparison shows that the dimensions of angular impulse and angular momentum are [moment] × [time], (lb. ft. sec.), whereas those for linear impulse and linear momentum are [force] × [time], (lb. sec.). Thus these quantities *cannot be added.*

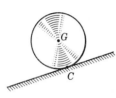

FIG. 51

The rolling wheel, Fig. 51, is an important special case of plane motion which deserves separate comment. It was shown in Art. 37 of Chapter 4 that the equation $\Sigma M_C = I_C \alpha$ holds with respect to the instant center $C$ of zero velocity at all times during the motion provided the wheel does not slip and provided the geometric center of the wheel is also the mass center. This motion equation may be written

$$\Sigma M_C = \frac{d}{dt}(I_C \omega)$$

or integrated to give

$$\int_0^t \Sigma M_C \, dt = I_C \omega - I_C \omega_0.$$

Integration is permitted since the same differential relation holds throughout rolling under the conditions stated. In this case the moment axis is not attached to the wheel but moves with it and always coincides with the instantaneous center $C$. The advantage of this equation for a rolling wheel is that the contact forces at $C$ are eliminated from the equation. Considerable caution is warranted, however, since the expression must *not* be used except for a symmetrical wheel which does not slip.

Equations 67 and 68 were developed for rigid body motion, but it is important to recognize more general applicability to any system of particles of constant mass. In Fig. 52 let $m_i$ be the mass of a representative particle of any system, and consider the components of its motion in the $x$–$y$ plane. From the principle of linear impulse and momentum the resultant force on $m_i$ in the

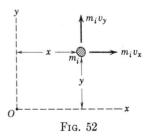

FIG. 52

$x$-direction and that in the $y$-direction are

$$F_x + f_x = \frac{d}{dt}(m_i v_x), \qquad F_y + f_y = \frac{d}{dt}(m_i v_y),$$

where $F_x$ and $F_y$ stand for forces applied from sources external to the system and $f_x$ and $f_y$ represent forces applied from sources internal to the system. The resultant moment in a counterclockwise sense about a fixed point $O$ is

$$M_i = (F_y + f_y)x - (F_x + f_x)y = x\frac{d}{dt}(m_i v_y) - y\frac{d}{dt}(m_i v_x).$$

Differentiation will show that this expression is the same as

$$M_i = \frac{d}{dt}(xm_i v_y) - \frac{d}{dt}(ym_i v_x),$$

or

$$M_i = \frac{d}{dt}(xm_i v_y - ym_i v_x) = \frac{dH_i}{dt}.$$

Thus the resultant moment $M_i$ about $O$ of all forces on $m_i$ equals the time rate of change of angular momentum about $O$. By adding all such equations written for every particle of the system there results

$$\Sigma M_i = \Sigma \frac{dH_i}{dt} = \frac{d}{dt}\Sigma H_i.$$

The contribution to $\Sigma M_i$ by the internal forces is zero since they occur in pairs of equal and opposite forces and their moments cancel. If the resultant moment of external forces about $O$ is denoted by $\Sigma M_O$ and the sum $\Sigma H_i$ of the angular momenta of all particles about $O$ by $H_O$, the impulse-momentum equation becomes

$$\Sigma M_O = \frac{dH_O}{dt}. \tag{71}$$

Similar analyses in the two other coordinate planes will disclose similar equations, and thus Eq. 71 may be considered the vector combination of these three relations. Consequently, it may be stated that the resultant vector moment about any fixed *point* for a system of particles of constant total mass equals the time rate of change of angular momentum of the system about an axis through the point parallel with the vector moment axis. Although the proof will not be given here, Eq. 71 also holds with respect to a moving axis through the center of mass of any such system.

The relation expressed by Eq. 71 applied either to a fixed point $O$ or to the mass center $G$ constitutes one of the most general of the derived relations of mechanics. It permits the writing of moment equations of motion where the angular momentum may be changing in direction as well as in magnitude. The case of change in direction of the angular momentum is dealt with briefly in Art. 52 on gyroscopic motion.

Equation 71 may also be applied to problems involving the steady flow of fluids where angular-momentum changes are involved. Figure

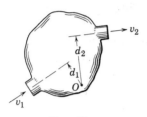

Fig. 53

53 represents a fixed body which supports a steady fluid flow at the mass rate $m'$ with inlet and outlet velocities of $v_1$ and $v_2$, respectively. In a manner analogous to that used in Art. 47 to obtain Eq. 62 the moment equation about some fixed point $O$ may be written directly from Eq. 71 as

$$\Sigma M_O = m'(v_2 d_2 - v_1 d_1). \qquad (72)$$

The terms $m'v_2 d_2$ and $m'v_1 d_1$ represent, respectively, the final and initial angular momentum rates about $O$, and their difference represents the corresponding rate at which angular momentum is changing about $O$. The moment sum $\Sigma M_O$ is the sum of the moments in the direction of the angular-momentum change of all forces acting on the system isolated and includes the moments of such forces as static-pressure forces acting across the inlet and outlet sections, forces acting on the cut sections of pipe, the weight of the body and fluid within it, and so forth.

### SAMPLE PROBLEMS

**564.** The force $P$ which is applied to the cable wrapped around the central hub of the symmetrical wheel is increased slowly according to $P = 1.50t$, where $P$ is in pounds and $t$ is in seconds. Determine the angular velocity $\omega$ of the wheel 10 sec. after $P$ is applied if the wheel is rolling to the left with a linear velocity of its center of 3 ft./sec. at time $t = 0$. The wheel weighs 120 lb. with a centroidal radius of gyration of 10 in. and rolls without slipping.

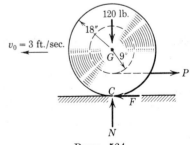

Prob. 564

*Solution I.* The free-body diagram of the wheel is shown. The correct direction of the friction force is established by the necessity for a positive clockwise moment of forces about $G$ to produce the resulting clockwise angular acceleration. Direct application of the angular impulse-momentum equation with respect to the mass center, Eq. 70, gives

$$\left[ \int_0^t \Sigma \overline{M} \, dt = \Delta(\overline{I}\omega) \right]$$

$$\int_0^{10} \left( \frac{18}{12} F - \frac{9}{12} \times 1.50t \right) dt = \frac{120}{32.2} \left( \frac{10}{12} \right)^2 \left[ \omega - \left( -\frac{3}{\frac{18}{12}} \right) \right],$$

where the positive direction is taken as clockwise. The force $F$ is a variable and so must be left under the integral sign. The second equation needed to eliminate $F$ is that of linear impulse and momentum which applies to the motion of the center of mass of any system. Thus

$$\left[ \int_0^t \Sigma F \, dt = \Delta(m\bar{v}) \right] \qquad \int_0^{10} (1.50t - F) \, dt = \frac{120}{32.2} \left[ \frac{18}{12} \omega - (-3) \right].$$

The integral involving $F$ is easily eliminated between the two equations, and the result is

$$\omega = 3.13 \text{ rad./sec. clockwise.} \qquad \qquad Ans.$$

*Solution II.* Since the wheel is symmetrical, an axis moving with the instant center $C$ may be used. The necessity of a simultaneous solution is eliminated since $F$ does not appear in the equation. Hence

$$\left[ \int_0^t \Sigma M_C \, dt = \Delta(I_C \omega) \right]$$

$$\int_0^{10} \frac{9}{12} \times 1.50t \, dt = \frac{120}{32.2} \left[ \left( \frac{10}{12} \right)^2 + \left( \frac{18}{12} \right)^2 \right] \left[ \omega - \left( -\frac{3}{\frac{18}{12}} \right) \right],$$

which gives $\omega = 3.13$ rad./sec.

Solution by use of the instant center is not permitted if any slipping occurs or if the geometric center and center of gravity do not coincide.

**565.** Determine the velocity $v$ of the 10 lb. weight 4 sec. after it is released from rest. The drum weighs 32.2 lb. with a radius of gyration of 8 in. and has negligible friction in its bearing at $O$.

*Solution.* The drum and the weight may be isolated separately with the angular impulse-momentum equation applied to the drum and the linear impulse-momentum equation applied to the weight. The tension $T$ in the cable may be eliminated and the resulting expression solved for $v$. A simpler

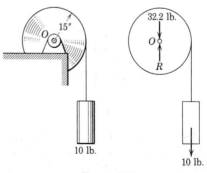

PROB. 565

method involves the application of Eq. 71 in integral form to a fixed axis for both parts considered a single system. The fixed axis will be taken at $O$ to eliminate the 32.2 lb. weight and the bearing reaction $R$ from the equation. From the free-body diagram of the entire system the resultant moment about $O$ of all external forces is that due to the weight only. Also the angular momentum of the weight about $O$ is the moment of its linear momentum. Thus

$$[\Sigma M_O t = \Delta H_O] \qquad 10 \times \frac{15}{12} \times 4 = \frac{32.2}{32.2} \left(\frac{8}{12}\right)^2 \frac{v}{\frac{15}{12}} + \left(\frac{10}{32.2} v\right) \times \frac{15}{12},$$

$$v = 67.2 \text{ ft./sec.} \qquad\qquad\qquad Ans.$$

## PROBLEMS

**566.** The rotor of a steam turbine weighs 80 lb. with a radius of gyration of 12 in. and requires 6 min. to come to rest from a speed of 10,000 rev./min. after the steam is shut off. Determine the average value of the resisting moment $M_f$ due to internal friction.

$Ans.$ $M_f = 7.23$ lb. ft.

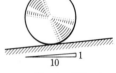

**567.** The center of the homogeneous solid cylinder is given an initial velocity of 2 ft./sec. up the incline. Determine the time $t$ required for it to reach a velocity of 4 ft./sec. down the incline if it rolls without slipping. $Ans.$ $t = 2.81$ sec.

PROB. 567

**568.** A 3 oz. bullet is traveling at a speed of 2000 ft./sec. in the plane of rotation of the uniform 10 lb. bar. If the bar is swinging and the bullet strikes it when in the vertical position, determine the angular velocity $\omega$ of the bar just before collision so that the angular momentum of the system about $O$ is zero at this instant. $Ans.$ $\omega = 31.3$ rad./sec.

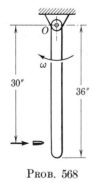

PROB. 568

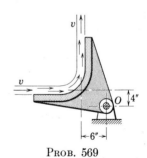

PROB. 569

**569.** Determine the torque $M$ which must be applied to the deflector at $O$ in order to support the 90 deg. diversion of an open stream of fresh water flowing in a horizontal plane with a velocity $v$ of 100 ft./sec. and at the rate of 4 lb./sec. $Ans.$ $M = 2.07$ lb. ft.

**570.** Determine the time $t$ required for the center of the homogeneous cylinder to reach a velocity of 6 ft./sec. when released from rest on the incline. The coefficient of friction is 0.40, and a sufficient length of cord is wrapped around the cylinder.

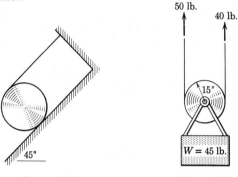

PROB. 570          PROB. 571

**571.** The pulley weighs 30 lb., has a radius of gyration of 10 in., and carries the 45 lb. load $W$. Constant tensions of 50 lb. and 40 lb. are applied to the vertical hoisting cables as shown. If the velocity $v$ of $W$ is 6 ft./sec. down and the angular velocity $\omega$ of the pulley is 8 rad./sec. counterclockwise at time $t = 0$, determine $v$ and $\omega$ after the cable tensions have been applied for 4 sec. Note the independence of the results.

*Ans.* $v = 19.8$ ft./sec. up, $\omega = 69.3$ rad./sec. clockwise

**572.** Find the torque $M$ required to prevent the lawn sprinkler from rotating if the total flow rate is 18 gal./min. Each nozzle is inclined 10 deg. above the horizontal and has an opening $\frac{1}{4}$ in. in diameter.

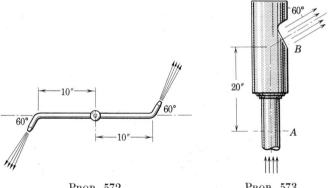

PROB. 572          PROB. 573

**573.** Saturated steam enters the steam whistle through pipe $A$ at the rate of 8 lb./sec. at a pressure of 200 lb./in.$^2$ gage and leaves the whistle at $B$ at atmospheric pressure. The specific volume of the steam at $A$ is 2.10 ft.$^3$/lb.

and at the exit $B$ is 26.3 ft.$^3$/lb.  The flow area in the pipe at $A$ is 6 in.$^2$ and at the exit $B$ is 10 in.$^2$ measured in a plane normal to the flow.  Determine the bending moment $M$ and shear $Q$ in the pipe at $A$.

**574.** Each identical bevel gear and attached shaft has a moment of inertia about its own axis of 0.200 lb. ft. sec.$^2$ and rotates in fixed bearings at a speed of 1000 rev./min. while in mesh.  Determine the magnitude of the total angular momentum $H$ of the system.        *Ans.*   $H = 10.84$ lb. ft. sec.

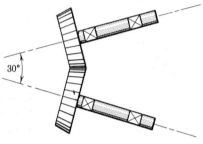

PROB. 574

**575.** The frictional moment $M_f$ acting on a rotating turbine disk and its shaft is given by $M_f = k\omega^2$ where $\omega$ is the angular velocity of the turbine.  If the source of power is shut off while the turbine is running at an angular velocity $\omega$, determine the time $t$ required for the speed of the turbine to drop to half of its initial value.  The moment of inertia of the turbine disk and shaft is $I$.

**576.** In the centrifugal-pump impeller shown water flows to the straight radial vanes in an axial direction and leaves the vanes with a velocity $v$ whose tangential component is the rim speed of the impeller.  If the pump handles 2000 gal./min. at a speed of 840 rev./min., what is the theoretical torque $M$ on the impeller shaft required to impart the angular momentum to the water?  If the actual power required to run the pump is 30 h.p., what is the efficiency $e$ of the pump?        *Ans.*   $M = 132.0$ lb. ft., $e = 70.4$ per cent

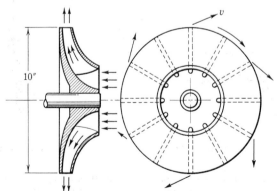

PROB. 576

**577.** An irregular bar is suspended by a long cord and receives the impact of a bullet at a distance $b$ above the center of mass $G$ of the bar. Find the coordinate $x$ to the instant center $C$ about which the bar begins to rotate during the impact. The centroidal radius of gyration of the bar is $\bar{k}$. *Ans.* $x = \bar{k}^2/b$

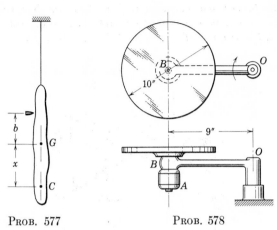

PROB. 577          PROB. 578

**578.** In the rotating assembly shown the arm $OB$ and attached motor frame $A$ together weigh 10 lb. and have a radius of gyration about $O$ of 7 in. The disk and attached motor armature together weigh 15 lb. and are mounted in bearings with negligible friction. A constant torque of 0.3 lb. ft. is applied to the shaft at $O$ initially at rest, and, as the arm $OB$ rotates, the disk moves with curvilinear translation with the motor $A$ turned off. Determine the angular velocity $\omega$ of $OB$ when the torque on the shaft at $O$ has been applied for 10 sec.

*Ans.* $\omega = 8.16$ rad./sec.

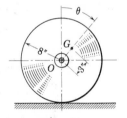

PROB. 579

**579.** The unbalanced wheel rolls to the right without slipping with a constant velocity of 4 ft./sec. of its center $O$. The wheel weighs 20 lb. with center of gravity at $G$ and has a radius of gyration about $O$ of 6 in. Determine the angular momentum $H_O$ of the wheel about $O$ at the instant ($a$) when $G$ passes directly over $O$ with $\theta = 0$ and ($b$) when $G$ passes the horizontal line through $O$ where $\theta = 90$ deg. *Ans.* ($a$) $H_O = 1.553$ lb. ft. sec., ($b$) $H_O = 0.932$ lb. ft. sec.

**580.** In the gear and rack unit of Prob. 325 the gear weighs 10 lb. with a radius of gyration of 4 in. Each rack weighs 12 lb., and there is negligible friction in the unit. Determine the constant torque $M$ applied to the gear for $\frac{3}{4}$ sec. which is required to reverse the motion of each rack from a velocity of 4 ft./sec. in one direction to a velocity of 4 ft./sec. in the opposite direction.

**581.** The header tank $A$ is supported entirely by the fixed pipe $B$. The valve $C$ is initially closed with the pipes and tank full of fresh water. When the valve is turned on, water flows through the system and is exhausted at $D$.

The flow area through the inlet pipe at section $E$ is 9 in.², and the static pressure across this section is 30 lb./in.² above atmospheric pressure. The water issues from the outlet pipe $D$ with a velocity of 21.1 ft./sec. through an exit area of 3 in.² For section $E$ calculate the increments in torsion $T$ about the axis of the pipe $B$, the bending moment $M$ about the $x$-axis, the vertical shear $Q$, and the tension $F$ in pipe $B$ which are due to turning on the water.

    *Ans.*    $\Delta Q = 18.0$ lb., $\Delta F = 276$ lb., $\Delta T = 270$ lb. in., $\Delta M = 108$ lb. in.

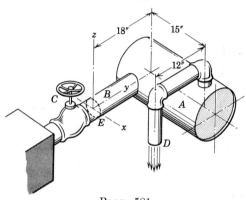

Prob. 581

**582.** The two gears shown rotate about their mass centers with negligible friction. Gear $A$ acquires a speed of 50 rad./sec. clockwise from rest under the action of a torque $M$. If the centroidal moments of inertia of $A$ and $B$ are 0.10 and 0.05 lb. ft. sec.², respectively, find the total angular momentum $H$ of the system. Is it permissible to equate $H$ to $\int M\,dt$?

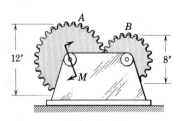

Prob. 582

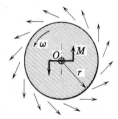

Prob. 583

\* **583.** The rotating circular disk disintegrates by throwing off particles from its rim in a uniform manner around the rim. At the instant considered the remaining part of the disk has a radius $r$, a moment of inertia $I_O$ about its center of rotation $O$, an angular velocity $\omega$, and is subjected to an applied torque $M$ as shown. If $I_O$ is treated as a function of time ($r$ changes with time), show that $M \neq \dfrac{d}{dt}(I_O\omega)$.

* **584.** Each of the circular disks has a weight $W$ and a negligible thickness parallel to the axis of the shaft. The disks are mounted in bearings on the shaft and roll without slipping in a circle of radius $R$ as the shaft is turned about a vertical axis through the center of the assembly by a moment $M$. If the angular velocity of the unit about the vertical is $\omega$, write an expression for the angular

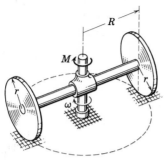

PROB. 584

momentum $H_D$ of the two disks about the vertical central axis. If $t$ sec. are required to establish this motion from rest under a constant moment $M$, would $Mt$ equal the total angular momentum of the disks and the shaft unit about the vertical axis?  Explain.

$$Ans. \quad H_D = \frac{2W\omega}{g}\left(R^2 + \frac{r^2}{4}\right)$$

* **585.** The centrifugal pump handles water at the rate of 4000 gal./min. The inside diameter of both the inlet and discharge pipes at $A$ and $B$ is 4 in. The tension in each of the connecting pipes at sections $A$ and $B$ balances the force on the pump due to pressure in the water. The pump shaft turns clockwise at 2000 rev./min., and the driving motor supplies 50 h.p. With the

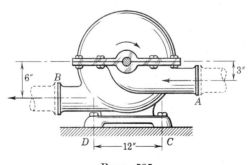

PROB. 585

pump filled but at rest the total force exerted on each of the mountings $C$ and $D$ is 60 lb. vertically up. Neglect any vertical restraint on the pump by the long connecting pipes and calculate the total vertical forces which act on the mountings while pumping.　　　　*Ans.*　$C = 250$ lb. down, $D = 370$ lb. up

*586. The two equal bevel gears and attached shafts are mounted in their bearings $A$, $B$, $C$, and $D$ with negligible friction. Each unit has a moment of inertia $I$ about its own axis. A moment $M$ applied to one shaft as shown will produce an angular acceleration $\alpha = M/(2I)$ for each gear and a corresponding angular velocity $\omega = Mt/(2I)$ in time $t$ from rest. After determining the bearing reactions at $C$ and $D$, isolate the two units together as a single system and show that $\Sigma M_x t$ gives the correct expression for the change in angular momentum of the system in the $x$-direction.

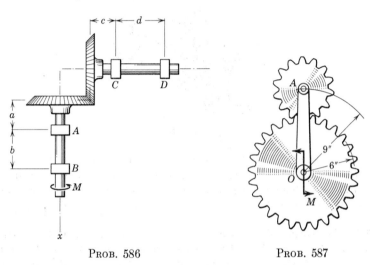

PROB. 586          PROB. 587

*587. The small gear is made to rotate in a horizontal plane about the large stationary gear by means of the torque $M$ applied to the arm $OA$. The small gear weighs 6 lb. and may be treated as a circular disk. The arm $OA$ weighs 4 lb. and has a radius of gyration about the fixed bearing at $O$ of 6 in. Determine the constant torque $M$ required to give the small gear an absolute angular velocity of 60 rad./sec. in 3 sec., starting from rest. Neglect friction and analyze the system consisting of the arm $OA$ and the small gear together.

*Ans.* $M = 1.256$ lb. ft.

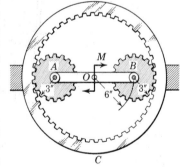

*588. The ring gear is fixed and cannot rotate. Arm $AB$, which weighs 15 lb. and may be considered a slender rod, is mounted on a shaft at $O$ and subjected to a constant torque $M$. Each of the

PROB. 588

small gears weighs 5 lb. and may be treated as a solid circular disk. The arm $AB$ is brought up to a speed of 400 rev./min. in 4 sec. from rest under the action of $M$. First, analyze one small gear to determine the tooth contact force on the ring gear. Next, isolate the entire system, and compute $M$ by the principle of angular impulse and momentum.     *Ans.*   $M = 1.627$ lb. ft.

**50. Conservation of Momentum.** The principle of linear impulse and momentum for any mass system is expressed by Eqs. 60 and states that the resultant external force in any direction on the system equals the time rate of change of the linear momentum of the system in that direction. If the resultant force in, say, the $x$-direction is zero during any interval of time, it follows that the time rate of change of the momentum in that direction is also zero. Hence

$$G_x = \Sigma mv_x = \text{constant}, \tag{73}$$

where $\Sigma mv_x$ is the sum of the linear momenta of the several parts of the system in the $x$-direction. This statement expresses the *law of conservation of linear momentum*. Thus the linear momentum in any direction for a system of bodies remains constant (is conserved) as long as there is no resultant external force on the system in that direction. This principle finds particular use in describing the interactions of bodies such as the recoil of a gun or the collision of two objects.

The principle of angular impulse and momentum about a fixed axis for any system of bodies is expressed by Eq. 71 and states that the resultant moment about a fixed axis $O$ equals the time rate of change of angular momentum of the system about that axis. If the resultant moment about any such axis is zero during an interval of time, it follows that the time rate of change of angular momentum about that axis is also zero. Hence

$$H_O = \Sigma I_O \omega = \text{constant}, \tag{74}$$

where $\Sigma I_O \omega$ is the sum of the angular momenta of all parts of the system about $O$. This statement expresses the *law of conservation of angular momentum*. Thus, when there are no externally applied moments on any system about a fixed axis, the angular momentum of each part may change, but the total angular momentum of the system about this axis remains constant (is conserved). Since Eq. 71 also applies to a moving axis through the mass center, it follows that the principle of conservation of angular momentum also holds for a moving centroidal axis.

### SAMPLE PROBLEMS

**589.** The 2 oz. bullet traveling at 2000 ft./sec. strikes the 10 lb. block centrally and is embedded within it. If the block is sliding on a smooth horizontal plane with a velocity of 40 ft./sec. in the direction shown just before impact, determine the velocity $v$ of the block and bullet and its direction $\theta$ immediately after impact.

*Solution.* Since the force of impact is internal to the system composed of the block and bullet and since there are no other external forces acting on the

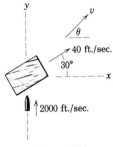

PROB. 589

system, it follows that the linear momentum of the system is conserved in both the $x$- and $y$-directions. Thus

$$[\Delta G_x = 0] \qquad 10 \times 40 \cos 30° + 0 = (10 + \tfrac{2}{16})v_x,$$

$$v_x = 34.2 \text{ ft./sec.},$$

$$[\Delta G_y = 0] \qquad 10 \times 40 \sin 30° + \tfrac{2}{16} 2000 = (10 + \tfrac{2}{16})v_y,$$

$$v_y = 44.4 \text{ ft./sec.}$$

The acceleration of gravity $g$ has been omitted since it appears in each term and cancels. The final velocity is given by

$$[v = \sqrt{v_x{}^2 + v_y{}^2}] \qquad v = \sqrt{(34.2)^2 + (44.4)^2} = 56.1 \text{ ft./sec.} \qquad Ans.$$

The direction of the final velocity is given by

$$\left[\tan \theta = \frac{v_y}{v_x}\right] \qquad \tan \theta = \frac{44.4}{34.2} = 1.30. \qquad Ans.$$

**590.** The uniform rectangular block of dimensions shown is sliding to the left on the horizontal surface with a velocity $v$ when it strikes the small step in the surface. Assume negligible rebound at the step, and compute the minimum value of $v$ which will permit the block to pivot about the edge of the step and just reach the standing position shown with no velocity. Compute the energy loss $\Delta E$ for $b = c$.

*Solution.* It will be assumed that the edge of the step $O$ acts as a latch on the corner of the block, so that the block pivots about $O$. Furthermore, the height of the step is assumed negligible compared with the dimensions of the block. During impact the only force which exerts a moment about $O$ is the weight $W$, but the angular impulse due to the weight is extremely small since the time of impact is negligible. Thus angular momentum about $O$ may be said to be conserved.

The initial angular momentum of the block about $O$ just before impact is the moment of its linear momentum and is $H_O = (W/g)v(b/2)$. The velocity of the center of mass $G$ immediately after impact is $\bar{v}$, and the angular velocity

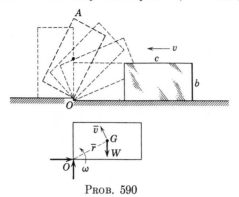

PROB. 590

is $\omega = \bar{v}/\bar{r}$. The angular momentum about $O$ just after impact when the block is starting its rotation about $O$ is

$[H_O = I_O\omega]$

$$H_O = \left[ \frac{1}{12} \frac{W}{g} (b^2 + c^2) + \frac{W}{g} \left( \left[ \frac{c}{2} \right]^2 + \left[ \frac{b}{2} \right]^2 \right) \right] \omega = \frac{W}{3g} (b^2 + c^2)\omega.$$

Conservation of angular momentum gives

$[\Delta H_O = 0]$
$$\frac{W}{3g} (b^2 + c^2)\omega = \frac{W}{g} v \frac{b}{2}, \qquad \omega = \frac{3vb}{2(b^2 + c^2)}.$$

This angular velocity will be sufficient to raise the block just past position $A$ if the kinetic energy of rotation equals the increase in potential energy. Thus

$[\Delta T + \Delta V_g = 0]$
$$\frac{1}{2} I_O\omega^2 - W \left( \sqrt{\left(\frac{b}{2}\right)^2 + \left(\frac{c}{2}\right)^2} - \frac{b}{2} \right) = 0,$$

$$\frac{1}{2} \frac{W}{3g} (b^2 + c^2) \left[ \frac{3vb}{2(b^2 + c^2)} \right]^2 - \frac{W}{2} (\sqrt{b^2 + c^2} - b) = 0$$

$$v = 2\sqrt{\frac{g}{3} \left( 1 + \frac{c^2}{b^2} \right)} \, (\sqrt{b^2 + c^2} - b). \qquad Ans.$$

The percentage loss of energy is

$$\frac{\Delta E}{E} = \frac{\frac{1}{2}mv^2 - \frac{1}{2}I_O\omega^2}{\frac{1}{2}mv^2} = 1 - \frac{k_O^2\omega^2}{v^2} = 1 - \left( \frac{b^2 + c^2}{3} \right) \left[ \frac{3b}{2(b^2 + c^2)} \right]^2$$

$$= 1 - \frac{3}{4 \left( 1 + \frac{c^2}{b^2} \right)} \cdot \quad \Delta E/E = 62.5 \text{ per cent for } b = c. \qquad Ans.$$

## PROBLEMS

**591.** The 4 oz. projectile is fired with a velocity of 2000 ft./sec. and picks up the four washers, each of which weighs 3 oz. Find the common velocity $v$ of projectile and washers following the interaction. Determine the energy loss $\Delta E$.                    *Ans.*  $v = 500$ ft./sec., $\Delta E = 11,650$ ft. lb.

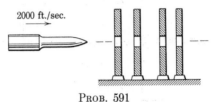

2000 ft./sec.

PROB. 591

**592.** The uniform 20 lb. circular disk $A$ is spinning freely at 400 rev./min. about the vertical shaft. Disk $B$ weighs 10 lb. with a radius of gyration of 4 in. If disk $B$ is spinning at 200 rev./min. in the opposite direction as it is allowed to drop onto disk $A$, determine the final common velocity $N$ of the two disks after slipping ceases.
                    *Ans.*  $N = 301$ rev./min.

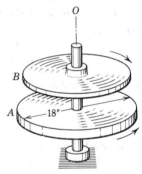

**593.** The barrel and breech of a 3 in. anti-aircraft gun weigh 1800 lb. The projectile weighs 15 lb. and has a muzzle velocity of 3000 ft./sec. The recoil of the gun is checked by a combination of springs and oil dampers so that the force $F$ of the recoil mechanism on the moving barrel is essentially constant. Determine $F$ if the recoil distance is 16 in. Neglect the weight of the gases and assume that the gun acquires its full recoil velocity before the recoil mechanism begins to act.                    *Ans.*  $F = 13,100$ lb.

PROB. 592

**594.** For a powder charge of 5 lb. in the anti-aircraft gun of Prob. 593 determine the recoil velocity of the gun as the projectile leaves the muzzle. The center of gravity of the corresponding weight of gases may be assumed to have a velocity of one half that of the shell.

**595.** The third and fourth stages of a rocket are traveling at 5000 mi./hr. when the third stage runs out of fuel and its thrust drops to zero. An instant after this occurs the fourth stage ignites, and its thrust against the third stage causes separation with no other forces of interaction between the two parts. At this condition the empty third-stage case has a mass of 4 lb. ft.$^{-1}$ sec.$^2$, and the fourth stage has a mass of 2 lb. ft.$^{-1}$ sec.$^2$ If the relative velocity of separation is 40 ft./sec. and separation occurs $\frac{1}{4}$ sec. after the fourth stage ignites, determine the velocity $v$ of the fourth stage as it leaves the third stage and the average thrust $T$ of the fourth stage during separation.
                    *Ans.*  $v = 5018$ mi./hr., $T = 213$ lb.

**596.** The horizontal rod has a moment of inertia about the vertical axis of 0.080 lb. ft. sec.$^2$, and each of the sliding balls with negligible dimensions weighs 2 lb. The assembly is rotating freely about $O$–$O$ at an angular velocity of 20 rad./sec. with the balls latched in the positions shown. If the latches are released, determine the new angular velocity of the system after the balls have come to rest against the stops. Find the loss of kinetic energy $\Delta E$.

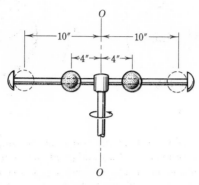

PROB. 596

**597.** A ballistic pendulum consists of a 100 lb. box of sand suspended by a wire as shown. A 2 oz. bullet traveling horizontally is embedded in the sand, and the pendulum is observed to swing through an angle $\theta = 10$ deg. Determine the initial velocity $v$ of the bullet. What percentage $e$ of the energy of the bullet is lost from the system? *Ans.* $v = 3070$ ft./sec., $e = 99.88$ per cent

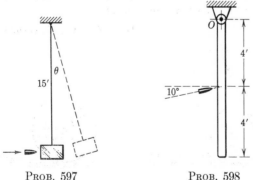

PROB. 597          PROB. 598

**598.** A 2 oz. bullet is fired with a velocity of 1000 ft./sec. in the direction shown and embeds itself into the uniform slender rod which weighs 50 lb. and is initially at rest. Determine the angle $\theta$ through which the bar swings if it is freely pivoted at $O$. *Ans.* $\theta = 10°\ 46'$

**599.** The two wheels shown are spinning freely with the angular velocities indicated. The axle of the right-hand wheel is moved to the left so that interference and slipping occur for a short period, and then the wheels are separated. Discuss the application of the principle of conservation of angular momentum to this situation. (*Hint:* Be certain to define and isolate clearly the system under consideration.)

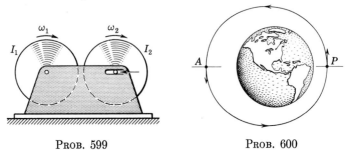

PROB. 599                              PROB. 600

**600.** An earth satellite encircles the earth in the elliptical orbit shown. (*a*) By using polar coordinates $r$, $\theta$ with origin at the center of the earth show that the equation of motion in the $\theta$-direction expresses the conservation of angular momentum for the satellite. (*b*) At the apogee $A$ (farthest point from the earth) the satellite is 1200 mi. from the earth's surface, and at the perigee (closest point to the earth) it is 200 mi. above the earth's surface. The radius of the earth is 3960 mi. Under these conditions the velocity of the satellite at $P$ is 18,170 mi./hr. What is the velocity $v$ at $A$?

**601.** A uniform pole of length $L$ is dropped at an angle $\theta$ with the vertical, and both ends have a velocity $v$ as end $A$ hits the ground. If end $A$ pivots about its contact point during the remainder of its motion, determine the velocity $v'$ with which end $B$ hits the ground.

*Ans.*  $v' = \sqrt{(9v^2/4)\sin^2\theta + 3gL\cos\theta}$

PROB. 601                              PROB. 602

**602.** A uniform circular disk which rolls without slipping with a velocity $v$ encounters an abrupt change in the direction of its motion as it rolls onto the incline $\theta$. Determine the new velocity $v'$ of the center of the disk as it starts up the incline, and find the fraction $n$ of the initial energy which is lost due to contact with the incline.

**603.** Determine the minimum velocity $v$ which the wheel may have and just roll over the obstruction. The centroidal radius of gyration of the wheel is $k$, and it is assumed that the wheel does not slip.

$$Ans. \quad v = \frac{r}{k^2 + r^2 - rh}\sqrt{2gh(k^2 + r^2)}$$

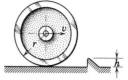

* **604.** A turntable of radius $r$ is initially at rest but is free to rotate about its central vertical axis about which its moment of inertia is $I$. A man of weight $W$ starts from rest at point $A$ marked on the rim and walks around the rim until he meets point $A$ again. Through what angle $\theta$ has the disk turned during this interval?

PROB. 603

$$Ans. \quad \theta = \frac{2\pi}{1 + (Ig/Wr^2)}$$

* **605.** The circular disk shown with Prob. 578 is coupled to the shaft and armature of the electric motor $A$, and together this unit weighs 15 lb. with a radius of gyration of 4 in. about the vertical axis of the motor. The motor frame at $A$ is rigidly attached to the arm $OB$ which is perfectly free to rotate about a vertical shaft through $O$. The arm and motor frame together weigh 10 lb. and have a radius of gyration about $O$ of 7 in. If the motor is turned on when the entire unit is at rest, determine the angular velocity $\omega$ of the arm $OB$ when the motor reaches a speed of 1500 rev./min. *relative* to the arm $OB$.

$$Ans. \quad \omega = 185 \text{ rev./min.}$$

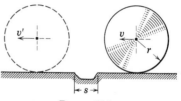

* **606.** A uniform circular disk is rolling freely to the left with a velocity $v$ when it encounters a depression of span $s$. Compute the new velocity $v'$ of the wheel after rolling over the depression. Assume that the wheel does not slip

PROB. 606

at either edge of the depression and that it contacts the edges only and without rebound.

$$Ans. \quad v' = \sqrt{v^2\left(1 - \frac{s^2}{3r^2}\right)^2 - \frac{4}{9}\frac{gs^2}{r}\left(1 - \sqrt{1 - \frac{s^2}{4r^2}}\right)\left(2 - \frac{s^2}{3r^2}\right)}$$

**51. Impact.** The collision between two bodies where relatively large contact forces exist during a very short interval of time is called *impact*. Experimental verification of impact theory is difficult by reason of the extremely short time during which the contact forces act. With the advent of modern instrumentation, however, reliable data for the description of impact phenomena have become available.

As an introduction to impact consider the collinear motion of two spheres of masses $m_1$ and $m_2$, Fig. 54a, traveling with velocities $v_1$ and $v_2$. If $v_2$ is greater than $v_1$, collision occurs, and a short period of deformation takes place, Fig. 54b, until the contact area between the spheres ceases to increase. After this deformation a period of restoration takes place, and the spheres regain their original shape if the blow is not too severe or else retain a deformed shape if the impact is more severe. The spheres then continue to move with final velocities $v_1'$ and $v_2'$ as in Fig. 54c. Inasmuch as the contact forces are equal and opposite, the linear momentum of the system remains unchanged. Thus the law of conservation of momentum applies, and

$$m_1v_1 + m_2v_2 = m_1v_1' + m_2v_2'.$$

All velocities are arbitrarily assumed positive to the right so that a negative sign will describe a velocity to the left.

In addition to the conservation of momentum, the energy of the colliding masses must be accounted for. The initial kinetic energy of

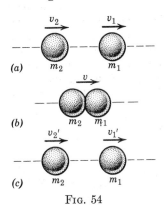

(a)

(b)

(c)

FIG. 54

the system before impact is divided into three parts after impact. First, some of the energy is retained in the form of kinetic energy on account of the rebound velocities of the spheres as a whole. Second, some of the initial energy is lost as a result of the generation of heat if the spheres are permanently deformed and by the generation of sound waves. Third, the impact forces cause internal vibrations of the spheres, and the resulting propagation and rebound of elastic waves within the spheres consume some of the initial energy. This third part of the total energy is usually difficult to account for and is by no means negligible in many impact problems involving bodies whose shapes are other than spherical.

The classical theory of impact as presented in most treatments on mechanics neglects the internal energy of vibration. With this neglect and for the case of perfectly elastic impact the final kinetic energy must equal the initial kinetic energy. Thus

$$\tfrac{1}{2}m_1v_1^2 + \tfrac{1}{2}m_2v_2^2 = \tfrac{1}{2}m_1v_1'^2 + \tfrac{1}{2}m_2v_2'^2,$$

or

$$m_1(v_1 + v_1')(v_1 - v_1') = m_2(v_2 + v_2')(v_2' - v_2).$$

The equation for the conservation of momentum may be written

$$m_1(v_1 - v_1') = m_2(v_2' - v_2).$$

Dividing the energy equation by the momentum equation gives

$$v_1 + v_1' = v_2 + v_2' \qquad \text{or} \qquad v_2 - v_1 = v_1' - v_2',$$

which shows that the relative velocity of approach equals the relative velocity of separation if the energy is conserved.

In most impact problems a rather large percentage of the energy of the system is lost, and the equation for the velocity difference is written

$$e(v_2 - v_1) = (v_1' - v_2').$$

The factor $e$, which may vary between zero and unity, is known as the *coefficient of restitution* and equals the ratio of the relative velocity of separation to the relative velocity of approach. If the impact occurs obliquely, only the components of the velocities in the direction of the force of impact should be used with the coefficient of restitution. In the classical theory of impact a coefficient of restitution of unity means *elastic impact* with no energy loss, and a coefficient of restitution of zero means an *inelastic* or *plastic impact,* where the bodies cling together after collision and the energy loss is a maximum.

Experimental determination of coefficients of restitution for spheres of various materials indicates that $e$ varies greatly with the impact velocity but approaches unity when this velocity approaches zero. This condition is explained on the basis that the energy loss due to permanent deformation becomes less as the impact velocity decreases. Experiment also has shown that for given materials and for a given impact velocity the coefficient of restitution changes appreciably with the size and shape of the colliding bodies. This effect is due largely to the corresponding change in induced internal energy of vibration. A handbook value for a coefficient of restitution is generally unreliable * unless conditions identical to those under which the measurement was made are known to exist.

### SAMPLE PROBLEMS

**607.** Two smooth steel spheres moving with the initial velocities shown collide with the line joining their centers in the direction of the velocity $v_2$. From previous experiments it is known that the coefficient of restitution for these conditions is 0.70. Determine the final velocity $v$ of each sphere and the percentage loss of kinetic energy.

PROB. 607

* Most of the values for coefficients of restitution reported in handbooks and in books on mechanics are taken directly from the early experiments by Eaton Hodgkinson in 1834 and P. G. Tait in 1890.

*Solution.* The equal and opposite force of contact on each sphere is along the $x$-direction so that the linear momentum of the system is conserved in that direction. Also, since there is no force on either sphere in the $y$-direction, there is no change in the $y$-component of either velocity. Thus

$$[\Delta G_x = 0]_{\text{system}} \qquad 2 \times 10 \times 0.866 - 4 \times 5 = 4v_2' - 2v_1' \cos \theta,$$

$$[\Delta v_y = 0]_{\text{each sphere}} \qquad v_1' \sin \theta = 10 \times 0.5, \qquad v_{2_y}' = 0.$$

The coefficient of restitution is the ratio of relative separation velocity to relative approach velocity both measured in the direction of the impact force. Therefore

$$\left[ e = \left| \frac{\Delta v_x'}{\Delta v_x} \right| \right] \qquad\qquad 0.70 = \frac{v_2' + v_1' \cos \theta}{5 + 10 \times 0.866}.$$

The simultaneous solution of these three equations gives

$$v_1' = 8.46 \text{ ft./sec.}, \qquad \theta = 36° \, 14', \qquad v_2' = 2.74 \text{ ft./sec.} \qquad Ans.$$

The initial kinetic energy of the system is

$$\frac{1}{2} \frac{2}{32.2} (10)^2 + \frac{1}{2} \frac{4}{32.2} 5^2 = 4.66 \text{ ft. lb.}$$

The final kinetic energy is

$$\frac{1}{2} \frac{2}{32.2} (8.46)^2 + \frac{1}{2} \frac{4}{32.2} (2.74)^2 = 2.69 \text{ ft. lb.}$$

The percentage loss is

$$\frac{4.66 - 2.69}{4.66} 100 = 42.3 \text{ per cent.} \qquad Ans.$$

## PROBLEMS

**608.** A steel ball is dropped from rest from a height $h$ above a horizontal steel plate of large weight and rebounds to a height $h'$. Determine the coefficient of restitution $e$.

$$Ans. \quad e = \sqrt{\frac{h'}{h}}$$

**609.** Cars $A$ and $B$ of equal weight collide at right angles at the intersection of two icy roads. The cars become entangled and move off together in the direction indicated by $v'$, their common velocity after impact. If car $A$ was traveling 30 mi./hr. at the instant of impact, determine the velocity $v_B$ of car $B$ just before impact.   *Ans.* $v_B = 52.0$ mi./hr.

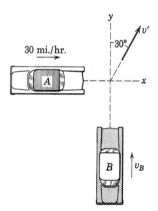

PROB. 609

**610.** Show that the moving billiard ball $A$ transfers all of its kinetic energy to the identical ball $B$ initially at rest. Assume direct central impact without permanent deformation or contact friction and neglect internal vibrational energy.

**611.** Describe the conditions under which elastic impact occurs with a coefficient of restitution of less than unity. Consider all energies involved.

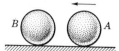

**612.** In selecting the ram of a pile driver for a certain job it is desired that the ram will give up all of its

PROB. 610

kinetic energy at each blow. Hence the velocity of the ram is zero immediately after impact. The piles to be driven weigh 800 lb. each, and experience has shown that a coefficient of restitution of 0.3 can be expected. What should be the weight $W$ of the ram? Compute the velocity $v$ of the pile immediately after impact if the ram is dropped from a height of 10 ft. onto the pile. Also compute the energy loss $\Delta E$ due to impact at each blow.

*Ans.* $W = 240$ lb., $v = 7.61$ ft./sec., $\Delta E = 1680$ ft. lb.

**613.** Two steel balls each weighing 4 lb. and connected 3 ft. apart by a light rod are dropped from rest in the position shown. The right-hand ball strikes a horizontal steel plate of considerable mass and suffers a rebound for which the coefficient of restitution is 0.60. Determine the angular velocity $\omega$ of the bar $(a)$ at the instant of maximum deformation of the right-hand ball and $(b)$ an instant after impact.

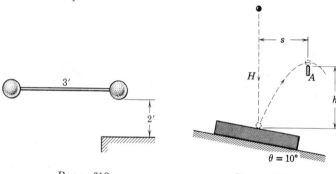

PROB. 613          PROB. 614

**614.** To pass inspection steel balls for ball bearings must clear the fixed bar $A$ at the top of their rebound when dropped from rest through a vertical distance of $H = 36$ in. onto the heavy inclined steel plate. If balls which have a coefficient of restitution of less than 0.7 with the rebound plate are to be rejected, locate the position of the bar by specifying $h$ and $s$. Neglect any friction during impact. *Ans.* $h = 1.262$ ft., $s = 1.131$ ft.

**615.** A pile driver consists of a 1200 lb. weight which falls freely through a height of 5 ft. above the top of a 300 lb. pile. Upon impact the weight is seen to move with the pile with no appreciable rebound, and the pile penetrates 15 in. into the ground at each blow. Determine the average resistance $R$ to penetration of the pile.

**616.** In a low-velocity impact study a steel ball weighing 0.055 lb. is dropped from rest through a vertical distance of 6 ft. onto a 0.610 lb. steel cylinder supported by a light rod which acts as a cantilever beam. A maximum deflection of 0.250 in. from the position of static equilibrium is observed for the cylinder as a result of the impact.   If a static calibration of the beam shows that an elastic deflection of 0.500 in. is produced by hanging a 12 lb. weight on the end of the beam, calculate the height $h$ of rebound of the ball and the coefficient of restitution $e$ which applies to these conditions.

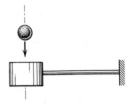

PROB. 616

*Ans.* $h = 14.56$ in., $e = 0.581$

**617.** If the billard ball $B$ is to be sent to the pocket $C$ by striking it with the cue ball $A$, determine the angle $\beta$ for the rebound of the cue ball.   Each ball is an identical $2\ \frac{1}{16}$ in. diameter ivory sphere for which the coefficient of restitution may be taken to be 0.9.       *Ans.* $\beta = 43° 48'$

**\*618.** Show that the loss of energy due to direct central impact of two masses $m_1$ and $m_2$ having velocities $v_1$ and $v_2$ directed toward each other is given by

$$\Delta E = \frac{1 - e^2}{2}\ \frac{m_1 m_2}{m_1 + m_2}(v_1 + v_2)^2,$$

where $e$ is the coefficient of restitution for these particular impact conditions and the internal vibrational energy is neglected. (*Hint:* The energy loss depends on the relative impact velocity $v_1 + v_2$. Thus the center of gravity of the system may be taken at rest to simplify the algebra so that $m_1 v_1 = m_2 v_2$.)

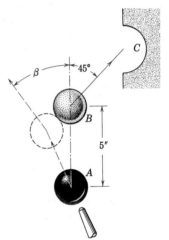

PROB. 617

**52. Gyroscopic Motion.**   One of the most interesting of all problems in dynamics is that of the gyroscope, which involves the rotation of a body about an axis which itself is rotating.   This problem is three dimensional and may be described by the general principle of angular impulse and momentum for a rigid body with respect to a fixed point as given by Eq. 71.

Consider the rotor in Fig. 55 which is pivoted at its point $O$ with negligible friction and which has an angular velocity of spin $\omega$ about its own axis.   The motion of this rotor under the action of its weight $W$ and the pivot reaction will be described.   The total angular momentum of the rotor about the fixed point $O$ may be represented by its three vector components in the orthogonal $x$–$y$–$z$ directions.   The

$z$-component is $H_z = I\omega$, where $I$ is the moment of inertia of the rotor about the $z$-axis and the vector stems from $O$. The component $H_y = I_y(d\alpha/dt)$ is due to rotation of the rotor axis about the $y$-axis at the instant represented, and likewise the component $H_x = I_x(d\theta/dt)$ is due to rotation about the $x$-axis. The resultant angular momentum about $O$ is the vector sum of these three components. The resultant moment about $O$ is $M_O = W\bar{r}\sin\alpha$ and is in the $y$-direction. Equation 71 requires that this moment be equal in magnitude and direction to the *time rate of change of the total angular-momentum vector.* Evaluation of this time rate of change where all three components of $H_O$ are accounted for is necessary for a complete description of the motion.

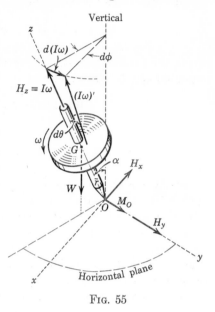

Fig. 55

The engineering aspects of the problem can be adequately explained by examining only the case where $H_z = I\omega$ is very large compared with $H_y$ and $H_x$. This condition occurs for a large rate of spin $\omega$.* Thus only the one component of angular momentum will be considered. With this simplification Eq. 71 may be written as

$$M_O dt = dH_O = d(I\omega),$$

where the moment about $O$ is $M_O = W\bar{r}\sin\alpha$. This relation states that the change in angular momentum is equal in magnitude and direction to the applied angular impulse. This impulse has the direction of $M_O$, which, vectorially, is along the $y$-axis, and hence $d(I\omega)$ has the same direction. Thus the change in angular momentum is at right angles to the momentum or spin axis. Adding this change to $I\omega$ gives the new angular momentum $(I\omega)'$ after time $dt$. The mo-

* If the rotor of Fig. 56a were a circular disk with a radius of 4 in. and a distance from $O$ of $\bar{r} = 8$ in., the angular momentum about the $x$-axis would be approximately 3 per cent of that about the $z$-axis for a spin velocity of 3000 rev./min. For a spin velocity of 9000 rev./min. the percentage would be only about 0.4 per cent.

mentum or spin axis of the rotor has moved through the angle $d\theta$ which is given by

$$d\theta = \frac{d(I\omega)}{I\omega}.$$

Combination with the preceding equation gives

$$M_O \, dt = I\omega \, d\theta \quad \text{or} \quad M_O = I\frac{d\theta}{dt}\omega.$$

From the figure it is seen that $d\theta = d\phi \sin \alpha$, and thus the resulting equation may be written also as

$$W\bar{r} \sin \alpha = I\left(\frac{d\phi}{dt} \sin \alpha\right)\omega,$$

or

$$W\bar{r} = I\frac{d\phi}{dt}\omega,$$

where $d\phi/dt$ is the rate of *precession* of the rotor axis about the vertical. This relation shows that for a given rotor and given spin velocity the rate of precession about the vertical is the same for all values of $\alpha$.

The reason that the rotor axis in Fig. 55 revolves about the vertical at a constant angle $\alpha$ instead of falling toward the $x$–$y$ plane lies in the fact that the precession described is the only motion which will make the vector change in angular momentum have the same direction as the applied moment and angular impulse. If the rotor had no spin velocity, it would indeed fall. Actually as the spin velocity decreases because of friction, the rotor axis will drop toward the horizontal plane in a rather complex manner which requires the retention of the momentum components $H_x$ and $H_y$ for description. In understanding the gyroscopic effect it is helpful to note that precession of the axis of spin occurs when a moment is applied whose vector is at *right angles* to the angular-momentum vector. In the problem of plane motion, on the other hand, the moment- and angular-momentum vectors are *parallel*.

In most engineering applications of gyroscopes the moment, spin, and precession axes are mutually perpendicular. This situation is illustrated in Fig. 56a where the axis of the rotor of the previous figure is now horizontal. The momentum equation becomes

$$M = I\Omega\omega, \tag{75}$$

where $\Omega$ is the rate of precession $d\phi/dt$ about the vertical and $M$ is the moment $W\bar{r}$ of the weight about $O$. The moment vector $M$ in Eq. 75 is normal to both the spin axis $\omega$ and the precession axis $\Omega$ and represents the moment in this direction about the pivot $O$ due to *all* forces acting *on* the gyro rotor. For the rotor illustrated Eq. 75 is not exact since it accounts for only the predominant momentum change in the direction of $M$. The error is exceedingly small, however, for the relatively high spin velocities normally used as indicated in the preceding footnote.

Equation 75 and the corresponding relationship between the senses of the three vectors $M$, $\Omega$, and $\omega$ will now be determined directly for the case illustrated in Fig. 56*a* as further aid to correct interpretation of the gyroscopic equation. Equation 71 requires that the angular

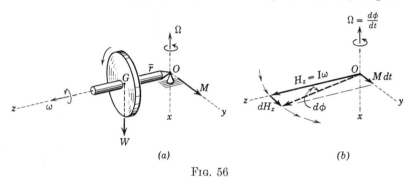

(a)                   (b)

Fɪɢ. 56

impulse $M\,dt$ during time $dt$ about the $y$-axis through the fixed point $O$ must equal the change $dH_z$ in angular momentum both in magnitude and direction. These vectors are shown in Fig. 56*b*, and it is seen that during the time $dt$ the momentum or spin axis has swung through the angle $d\phi$ in order that $dH_z$ equal $M\,dt$. It follows, then, that $M\,dt = dH_z = I\omega\,d\phi$, and division by $dt$ yields $M = I\Omega\omega$.

It should be carefully noted that the direction of the precession is determined by the fact that the vector change $dH_z$ in angular momentum has the same sense as the applied moment $M$, and hence the spin axis will always rotate *toward* the moment axis. The three vectors $M$, $\Omega$, and $\omega$ constitute a right-handed set of axes. Thus in rotating from the $M$-axis to the $\Omega$-axis through the 90-deg. angle, advancement for a right-hand screw is along the $\omega$-axis. Likewise a right-hand screw would advance in the $M$-direction when rotated from the $\Omega$-axis to the $\omega$-axis or would advance in the $\Omega$-direction when rotated from the $\omega$-axis to the $M$-axis. Use of this right-hand rule requires memory of the sequence $M$-$\Omega$-$\omega$ of these vectors. This sequence can be established quickly by recognizing, basically, that the momentum axis rotates toward the moment axis since the vector change in the spin momentum must have the same sense as the applied moment.

In the event an additional moment about $O$ is applied to the rotor a corresponding additional precession will occur which obeys the rules just cited. Thus, if a force $F$ were applied to the rotating end of the rotor shaft, Fig. 57, in the positive $y$-direction, the corresponding moment vector would be in the negative $x$-direction. The momentum or

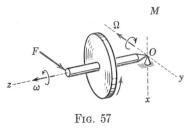

spin axis $\omega$ would have a vector change in the direction of the moment axis $M$ which is vertically up, and the spin axis would rise. Conversely, if a force were applied to the end of the rotor shaft in the direction to oppose the precession (negative $y$-direction), the spin axis would fall.

Fᴵɢ. 57

If the rotor axis of a gyro precesses in a given plane, the center of gravity of the rotor remains in that plane and can have no acceleration normal to it. It follows that the resultant of *all* forces acting *on* the rotor in a plane normal to the precession plane and containing the rotor axis cannot be a force and, if not zero, must be a couple. Thus the moment $M$ in Eq. 75 is a couple and is known as the *gyroscopic couple*. Since the value of a couple is independent of which parallel axis is chosen for evaluating its moment, a moment summation about *any* axis normal to the rotor axis and lying in the precession plane may be used for evaluating $M$. Thus for the rotor in Fig. 56a, there is no vertical acceleration of $G$ during the horizontal precession, and the upward force exerted by the pivot on the rotor at $O$ equals the weight $W$ and together with the weight constitute the gyroscopic couple $W\bar{r}$. The correct value of the couple may be obtained by taking moments about an axis parallel to the $y$-axis through $O$, $G$, or any other point.

When $\omega$ becomes small for the rotor of Fig. 56a, the axis begins to droop, and Eq. 75 is no longer a good approximation. On the other hand, if the rotor axis is confined to rotate in the horizontal plane about the vertical by some type of restraining guides, there can be no angular momentum about the $y$-axis at all, and the only change in angular momentum in the $y$-direction comes from the directional change in $H_z = I\omega$ as expressed by Eq. 75. Therefore Eq. 75 is *exact* whenever the axis of a symmetrical rotor is confined to precess exclusively in one plane. If the end of the rotor axis in Fig. 57 were constrained by smooth guides (not shown) to move only in the horizontal $y$-$z$ plane, then the force $F$ would cause accelerated rotation of the shaft about the $x$-axis given by $Fl = I_x\alpha$ where $l$ is the moment arm to $O$, $\alpha$ is the angular acceleration of the shaft axis about the vertical, and $I_x$

is the moment of inertia of the rotor about the vertical. Accompanying this rotation there would be a downward force exerted by the
guide on the shaft whose moment $M$ about $O$ obeys Eq. 75 exactly at
any instant.

In addition to being a toy the gyroscope has important engineering
application. First it is used extensively as a directional device. With
a mounting in gimbal rings, Fig. 58, the gyroscope is free from external
moments, and its axis will retain a fixed direction irrespective of the

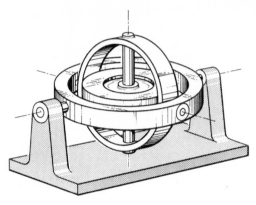

FIG. 58

rotational movement of its base. Independence from the rotational
movement of the surroundings is used as a positioning control device.
By adding a pendulous weight to the inner gimbal ring the attraction
of the earth may be used to cause precession of the gyro so that the
spin axis always points north. This action forms the basis of the gyro
compass. Gyroscopic action also forms the basis for inertial-guidance
systems. The gyroscope has found important use as a stabilizing
device. The controlled precession of a large gyro mounted in a ship
is used to produce a moment to counteract the rolling of the ship at
sea. The gyroscopic effect is an extremely important consideration
in the design of bearings for the shafts of rotors subject to forced
precession.

### SAMPLE PROBLEM

**619.** The turbine rotor in a ship's power plant weighs 2600 lb. with center
of gravity at $G$ and has a radius of gyration of 8 in. The rotor is mounted in
bearings $A$ and $B$ with its axis in the horizontal fore-and-aft direction and turns
counterclockwise at 5000 rev./min. when viewed from the stern. Determine
the vertical components of the bearing reactions at $A$ and $B$ if the ship is mak-

ing a turn to port (left) of 400 yd. radius at a speed of 22 knots (1 knot = 1.152 mi./hr.).

*Solution.* The vertical components of the bearing reactions will equal the static reactions $R_1$ and $R_2$ plus or minus the increment $\Delta R$ due to the gyroscopic effect. The moment principle easily gives $R_1 = 1560$ lb. and $R_2 = 1040$ lb. The direction of the spin velocity $\omega$ and the precessional velocity $\Omega$ are indicated with the free-body diagram. Since the spin axis tends to rotate toward the torque axis, the gyroscopic couple $M$ due to the $\Delta R$'s points to starboard, and

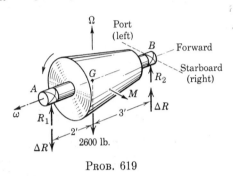

Prob. 619

thus the reaction at $B$ is $R_2 + \Delta R$ and that at $A$ is $R_1 - \Delta R$. Equation 75 is applied about the center of gravity of the rotor and gives

$$[M = I\Omega\omega] \qquad 5\Delta R = \frac{2600}{32.2}\left(\frac{8}{12}\right)^2\left(\frac{22 \times 1.152 \times 44}{400 \times 3 \times 30}\right)\left(\frac{5000 \times 2\pi}{60}\right),$$

$$\Delta R = 116 \text{ lb.}$$

The required reactions are then

$$A = 1560 - 116 = 1444 \text{ lb.,} \qquad B = 1040 + 116 = 1156 \text{ lb.} \qquad Ans.$$

The horizontal components of the bearing reactions necessary to give the rotor its centripetal acceleration in the turn may be computed, and each total bearing reaction determined if desired.

### PROBLEMS

**620.** If the bow of the ship of Sample Prob. 619 is rising as a wave passes under it, determine the direction of the gyroscopic moment exerted *by* the turbine rotor *on* the hull structure.

**621.** One type of aircraft-engine supercharger consists of the 4.10 lb. blower $A$ with a radius of gyration of 2.90 in. which is driven at 18,000 rev./min. by the 12.20 lb. exhaust turbine $B$ with a radius of gyration of 2.75 in. Determine the radial forces on the bearings $C$ and $D$ if the shaft is mounted in a vertical

position and the airplane is rolling (turning about the horizontal flight axis) at
the rate of 3 rad./sec.    *Ans.*  $|C| = |D| = 232$ lb.

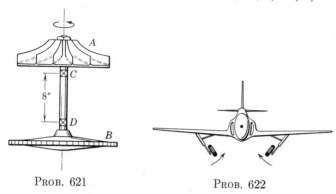

PROB. 621                    PROB. 622

**622.** An airplane has a take-off speed of 150 mi./hr. and retracts its main
landing gear in the manner shown. Each of the two 36 in. diameter wheels
weighs 74 lb. and has a radius of gyration of 12 in. If the retracting gear folds
into the wing with an angular velocity of 0.5 rad./sec., find the added bending
moment $M$ in the wheel bearing due to the gyroscopic action with the wheels
still spinning at take-off speed.

**623.** The 400 lb. rotor for a turbojet engine has a radius of gyration of 10 in.
and rotates clockwise at 15,000 rev./min. when viewed from the front of the
airplane. If the airplane is traveling at 600 mi./hr. and making a turn to the
right of 2 mi. radius, compute the gyroscopic moment $M$ which the rotor bearings must support. Does the nose of the airplane tend to rise or fall as a result
of the gyroscopic action?    *Ans.*  $M = 1130$ lb. ft., nose tends to rise

**624.** The two identical disks are rotating freely on the shaft with angular
velocities equal in magnitude and opposite in direction as shown. The shaft
in turn is caused to rotate about the vertical axis in the sense indicated. Prove
whether the shaft bends as in $A$ or as in $B$.    *Ans.*  $A$

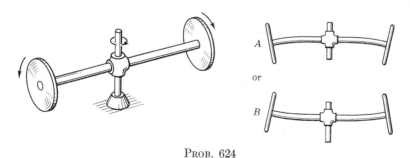

PROB. 624

**625.** The rotor axis of a gyro which is pivoted about its center of gravity
like the one shown in Fig. 58 is in the vertical position at 12:00 noon. What

angle $\alpha$ will the axis make with the vertical at 2:00 P.M. if the gyro is at a latitude of 40 deg. N and if the rotor is kept spinning at high speed with negligible friction in its gimbal bearings?        *Ans.*   $\alpha = 22° 52'$

**626.** In the figure is shown one of three gyros mounted with vertical axis and used to stabilize a large ship against rolling.   The motor $A$ turns the pinion which precesses the gyro by rotating the large precession gear $B$ and attached rotor assembly about a horizontal transverse axis in the ship.   The rotor turns inside the housing at a clockwise speed of 800 rev./min. when viewed from the

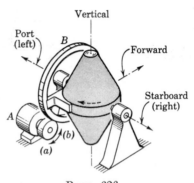

PROB. 626

top and has a weight of 100 tons with a radius of gyration of 4.85 ft.   Determine the moment exerted on the hull structure by the gyro if the motor turns the precession gear at the rate of 0.420 rad./sec.   In which of the two directions, $(a)$ or $(b)$, should the motor turn to counteract a roll of the ship to starboard?
        *Ans.*   $M = 5.14 \times 10^6$ lb. ft., $(a)$

**627.** An experimental car is equipped with a gyro stabilizer to counteract completely the tendency of the car to tip when rounding a curve (no change in normal force between tires and road).   The rotor of the gyro has a weight $w$ and a radius of gyration $k$, and is mounted in fixed bearings on a shaft which is parallel to the rear axle of the car.   The center of gravity of the car is a distance $h$ above the road, and the car is rounding an unbanked level turn at a speed $v$.   At what speed $\omega$ should the rotor turn and in what direction to counteract completely the tendency of the car to overturn for either a right or a left turn?

**\* 628.** A solid cone of weight $W$, base radius $r$, and altitude $h$ is set to spinning about its own axis with a high rate of spin $\omega$.   If the cone is released with its point supported at $O$, determine the direction of the precession and the period $\tau$ of one complete rotation about the vertical.

        *Ans.*   $\tau = \dfrac{4\pi\omega r^2}{5gh}$

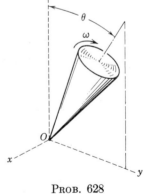

PROB. 628

*629. Derive Eq. 75 by relating the forces to the accelerations for an element of the thin ring of mass $m$. The ring has a constant angular velocity $\omega$ about the $x$-axis and is given an additional constant angular velocity $\Omega$ about the $z$-axis by the application of an external moment $M$ not shown. (*Hint:* The acceleration of the element in the $x$-direction is due to ($a$) the change in magnitude of the velocity component in this direction resulting from $\Omega$ and ($b$) the change in the direction of the $t$-component of the velocity which depends upon $\omega$.)

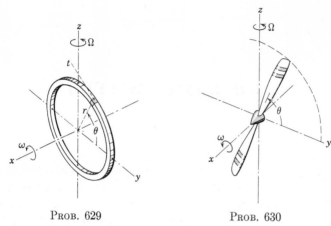

PROB. 629             PROB. 630

*630. The two-bladed airplane propeller has a constant angular velocity $\omega$ about its shaft axis $x$ and a moment of inertia $I$ about this same axis. The airplane is turning so that the propeller also has a constant angular velocity $\Omega$ about the $z$-axis. The moment $M_B = M_y \nrightarrow M_z$ acting on the propeller is supported by bending of the shaft, and the moment $M_x$ is supported by torsion of the shaft. Determine each moment as a function of $\theta = \omega t$.

*Ans.* $M_B = 2I\omega\Omega \sin \theta$ (Vector lies in the $y$–$z$ plane perpendicular to blade),
$M_x = \frac{1}{2}I\Omega^2 \sin 2\theta$

# PERIODIC MOTION

**53. Introduction.** Any motion which repeats itself after a certain time interval is said to be *periodic*. All oscillations and vibrations of bodies come under this heading and constitute one of the most important applications of dynamics. In particular the high operating speeds of machines and the requirement of structural resistance to shock and periodic loading require thorough study of the mechanics of vibrations.

Most vibrations are detrimental to the performance and life of the machine or structure, and effort is made to avoid or reduce them as much as possible. In a few instances vibrations are useful, as in the reduction of friction in delicate instruments by continued vibratory movement.

Vibrations are of two types, free and forced. A *free vibration* is one which is sustained by internal elastic forces and gravity forces such as in the vibration of an elastic beam. A *forced vibration* is one which is sustained by an external periodic force. Vibrations are also classified as to the number of possible modes of motion. The number of independent coordinates needed to specify completely the configuration of the system at any instant is known as the number of *degrees of freedom* of the system. In general, motion with more than a single degree of freedom calls for methods beyond the scope of this book, so that discussion will be confined to motion with a single degree of freedom, where only one independent coordinate is needed to specify the position of the vibrating body at any instant.

If the restoring force which acts on a vibrating body is proportional to the deflection, the vibration is said to be *linear*. If the restoring force is a nonlinear function of the deflection, the motion is said to be *nonlinear*. Only linear vibrations will be discussed in this chapter.

The dynamics of periodic motion is based on the same fundamental laws discussed and illustrated in the previous chapters. There are certain important characteristics common to the solution of vibration problems which make it convenient to discuss periodic motion in a separate chapter. The analysis of this type of motion is handled by the solution of a differential equation which will be illustrated in detail for several cases.

**54. Free Vibrations.** Consider a body of weight $W$, Fig. 59a, which is suspended by an elastic spring of negligible weight and of stiffness $k$. In the equilibrium position of the body the spring has a

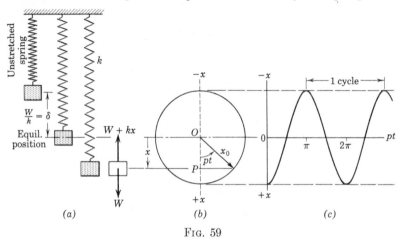

Fig. 59

static deflection $\delta = W/k$. If the body is pulled downward a distance $x_0$ from the equilibrium position and released from rest, it will vibrate in the vertical direction between the limits $x_0$ and $-x_0$. The free-body diagram of the weight at any position $x$ during its motion shows the weight $W$ and the force $k(\delta + x) = W + kx$ exerted by the spring. The equation of motion in the $x$-direction is $\Sigma F_x = ma_x$, which becomes

$$W - (W + kx) = \frac{W}{g}\frac{d^2x}{dt^2},$$

or

$$\frac{d^2x}{dt^2} + \frac{kg}{W}x = 0. \tag{76}$$

Equation 76 is the equation of motion for $W$ written as a differential equation, and its solution will give the displacement $x$ as a function of the time $t$. It should be noted that, since $x$ is taken positive down, $d^2x/dt^2$ will also be positive down. In writing the differential equation of motion it is necessary to be consistent with the arbitrary convention of sign.

The differential equation is of *second order*, so *two* integration constants will appear in its general solution. For this relatively simple physical problem it is not difficult to guess at the form of the solution and then to verify the assumption by direct substitution. The expression to be tried will be a periodic function of time

$$x = A \cos pt + B \sin pt.$$

The constants $A$ and $B$ are arbitrary, and $p$ is a constant quantity having the dimensions of angular velocity to make the argument of the sine and cosine a dimensionless angle. Substitution into the differential equation requires two differentiations. The first is

$$\frac{dx}{dt} = -Ap \sin pt + Bp \cos pt,$$

and the second is

$$\frac{d^2x}{dt^2} = -Ap^2 \cos pt - Bp^2 \sin pt.$$

Substitution into Eq. 76 and grouping terms give

$$A\left(-p^2 + \frac{kg}{W}\right) \cos pt + B\left(-p^2 + \frac{kg}{W}\right) \sin pt = 0.$$

If the assumed solution is valid, the expression just obtained must hold for *all* values of the time. The only way in which this expression can hold for all $t$ is for the coefficients of both the sine and cosine terms to vanish at all times. Since both $A$ and $B$ cannot be zero, the requirement yields

$$-p^2 + \frac{kg}{W} = 0 \quad \text{or} \quad p = \sqrt{\frac{kg}{W}}.$$

With this constant value of $p$ the assumed relation will satisfy Eq. 76 for all values of the time and, consequently, is the general solution to the differential equation.

To give a simple interpretation to the solution just obtained assume that the time $t$ is measured from the instant of release from rest at

$x = x_0$. Thus the two boundary conditions needed to evaluate the two arbitrary constants $A$ and $B$ are $dx/dt = 0$ when $t = 0$ and $x = x_0$ when $t = 0$. Substitution of the first condition into the expression for $dx/dt$ requires

$$0 = 0 + Bp, \qquad B = 0.$$

The solution is reduced to $x = A \cos pt$, and the second condition gives $A = x_0$. Hence for the boundary conditions imposed the solution is

$$x = x_0 \cos pt \quad \text{where } p = \sqrt{\frac{kg}{W}}. \tag{77}$$

The significance of this solution may be seen graphically in Figs. 59$b$ and $c$, where the variation of $x$ with $pt$ is shown. The displacement $x$ may be viewed as the projection $P$ on the $x$-axis of a vector of length $x_0$ which rotates counterclockwise with an angular velocity $p$. The motion of $W$ is that of this projection and is known as *simple harmonic motion*. Simple harmonic motion may be defined as that motion wherein the acceleration is proportional to the displacement and is directed opposite to the displacement as described by Eq. 76. The maximum displacement $x_0$ from the neutral position is known as the *amplitude* of the motion. The time for one complete cycle is the *period* $\tau$ and is the time required to change the argument of the cosine term by $2\pi$. Also the number of cycles per unit time is the *frequency* $f$ and is the reciprocal of the period. Thus

$$\tau = \frac{2\pi}{p} = 2\pi \sqrt{\frac{W}{kg}} \qquad \text{and} \qquad f = \frac{1}{\tau} = \frac{p}{2\pi} = \frac{1}{2\pi} \sqrt{\frac{kg}{W}}.$$

The angular velocity $p$ of the rotating reference vector is known as the *circular frequency*.

If this same vibration is described by counting time from the instant the body passes the origin with the velocity $v_0$, then the boundary conditions are $x = 0$ when $t = 0$ and $dx/dt = v_0$ when $t = 0$. By substitution into the expressions for $x$ and $dx/dt$ the first condition gives $A = 0$ and the second yields $B = v_0/p = x_0$ where $x_0$ is the amplitude of the vibration. Thus

$$x = x_0 \sin pt,$$

which, of course, has the same period and frequency as the cosine expression.

If time is counted from some other position, as shown in Fig. 60, the solution for this same vibration may be expressed as

$$x = x_0 \sin (pt + \phi),$$

where $\phi$ is a *phase angle*. For this condition both the constants $A$

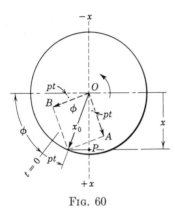

and $B$ must be retained in the general solution, and it may be seen from the figure that $x_0 = \sqrt{A^2 + B^2}$ and $\phi = \tan^{-1} (A/B)$.

Equation 76 is the basic equation which describes simple harmonic motion. This equation together with its solution and the expressions for the period and frequency are common to many types of oscillatory motion which occur in engineering. Once the governing equation of motion for a given problem has been shown to be of the form of Eq. 76, it is then known that

Fig. 60

the solution will be the same as that for Eq. 76 except for whatever change of symbols is called for.

### SAMPLE PROBLEMS

**631.** Determine the natural frequency $f$ for small vibrations of the system about the equilibrium position shown. Each spring has a constant $k$. Neglect the weight of the supporting arms compared with $W$.

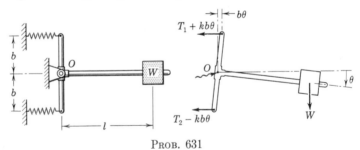

Prob. 631

*Solution.* The free-body diagram of the system is represented for a small angular displacement $\theta$ away from the equilibrium position. The tension in the top spring is its initial equilibrium value $T_1$ plus the increment $kb\theta$ due to the stretch $b\theta$. The arc length $b\theta$ is a good approximation to the actual stretch for a small angle. Likewise the tension in the bottom spring is the initial equilibrium value $T_2$ minus the increment $kb\theta$.

The motion is one of rotation about the fixed point $O$, so the equation of motion $\Sigma M_O = I_O\alpha$ must be used. This equation gives

$$Wl + (T_2 - kb\theta)b - (T_1 + kb\theta)b = \frac{W}{g} l^2 \frac{d^2\theta}{dt^2}.$$

In using the moment arm $l$ for $W$ the difference between $\cos\theta$ and unity is neglected for small angular movements. The initial tensions are found from the balance of statical moments for the equilibrium position which gives

$$Wl = (T_1 - T_2)b.$$

Substitution into the equation of motion and rearrangement of terms give

$$\frac{d^2\theta}{dt^2} + 2\frac{kg}{W}\left(\frac{b}{l}\right)^2 \theta = 0.$$

This equation is seen to be of the same mathematical form as Eq. 76, and the circular frequency of this simple harmonic motion is

$$p = \sqrt{2\frac{kg}{W}\left(\frac{b}{l}\right)^2}.$$

Thus the natural frequency for small vibrations is

$$f = \frac{p}{2\pi} = \frac{1}{\pi\sqrt{2}} \frac{b}{l} \sqrt{\frac{kg}{W}}. \qquad \textit{Ans.}$$

For large amplitudes the geometrical approximations made become invalid.

**632.** A homogeneous solid cylinder of weight $W$ and radius $r$ rolls without slipping during its oscillation on the circular surface of radius $R$. If the motion is confined to small amplitudes, determine the period $\tau$ of oscillation and the angular velocity $\omega$ of the cylinder as it crosses the vertical. The amplitude of motion is $\theta = \theta_0$.

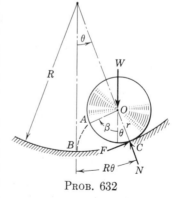

PROB. 632

*Solution.* The free-body diagram of the cylinder in a displaced position is shown. The angular displacement of the wheel is the angular displacement $\beta$ of line $OA$ which was in the vertical position for $\theta = 0$. With the clockwise direction of $\beta$ as positive the equation of motion for the symmetrical wheel about the instant center $C$ gives

$$\Sigma M_C = I_C \alpha] \qquad\qquad -Wr\sin\theta = I_C \frac{d^2\beta}{dt^2}.$$

The relation between $\beta$ and $\theta$ is obtained by equating the arc lengths $AC$ and $BC$ which gives

$$R\theta = r(\theta + \beta) \qquad \text{or} \qquad \beta = \frac{R - r}{r}\theta.$$

This substitution together with the expression $I_C = \frac{3}{2}mr^2$ and the replacement of $\sin \theta$ by $\theta$ for small movements gives

$$\frac{d^2\theta}{dt^2} + \frac{2g}{3(R - r)}\theta = 0.$$

The form of this equation is that of simple harmonic motion, and the circular frequency is

$$p = \sqrt{\frac{2g}{3(R - r)}}.$$

Thus the period for each complete small oscillation is

$$\tau = \frac{2\pi}{p} = 2\pi\sqrt{\frac{3(R - r)}{2g}}. \qquad Ans.$$

From Eq. 77 the displacement $\theta$ and the angular velocity $d\theta/dt$ may be written as

$$\theta = \theta_0 \cos pt \qquad \text{and} \qquad \frac{d\theta}{dt} = -\theta_0 p \sin pt,$$

where the time is measured from the extreme position $\theta_0$. The maximum angular velocity of the cylinder occurs at $\theta = 0$ and is, therefore,

$$\omega = \left|\frac{d\beta}{dt}\right|_{max.} = \frac{R - r}{r}\left|\frac{d\theta}{dt}\right|_{max.} = \frac{R - r}{r}\theta_0 p = \frac{\theta_0}{r}\sqrt{\frac{2g(R - r)}{3}}. \qquad Ans.$$

### PROBLEMS

Neglect the weight of all springs in the following problems.

**633.** Replace the springs in each of the two cases shown by a single spring of constant $k$ (equivalent spring constant) which will cause each weight to vibrate with its original frequency.

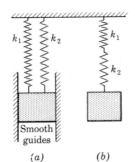

$Ans.$   $(a)$ $k = k_1 + k_2$, $(b)$ $\dfrac{1}{k} = \dfrac{1}{k_1} + \dfrac{1}{k_2}$

**634.** The weight of the elastic cantilever beam is negligible. If a force $F$ of 6 lb.

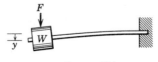

$(a)$        $(b)$

PROB. 633            PROB. 634

causes a static deflection $y = 0.04$ in., determine the necessary weight $W$ which will result in a natural frequency of vibration of 10 cycles/sec. upon sudden removal of the force.                    *Ans.*  $W = 14.67$ lb.

**635.** A certain simple pendulum has a period of 2 sec. measured on the surface of the earth. What would be the period $\tau$ of the same pendulum if the same experiment were conducted on the surface of the moon whose gravity is roughly $\frac{1}{6}$ that of the earth?                    *Ans.*  $\tau = 4.90$ sec.

**636.** A compound pendulum in the form of a slender rod of length $l$ pivoted freely about one end oscillates with a small angular displacement under the action of its own weight. Find the period $\tau$ of its motion.

**637.** The semicircular disk of radius $r$ is set into oscillation about its bearing $O$. Determine the period $\tau$ of the motion for small amplitude of vibration about $O$.

$$Ans. \quad \tau = \pi \sqrt{\frac{3\pi r}{2g}}$$

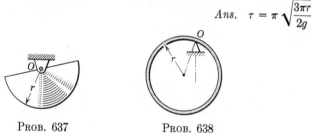

PROB. 637                    PROB. 638

**638.** The ring of radius $r$ and negligible thickness oscillates with a small amplitude about the pivot at $O$. Determine the period $\tau$ of the motion.

**639.** The 10 lb. weight together with its attached spring and base $B$ are allowed to fall as a unit through the vertical distance of $h = 4$ in. from rest with the spring undeformed. When $B$ strikes the fixed support, a latch secures it in place, and the weight is observed to drop an additional 2 in. as it stretches the spring. Find the frequency $f$ of the subsequent vibration.

$Ans.$  $f = 5.42$ cycles/sec.

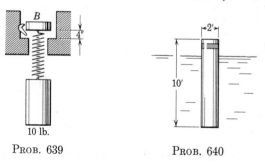

PROB. 639                    PROB. 640

**640.** The cylindrical buoy shown floats in salt water (64 lb./ft.³) and has a total weight of 1600 lb. with a low center of gravity so that it is stable in the upright position. Determine the frequency $f$ of vertical motion of the buoy when given a vertical displacement and then released. Assume that the water surface is undisturbed, and neglect frictional resistance in the water.

**641.** The plunger weighs 5 lb. and is subjected to the action of the two springs. Determine the natural frequency $f$ of the vertical vibration if friction in the guide is negligible and both springs remain in compression at all times. *Ans.* $f = 7.67$ cycles/sec.

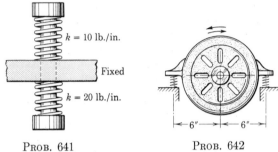

$k = 10$ lb./in.

Fixed

$k = 20$ lb./in.

Prob. 641          Prob. 642

**642.** The motor shown weighs 50 lb. and is set into small angular oscillation about its center of gravity which lies on the shaft axis. Each of the four identical spring pads (two on a side) has a modulus of 18 lb./in., and the measured frequency of oscillation is 4 cycles/sec. Determine the centroidal radius of gyration $\bar{k}$ of the motor.

**643.** The 20 lb. wheel has a centroidal radius of gyration of 4 in. and is connected to the two springs of indicated stiffness by a light steel band which does not slip on the rim of the wheel. The dimension $h$ is adjusted until the bearing $O$ supports a total force of 40 lb. in the static condition. Determine the frequency $f$ of angular oscillation of the wheel when it is given an angular displacement and then released. *Ans.* $f = 3.50$ cycles/sec.

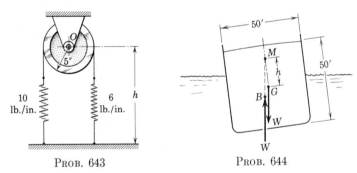

10 lb./in.     6 lb./in.     $h$

Prob. 643          Prob. 644

**644.** The center of gravity $G$ of the ship may be assumed to be at the center of the equivalent 50 ft. square section. The metacentric height $h$, determined from the intersection $M$ of the force $W$ acting through the center of buoyancy $B$ with the center line of the ship, is 3 ft. Determine the period $\tau$ of one complete roll of the ship if the amplitude is small and the resistance of the water is neglected. Neglect also the change in cross section of the ship at the bow and stern, and treat the ship as a uniform solid block of square section.

*Ans.* $\tau = 13.06$ sec.

**645.** Determine the expression for the frequency $f$ for small amplitudes of oscillation of the weight $W$ about the fixed bearing. Each spring has a stiffness $k$ and is under a compressive force $C$ when $W$ is in the vertical equilibrium position. Consider $W$ to be concentrated and neglect the mass of the other parts. Find the minimum $k$ to insure vibration.

$$Ans. \quad f = \frac{1}{2\pi}\sqrt{\frac{g}{b}\left(\frac{2ka^2}{Wb} - 1\right)}, \quad k_{min.} = \frac{Wb}{2a^2}$$

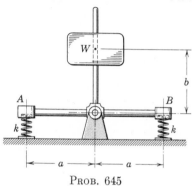

PROB. 645

**646.** Each end of the connecting rod is "weighed" as shown. The scales register 0.83 lb. for end $A$ and 1.38 lb. for end $B$. Next the rod is suspended from a knife edge in the wrist pin bearing at $O$ and a period of 0.920 sec. is measured for small free oscillations. Determine the centroidal radius of gyration $\bar{k}$ for the rod.

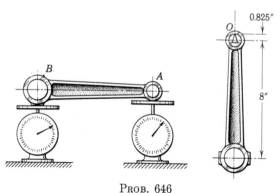

PROB. 646

\* **647.** The 1000 lb. load is supported by the spring-loaded frame in the equilibrium position shown. The weights of the members are negligible compared with the 1000 lb. load. Static application of the load to the frame results in a vertical deflection of 2 in. Determine the natural frequency $f$ for the vertical vibration of the load for small amplitudes.      *Ans.* $f = 2.21$ cycles/sec.

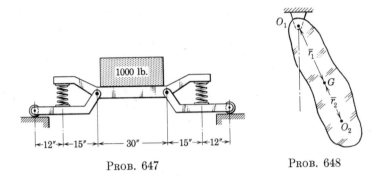

PROB. 647                                        PROB. 648

**\*648.** A compound pendulum with center of gravity at $G$ and with centroidal radius of gyration $\bar{k}$ is freely suspended, first, at $O_1$, and, second, at $O_2$. Determine the relation between $\bar{r}_1$ and $\bar{r}_2$ (other than the obvious one $\bar{r}_1 = \bar{r}_2$) which will make the period for small oscillations the same for each suspension point.                                              *Ans.* $\bar{r}_1\bar{r}_2 = \bar{k}^2$

**55. Torsional Vibrations.**   Consider a body suspended at its center of gravity by a light rod of small cross section, Fig. 61. The rod is assumed to be elastic within the range of angles through which it is twisted. In this event the resisting moment $M$ is proportional to the angle $\theta$ through which the suspended body is twisted. From elementary elasticity theory the magnitude of this moment is found to be $(JG/L)\theta$, where $J$ is the polar moment of inertia of the cross section of the rod and $G$ is the shear modulus (resistance to shear stress) of the shaft. If the body is twisted through a small angle and then released, angular oscillation will take place. For any position for which the angular displacement is $\theta$ the moment applied to the body in the direction of $\theta$ is $M = -JG\theta/L$. If the moment of inertia of the body about the centroidal axis is $I$, the equation of motion $\Sigma M = I\alpha$ applied in the arbitrary direction of positive $\theta$ gives

FIG. 61

$$-\frac{JG}{L}\theta = I\frac{d^2\theta}{dt^2} \qquad \text{or} \qquad \frac{d^2\theta}{dt^2} + \frac{JG}{IL}\theta = 0.$$

This equation is of the form of Eq. 76 and so describes simple harmonic motion with a period

$$\tau = \frac{2\pi}{p} = 2\pi \sqrt{\frac{IL}{JG}}.$$

The unknown moment of inertia of a body may be determined experimentally by measurement of the period $\tau$ for the body suspended as in Fig. 61 from a wire of known properties and by substitution into the expression for $\tau$.

Torsional vibrations are commonly encountered when two rotors are connected by a shaft as in Fig. 62. If the rotors are twisted in the opposite directions and then released, a torsional vibration will occur.

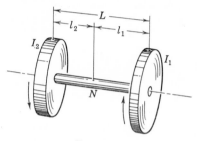

Fɪɢ. 62

The resulting motion may be analyzed by neglecting the mass of the shaft compared with that of the rotors. There will be some section $N$, known as the *nodal section*, which will have no angular motion. The periods of both rotors will be equal since the periodic twisting moment acting on one rotor is transmitted through the shaft and acts equally on the other rotor but in the opposite sense. By reason of equal periods the expression for $\tau$ gives

$$I_1 l_1 = I_2 l_2.$$

Combination with $l_1 + l_2 = L$ yields

$$l_1 = \frac{I_2}{I_1 + I_2} L \quad \text{and} \quad l_2 = \frac{I_1}{I_1 + I_2} L.$$

The natural period of vibration for either rotor now becomes

$$\tau = 2\pi \sqrt{\frac{I_1 I_2 L}{(I_1 + I_2)JG}}.$$

### PROBLEMS

**649.** The generator $A$ is driven by the motor $B$ through the 1 in. diameter shaft $C$ which is 2 ft. long. The rotor of $A$ weighs 40 lb. and has a radius of gyration of 3 in. The flywheel and rotating parts of $B$ are equivalent to a single 80 lb. rotor with a radius of gyration of 6 in. The connecting steel shaft has a shear modulus of $11.4 \times 10^6$ lb./in.$^2$ Find the speed $N$ at which the system should not be run if this speed corresponds to the natural frequency of torsional vibration.      *Ans.*   $N = 2270$ rev./min.

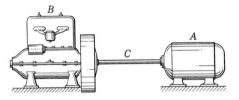

PROB. 649

**650.** The flywheel is suspended from its center by a wire from a fixed support, and a period $\tau_1$ is measured for torsional oscillation of the flywheel about the vertical axis. Two small weights each of mass $m$ are next attached to the flywheel in opposite positions at a distance $r$ from the center. This additional mass results in a slightly longer period $\tau_2$. Write an expression for the moment of inertia $I$ of the flywheel in terms of the measured quantities.     *Ans.*   $I = \dfrac{2mr^2}{(\tau_2/\tau_1)^2 - 1}$

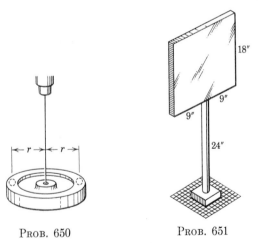

PROB. 650             PROB. 651

**651.** The homogeneous square plate weighs 38 lb. and is welded to the shaft which is a steel tube. The tube has a diameter of 1 in. and a wall thickness of

0.063 in. If the shear modulus $G$ is $11.4 \times 10^6$ lb./in.$^2$, determine the natural frequency $f$ of oscillation of the plate about the axis of the shaft.

**652.** The bar $A$ weighs 12 lb. and may be considered a uniform slender rod fastened at its end to the short shaft. The shaft is supported freely in the bearing $B$ and is fixed in a rigid support at $C$. If the shear modulus for the

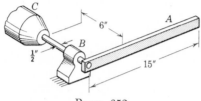

PROB. 652

shaft is $11.4 \times 10^6$ lb./in.$^2$, determine the natural frequency $f$ for small torsional vibration of the shaft when the bar is given an angular movement and then released.      *Ans.* $f = 11.26$ cycles/sec.

**653.** The motor armature of the computer mechanism shown with Prob. 341 has a moment of inertia of 0.008 lb. ft. sec.$^2$ The shaft has a torsional stiffness of 2 lb. ft. per degree of twist between its ends. If the positive clutch is engaged at the instant the power to the motor is shut off from a speed of 1800 rev./min., determine the maximum amplitude $\theta_0$ and the frequency $f$ of the resulting torsional vibration.

**654.** The flywheel $A$ weighs 80 lb. and has a radius of gyration of 10 in. The diameter of the solid steel shaft to which the flywheel is secured is stepped down from $1\frac{1}{2}$ in. to 1 in. as shown. The shaft is prevented from rotating by the taper pin through the shaft and bearing at $B$. If the wheel is given a twist about the

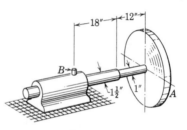

PROB. 654

axis of the shaft, determine the natural frequency $f$ of angular oscillation of the wheel. The shear modulus of the shaft is $G = 11.4 \times 10^6$ lb./in.$^2$, and the weight of the shaft may be neglected.      *Ans.* $f = 9.34$ cycles/sec.

**56. Work-Energy Solution.** The equation of motion for a body which vibrates without energy loss may be obtained by the principle of conservation of energy. For any conservative vibrating system the total energy remains constant and at any general position is partly kinetic and partly potential. The potential energy will include both potential energy of position $V_g$, if there is motion in the vertical direction, and elastic potential energy $V_e$ of the supporting members. Thus

$$T + V = \text{constant} \quad \text{and} \quad \frac{d}{dt}(T + V) = 0.$$

For the simple vibrating weight in Fig. 59a the kinetic energy at any displacement $x$ is

$$T = \frac{1}{2}\frac{W}{g}\left(\frac{dx}{dt}\right)^2.$$

If $x = 0$ is selected as the position for zero potential energy, the elastic potential energy of the spring due to the stretch $x$ is

$$V_e = \int_0^x (W + kx)\,dx = Wx + \tfrac{1}{2}kx^2,$$

and the potential energy of position is $V_g = -Wx$. Thus $V = V_e + V_g = \tfrac{1}{2}kx^2$, and the total energy is

$$\frac{1}{2}\frac{W}{g}\left(\frac{dx}{dt}\right)^2 + \frac{1}{2}kx^2 = \text{constant}.$$

Differentiation of this total constant energy with respect to the time gives

$$\frac{W}{g}\frac{dx}{dt}\frac{d^2x}{dt^2} + kx\frac{dx}{dt} = 0 \qquad \text{or} \qquad \frac{d^2x}{dt^2} + \frac{kg}{W}x = 0,$$

which is Eq. 76

Determination of the equation of motion by differentiation of the energy equation has great advantage for systems subjected to reactive forces which do no work. Attention was called to this advantage of the energy method in Art. 44 following Eq. 55. Here it was pointed out that the derivative of the energy equation established the relation between the forces and the accelerations directly without the need for dismembering the system. For elastic vibrations of a conservative mechanical system of one degree of freedom, this relation between acceleration and displacement will always have the same general form as that of the simple spring-mass system of Fig. 59 characterized by Eq. 76. The only difference is in the form of the constant coefficient of the displacement.

Work-energy consideration also leads directly to the determination of the frequency or period of an elastic vibrating system without the necessity for establishing the equation of motion. When the body reaches an extreme position, the entire energy is potential $V_{max.}$, and when the body passes the neutral or equilibrium position for which the potential energy is taken as zero, the energy is entirely kinetic $T_{max.}$. Conservation of energy requires, therefore, that

$$T_{max.} = V_{max.}.$$

This equality leads directly to the determination of the circular frequency for simple harmonic motion as may be shown for the vibrating body of Fig. 59a. Simple harmonic motion gives

$$x = x_0 \cos pt \quad \text{and} \quad \left|\frac{dx}{dt}\right|_{max.} = x_0 p.$$

Thus, for this type of motion, the maximum velocity equals the amplitude of motion multiplied by the circular frequency. The maximum kinetic energy becomes $T_{max.} = \frac{1}{2}(W/g)x_0^2 p^2$, and the maximum potential energy is $V_{max.} = \frac{1}{2}kx_0^2$. Hence

$$\frac{1}{2}\frac{W}{g}x_0^2 p^2 = \frac{1}{2}kx_0^2 \quad \text{and} \quad p = \sqrt{\frac{kg}{W}}.$$

The period and frequency are then obtained from $p$ in the usual manner.

### SAMPLE PROBLEM

**655.** Determine the equation of motion and the period of motion for the rolling cylindrical disk of Sample Prob. 632 by the energy method.

*Solution.* The kinetic energy at any position is

$$T = \frac{1}{2}I_c\omega^2 = \frac{1}{2}\left(\frac{3}{2}\frac{W}{g}r^2\right)\left(\frac{d\beta}{dt}\right)^2 = \frac{3}{4}\frac{W}{g}(R-r)^2\left(\frac{d\theta}{dt}\right)^2,$$

where the variable is changed to $\theta$ by the relation $\beta = (R-r)\theta/r$. The potential energy may be measured from the bottom position and is

$$V_g = W(R-r)(1 - \cos\theta).$$

The total energy of the system is

$$\frac{3}{4}\frac{W}{g}(R-r)^2\left(\frac{d\theta}{dt}\right)^2 + W(R-r)(1 - \cos\theta) = \text{constant},$$

and differentiation with respect to the time gives

$$\frac{3}{2}\frac{W}{g}(R-r)^2\frac{d\theta}{dt}\frac{d^2\theta}{dt^2} + W(R-r)\sin\theta\frac{d\theta}{dt} = 0.$$

Thus the equation of motion reduces to

$$\frac{d^2\theta}{dt^2} + \frac{2g}{3(R-r)}\theta = 0,$$

if motion is restricted to small angles for which $\sin\theta$ is replaced by $\theta$. This expression agrees with that obtained in Sample Prob. 632.

The circular frequency is evident from the foregoing equation but could have been obtained at the outset by assuming simple harmonic motion for which $|d\beta/dt|_{max.} = \beta_0 p$, where $\beta_0$ is the amplitude of $\beta$. The maximum kinetic energy is then

$$T_{max.} = \frac{1}{2}I_C\omega^2 = \frac{1}{2}\left(\frac{3}{2}\frac{W}{g}r^2\right)(\beta_0 p)^2 = \frac{3}{4}\frac{W}{g}(R-r)^2\theta_0{}^2p^2.$$

The maximum potential energy is

$$V_{max.} = W(R-r)(1-\cos\theta_0) \approx W(R-r)\frac{\theta_0{}^2}{2},$$

where only the first two terms in the series expansion for $\cos\theta_0$ have been used for $\theta_0$, a small angle. Equating the two energies gives

$$p = \sqrt{\frac{2g}{3(R-r)}},$$

which is the same expression as obtained previously.

## PROBLEMS

**656.** Neglect friction on the walls of the U-tube and determine the period $\tau$ of motion of the liquid if its total length in the tube is $l$.

$$Ans. \quad \tau = 2\pi\sqrt{\frac{l}{2g}}$$

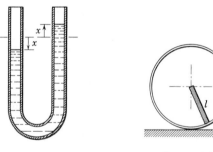

PROB. 656        PROB. 657

**657.** One end of the slender bar of length $l$ is secured to the rim of the light hoop, and the other end of the bar is at the center of the hoop. Determine the period $\tau$ for small angular oscillations about the vertical equilibrium position of the bar. The hoop rolls on the horizontal surface without slipping.

$$Ans. \quad \tau = 2\pi\sqrt{\frac{2l}{3g}}$$

**658.** Solve Prob. 647 by the work-energy approach.

**659.** The uniform slender bar of weight $W$ is supported as a bifilar pendulum. Determine the period $\tau$ for small angular oscillations about the central vertical axis $O-O$.

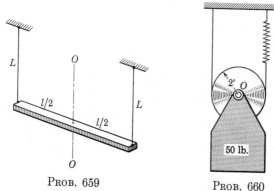

PROB. 659

PROB. 660

**660.** Determine the natural frequency $f$ of vertical vibration of the 50 lb. weight after it is released from a displaced position. The pulley weighs 30 lb. with a centroidal radius of gyration of 18 in., and the spring has a stiffness of 36 lb./ft.

*Ans.* $f = 1.10$ cycles/sec.

**661.** Solve Prob. 645 by the work-energy approach.

**662.** The two circular disks and their connecting links form a single rigid unit. The weight of the links may be neglected compared with the weight of the disks. If the upper disk rolls without slipping, determine the period $\tau$ for small oscillations of the system on the fixed horizontal rail.

$$Ans. \quad \tau = 2\pi \sqrt{\frac{l}{g}\left(3\frac{r^2}{l^2} - 2\frac{r}{l} + 1\right)}$$

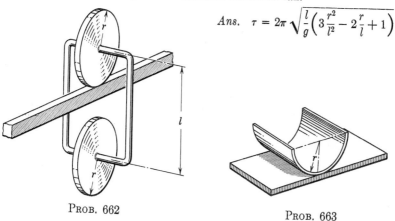

PROB. 662

PROB. 663

**663.** The semicylindrical shell with negligible but uniform wall thickness rocks with a small amplitude on a horizontal surface without slipping. Determine the period $\tau$ of the oscillation.

$$Ans. \quad \tau = 2\pi \sqrt{\frac{r}{g}(\pi - 2)}$$

**664.** The system shown is displaced from its equilibrium position and then released. Find the natural frequency $f$ of the resulting vibration if the spring is in contact with the central rack at all times. Each gear weighs 15 lb. with a radius of gyration of 4 in., the central rack weighs 12 lb., and the spring constant is 6 lb./in.

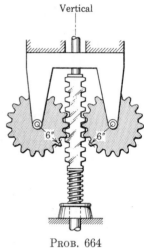

*Vertical*

> *Ans.* $f = 1.520$ cycles/sec.

**57. Damped Free Vibrations.** Frictional retardation or damping is present to some degree in all vibrating systems, and the amplitude of any free vibration will diminish steadily with time. There are three sources of damping forces: *fluid damping*, which is caused by the frictional resistance offered by the surrounding fluid to motion; *Coulomb damping*, which is caused by kinetic friction force $F = fN$ between sliding dry surfaces; and *solid damping*, which is due to internal friction or

Prob. 664

*hysteresis* in the body which undergoes periodic change of shape. In the case of fluid damping moderate velocity through the fluid results in a frictional retardation

$$F_x = -c\frac{dx}{dt},$$

which is proportional to the first power of the velocity and which is in the direction opposite to the velocity. This type of damping is known as *viscous damping*, and the damping constant $c$ depends on the viscous properties of the fluid.

The free vibrations of a simple spring-mass system, Fig. 63, may be retarded with viscous damping by attaching the weight to the plunger of a dashpot. The equation of motion is applied to the free-body diagram and gives

$$W - (W + kx) - c\frac{dx}{dt} = \frac{W}{g}\frac{d^2x}{dt^2},$$

which becomes

$$\frac{d^2x}{dt^2} + \frac{cg}{W}\frac{dx}{dt} + \frac{kg}{W}x = 0. \qquad (78)$$

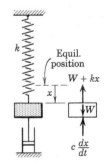

*Equil. position*

$W + kx$

$W$

$c\dfrac{dx}{dt}$

The solution of Eq. 78 will involve a factor which diminishes with time, an oscillatory term for the

Fig. 63

vibration, and two integration constants. Assume, therefore, a solution of the form

$$x = x_0 e^{-bt} \cos (pt - \phi). \tag{79}$$

By direct substitution it may be verified that this expression satisfies Eq. 78 for all values of the time where

$$b = \frac{cg}{2W} \quad \text{and} \quad p = \sqrt{\frac{kg}{W} - \left(\frac{cg}{2W}\right)^2}$$

and provided $kg/W > (cg/2W)^2$. Equation 79 is plotted in Fig. 64.

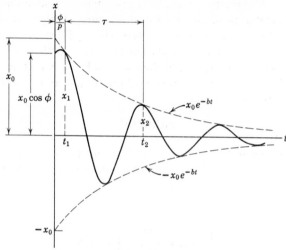

FIG. 64

The vibration has a period of

$$\tau = \frac{2\pi}{p} = \frac{2\pi}{\sqrt{\dfrac{kg}{W} - \left(\dfrac{cg}{2W}\right)^2}},$$

which is greater than that with no damping. The motion is limited between the two curves $x = x_0 e^{-bt}$ and $x = -x_0 e^{-bt}$.

The damping constant $c$ may be determined from an experimental record of the vibration, as represented in Fig. 64, by the measurement of two successive ordinates at times $t_1$ and $t_2 = t_1 + \tau$. These ordinates are $x_1 = x_0 e^{-bt_1}$ and $x_2 = x_0 e^{-b(t_1+\tau)}$, and their ratio is

$$\frac{x_1}{x_2} = \frac{x_0 e^{-bt_1}}{x_0 e^{-b(t_1+\tau)}} = e^{b\tau}.$$

This expression may be written

$$b\tau = \log \frac{x_1}{x_2},$$

and $b\tau$ is known as the *logarithmic decrement*. Measurements of $x_1$, $x_2$, and $\tau$ enable the calculation of $b$ and hence $c$ to be made.

If $(cg/2W)^2 > kg/W$, the solution given by Eq. 79 does not hold. The correct solution for this case is

$$x = A_1 e^{-(b+K)t} + A_2 e^{-(b-K)t},$$

where $K = \sqrt{(cg/2W)^2 - (kg/W)}$. This motion is nonvibratory since both exponential terms are positive and represents the case of damping so severe that the body never crosses the equilibrium position when released from an initial displacement. If $(cg/2W)^2 = kg/W$, the motion is said to be critically damped, and this condition represents the transition between a damped vibration and an overdamped nonvibratory motion.

### PROBLEM

\* **665.** Investigate the case of Coulomb damping for the block shown, where the coefficient of kinetic friction is $f$ and each spring has a stiffness $k$. The

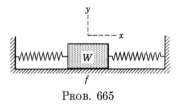

PROB. 665

block is displaced a distance $x_0$ from the neutral position and released. Determine the differential equation of motion and solve. Plot the resulting vibration and indicate the rate of decay of amplitude with time.

$$Ans. \quad x = \left(x_0 - \frac{fW}{2k}\right) \cos \sqrt{\frac{2kg}{W}} \, t + \frac{fW}{2k} \; ; \text{ for the first half cycle}$$

**58. Forced Vibrations.** When the vibration of a system is generated and sustained by the application of an external periodic force or by the periodic movement of the foundation of the system, the vibration is said to be *forced*. Forced vibration constitutes the most important type of vibration found in engineering work.

In Fig. 65a is shown a simple spring-mass system subjected to an external alternating force $P \sin \omega t$. It is assumed that the system is constrained to move in the vertical direction, so that only the one coordinate $x$ is needed to specify the position of the system. Also, damping forces are assumed absent for the time being. From the free-body diagram the equation of motion is seen to be

$$P \sin \omega t + W - (W + kx) = \frac{W}{g} \frac{d^2x}{dt^2},$$

or

$$\frac{d^2x}{dt^2} + \frac{kg}{W} x = \frac{Pg}{W} \sin \omega t. \tag{80}$$

In Fig. 65$b$ is represented a spring-supported mass which is vibrating by reason of an assumed harmonic movement $\delta \sin \omega t$ of the foundation.

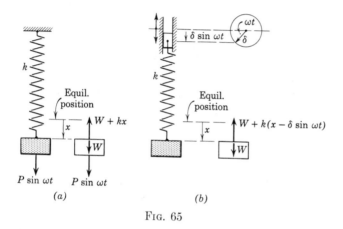

FIG. 65

The net stretch of the spring in any general displaced position is $x - \delta \sin \omega t$, so that the equation of motion is

$$W - [W + k(x - \delta \sin \omega t)] = \frac{W}{g} \frac{d^2x}{dt^2},$$

or

$$\frac{d^2x}{dt^2} + \frac{kg}{W} x = \frac{kg}{W} \delta \sin \omega t. \tag{81}$$

Equations 80 and 81 are of the same form, so that solution of the first will apply to the second if $k\delta$ is substituted for $P$.

When the right-hand side of a linear differential equation is not zero, the complete solution will equal the general solution $x_c$ of the homogeneous equation (right side equal to zero) plus *any* particular solution

$x_p$ of the complete equation. The complementary solution is that for the free vibration of $W$ and was found in Art. 54 to be

$$x_c = A \cos pt + B \sin pt, \quad \text{where } p = \sqrt{\frac{kg}{W}}.$$

For the particular solution of Eq. 80 try the expression

$$x_p = C \sin \omega t,$$

where $C$ is a constant. The second time derivative of $x_p$ is

$$\frac{d^2 x_p}{dt^2} = -C\omega^2 \sin \omega t.$$

Substitution into Eq. 80 gives

$$C\left(-\omega^2 + \frac{kg}{W}\right) \sin \omega t = \frac{Pg}{W} \sin \omega t.$$

This expression is satisfied for all values of the time if the two coefficients of the sine terms are equal. Thus

$$C = \frac{Pg/W}{(kg/W) - \omega^2} = \frac{P/k}{1 - (\omega/p)^2}.$$

With this value for the constant $C$ the assumed particular solution is valid, and the complete solution to Eq. 80 is $x = x_c + x_p$ or

$$x = A \cos pt + B \sin pt + \frac{P/k}{1 - (\omega/p)^2} \sin \omega t. \tag{82}$$

The constants $A$ and $B$ are dependent on the starting conditions as was shown in Art 54 for the case of free vibrations.

The periodic force may also be expressed as $P \cos \omega t$ or as $P$ times the sine or cosine of $\omega t - \phi$, where $\phi$ is a phase angle dependent on the exact instant at which the alternating force is first applied.

The first two terms of Eq. 82 represent the complementary or *transient* solution which disappears shortly because of the presence of even a small amount of damping as shown in Fig. 66. If a description is desired of the first few cycles immediately after application of the alternating force, it is necessary to know the exact phase at which the external force is applied at time $t = 0$ in order that the appropriate function $\sin \omega t$, $\cos \omega t$, or sine or cosine of $\omega t - \phi$ be employed.

After the initial or transient vibration has been damped out the particular solution

$$x_p = \frac{P/k}{1 - (\omega/p)^2} \sin \omega t \qquad (83)$$

remains and represents the *steady-state* forced vibration. When $P/k$ is replaced by $\delta$, Eq. 83 also represents the solution for the steady-state forced vibration due to harmonic movement of amplitude $\delta$ of the foundation of the spring-mass system in Fig. 65b. If the symbol $\delta$

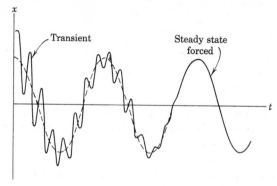

Fig. 66

is additionally used for the static deflection $P/k$ of the spring due to a static load equal to $P$ in the case of Fig. 65a, the amplitude $x_0$ of motion may be written in nondimensional form as

$$\frac{x_0}{\delta} = \frac{1}{1 - (\omega/p)^2}. \qquad (84)$$

The ratio $x_0/\delta$ is called the *magnification factor* and compares the actual amplitude $x_0$ with the static deflection $\delta$. The term $\omega/p$ is known as the *frequency ratio* and compares the applied frequency with the natural frequency of free vibration. The magnification factor is plotted against the frequency ratio in the full line of Fig. 67. For the limiting case of zero damping the amplitude of the forced vibration is seen to approach infinity as $\omega$ approaches $p$. For values of $\omega$ greater than $p$ the magnification factor is actually negative but is plotted above the axis for convenience. The negative value indicates that the resulting vibration is 180 deg. out of phase with the impressed force or foundation movement. The value $\omega = p$ is known as the *resonant frequency* or *critical speed* and clearly represents an operating condition to be avoided.

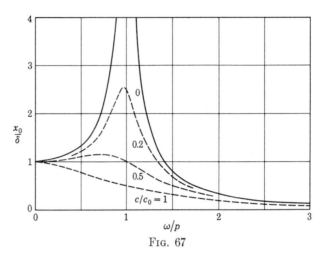

Fig. 67

The viscous effect of damping may be calculated by retaining the term $c(dx/dt)$ in the differential equation. The results of this analysis yield a steady-state motion of

$$x_p = \frac{P/k}{\sqrt{\left[1 - \left(\dfrac{\omega}{p}\right)^2\right]^2 + \left[\dfrac{c\omega}{k}\right]^2}} \sin(\omega t - \phi), \text{ where } \tan\phi = \frac{c\omega/k}{1 - \left(\dfrac{\omega}{p}\right)^2}.$$

The magnification factor may be written

$$\frac{x_0}{\delta} = \frac{1}{\sqrt{\left[1 - \left(\dfrac{\omega}{p}\right)^2\right]^2 + \left[2\dfrac{c\omega}{c_0 p}\right]^2}},$$

where $c/c_0$ is the damping factor and $c_0 = 2\sqrt{kW/g}$ is the critical damping constant. The quantity $c_0$ represents the maximum value which $c$ may have and still permit oscillatory motion. The curves for three values of $c/c_0$ are shown by the dotted lines in Fig. 67. Such curves are used to select suitable damping constants to limit the amplitude of motion when operation is in the critical range.

It is usually desirable to reduce as much as possible the forced vibrations which are generated in engineering structures and machines. Vibration reduction is normally accomplished in any of four ways: (1) elimination or reduction of the exciting force by balancing or other removal, (2) introduction of sufficient damping to limit the amplitude, (3) isolation of the body from the vibration source by providing elastic mountings of the proper stiffness, and (4) operation at a forced frequency sufficiently different from the natural frequency so as to avoid resonance.

The foregoing discussion of forced vibrations is only a brief introduction to this subject. Further study includes the analysis of systems with a number of degrees of freedom, and more advanced methods of solution are available.

### SAMPLE PROBLEM

**666.** The armature of an electric motor weighs 36 lb. and has a center of gravity midway between the two bearings and 0.015 in. off center from the bearing axis. The entire motor weighs 80 lb. and causes a static deflection of 0.125 in. in each of the four spring mounts under the base of the motor. Determine the speed $N$ at which the motor should *not* be run and find the amplitude $x_0$ of vertical vibration of the motor when running at twice this speed.

*Solution.* The spring constant for an equivalent single spring is

$$k = \frac{F}{\delta} = \frac{80}{0.125} = 640 \text{ lb./in.}$$

Thus the critical frequency is

$$\frac{p}{2\pi} = \frac{1}{2\pi}\sqrt{\frac{kg}{W}} = \frac{1}{2\pi}\sqrt{\frac{640 \times 32.2 \times 12}{80}} = 8.84 \text{ cycles/sec.,}$$

or

$$N = 8.84 \times 60 = 530 \text{ rev./min.} \qquad Ans.$$

The amplitude of the applied harmonic force for a speed of 1060 rev./min. is

$$P = me\omega^2 = \frac{36}{32.2}\frac{0.015}{12}\left(\frac{1060 \times 2\pi}{60}\right)^2 = 17.22 \text{ lb.}$$

The equivalent static deflection due to this load is $\delta = P/k = 17.22/640 = 0.0269$ in. The maximum amplitude of motion is therefore

$$x_0 = \left|\frac{\delta}{1 - (\omega/p)^2}\right| = \left|\frac{0.0269}{1 - (2)^2}\right| = 0.0090 \text{ in.} \qquad Ans.$$

### PROBLEMS

**667.** Each 1 lb. weight is attached to the end of the light elastic rod and deflects 0.250 in. because of a vertical load of 8 oz. applied statically to the weight. If the central collar is given a vertical harmonic movement with a frequency of 4 cycles/sec. and an amplitude of ⅛ in., find the amplitude $x_0$ of vertical vibration of the weight. *Ans.* $x_0 = 0.687$ in.

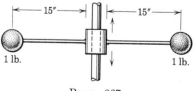

PROB. 667

**668.** The electric motor weighs 50 lb. and causes a static deflection of 0.125 in. of the center of the light elastic beam. The armature of the motor weighs 20 lb. and its center of gravity is 0.002 in. off center. Determine the vertical amplitude $x_0$ of the forced vibration of the middle of the beam when the motor is running at 600 rev./min.    $Ans.$   $x_0 = 0.00368$ in.

PROB. 668

**669.** A delicate instrument weighing 15 lb. is used in the vicinity of a punch press which operates at the rate of 4 blows per second. The instrument is placed on three equal spring pads each of which has a stiffness of 2 lb./in. If the instrument executes a vibration with an amplitude of 0.004 in., compute the amplitude $\delta$ of the vibration of the base to which the instrument is attached.          $Ans.$   $\delta = 0.0123$ in.

**670.** It is desired to limit the amplitude of vertical vibration for the motor described in Sample Prob. 666 to 0.010 in. when operating at a speed of 800 rev./min. by providing suitable viscous damping. Determine the necessary damping factor $c/c_0$.          $Ans.$   $c/c_0 = 0.28$

**671.** Show that an electrical circuit consisting of a resistance $R$, a capacitance $C$, and an inductance $L$ in series with an a-c voltage supply $E = E_0 \sin \omega t$ forms the analog of the linear mechanical oscillator with damping and a periodic driving force. The sum of the voltage drops across each element must equal the impressed voltage. If $i$ is the current, the voltage drop across the resistance is $Ri$ and that across the inductance is $L\, di/dt$. The voltage drop across the capacitance is $Q/C$ where $Q$ is the charge and $i = dQ/dt$.

**672.** The disk of weight $W$, mounted on the light elastic shaft, has a center of gravity $G$ a distance $e$ off center. When the shaft rotates at an angular velocity $\omega$, the unbalanced force $F$ deflects the shaft an amount $r$. This force equals $kr$, where $k$ is the equivalent spring constant or lateral force required to produce a unit deflection of the middle of the shaft. Equate $F$ and $kr$ and find the relation between $r$ and the natural circular frequency $p = \sqrt{kg/W}$ for lateral vibration of the shaft. At what angular velocity $\omega_c$ would the shaft vibrate excessively?

**673.** In the case of an elastically mounted motor of total weight $W$, where the forced vibration is excited by the out-of-balance of its rotor of weight $W'$, it is convenient to define the magnification factor as the ratio of $Wx_0$ to the product $W'e$, where $x_0$ is the amplitude of the motor vibration and $e$ is the eccentricity or distance from the center of gravity of the rotor to the axis of revolution. With this definition derive and plot the relation between $Wx_0/(W'e)$ and the frequency ratio $\omega/p$.

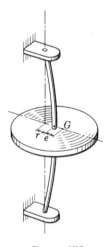

PROB. 672

$$Ans. \quad \frac{Wx_0}{W'e} = \frac{(\omega/p)^2}{1 - (\omega/p)^2}$$

**674.** A device to produce vibrations consists of the two counter-rotating wheels each carrying an eccentric weight $w = 3$ lb. with a center of gravity at a distance $e = \frac{1}{2}$ in. from its axis of rotation. The wheels are synchronized so that the vertical positions of the unbalanced weights are always identical. The total weight of the device is 15 lb. Determine the two possible values of the equivalent spring constant $k$ for the mounting which will permit the magnitude of the periodic force transmitted to the fixed mounting to be 300 lb. due to the unbalance of the rotors at a speed of 1500 rev./min.

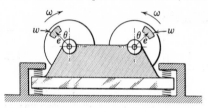

PROB. 674

**675.** A 60 lb. motor operates at 1250 rev./min. and has an unbalance in its rotor. When the motor is mounted on four identical spring pads, the alternating part of the force which is transmitted to the foundation is cut in half. Determine the constant $k$ of each pad. *Ans.* $k = 222$ lb./in.

**676.** The vibrometer shown is fastened to a ship's deck near the stern where the propeller vibration is most pronounced. The ship has a single 3-bladed propeller which turns at 125 rev./min. partly out of water, thus causing a shock as each blade breaks the surface. The natural frequency of vibration of the instrument is 2 cycles/sec., and the observed vertical amplitude of motion of the weight $A$ relative to the frame and deck is 0.030 in. Find the amplitude $\delta$ of vibration of the deck. (*Hint:* Note that the vibration of the weight is 180 deg. out of phase with the deck for operation above the natural frequency of 2 cycles/sec.) *Ans.* $\delta = 0.0269$ in.

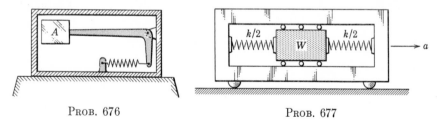

PROB. 676            PROB. 677

**677.** The outer frame of the spring-mass system is given a constant acceleration $a$ to the right. The equivalent spring constant is $k$. If the system starts from rest at time $t = 0$ with the weight $W$ in its equilibrium position, determine the expression for the absolute velocity $v$ of $W$. The springs remain in compression at all times.

$$Ans. \quad v = a\left[t - \sqrt{\frac{W}{kg}}\sin\sqrt{\frac{kg}{W}}\,t\right]$$

*678. Determine the amplitude of vertical vibration of the spring-mounted trailer as it travels at a velocity of 15 mi./hr. over the corduroy road whose contour may be expressed by a sine or cosine term. The weight of the trailer is 800 lb. and that of the wheels alone may be neglected. During the loading each 100 lb. increment of load caused the trailer to sag $\frac{1}{8}$ in. on its springs. Assume that the wheels are in contact with the road at all times. At what critical speed $v_c$ is the vibration of the trailer greatest?

*Ans.*   $x_0 = 0.223$ in., $v_c = 6.4$ mi./hr.

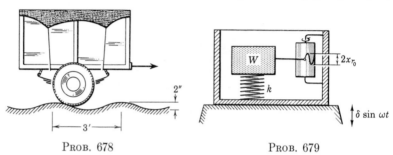

Prob. 678               Prob. 679

*679. A *seismic* type of vibration-recording instrument, represented schematically in the figure, consists of a spring-mounted mass within a case. The case in turn is secured to the body whose vibration is to be determined, and the *relative* movement $x_r$ between the mass and the case is measured and recorded. Derive the equation of motion for the mass in terms of $x_r$ and obtain the expression for the ratio of the amplitude $x_{r_0}$ to the amplitude $\delta$ of the given body vibration. Note that the equation derived for the system in Fig. 65*b* needs to be modified only by the change of variable from $x$ to $x_r$. Represent the relation between $x_{r_0}/\delta$ and $\omega/p$ graphically and indicate the conditions under which the measurement $x_r$ may be used with satisfactory accuracy to represent $\delta$.

*Ans.*   $\dfrac{x_{r_0}}{\delta} = \dfrac{(\omega/p)^2}{1 - (\omega/p)^2}$

---

# REVIEW PROBLEMS

In the preceding chapters the problems which are included with the various articles illustrate application of the particular topic involved. Thus the problem category and method of solution for these problems are to a great extent indicated automatically by their association with the article. The student of mechanics should develop ability to classify a new problem by recognizing the topic or topics involved and by selecting the appropiate method or methods of solution. The following review problems in Appendix A are included to help the student develop this ability. The problems are arranged only approximately in order of increasing difficulty. Some problems include more than one topic or may be worked by more than one method. It is suggested that the student use his time to outline the solution to as many of the problems as possible rather than to concentrate on the complete solution of only a limited few of them. In this way considerably more ground can be covered. The answers to all of the problems are included for those who wish them.

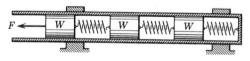

Prob. A1

**A1.** The system of three identical sliders each of weight $W$ and three springs of identical length and stiffness is initially held in an equilibrium position in the fixed horizontal tube by force $F$. If $F$ is suddenly released, find the initial accelerations $a$ of the center slider and $\bar{a}$ of the mass center. Neglect friction.    *Ans.* $a = 0,\ \bar{a} = Fg/3W$

**A2.** The conveyor belt travels at the lineal speed of 3 ft./sec. and delivers boxes which weigh 80 lb. each to the upper level at the rate of one every 2 sec. On the average there are 5 boxes on the belt at any one time. With the belt empty and the motor disconnected a moment of 84 lb. ft. applied to the lower driving pulley *A* is required to turn it against friction in all the parts. Specify the necessary power capacity of the motor sufficient to allow for a 50 per cent total overload.     *Ans.  P = 3.0 h.p.*

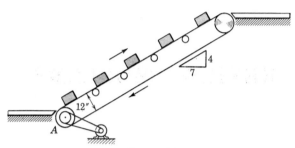

PROB. A2

**A3.** The ventilator door shown is a uniform rectangular plate weighing 100 lb. and hinged about a horizontal axis through *A*. The spring, which has a stiffness of 8 lb./ft., is compressed by the rod which is pinned to the lower end of the door and which passes through the swivel block at *B*. The spring is undeformed when θ is essentially zero. Determine the angular velocity ω of the door when it reaches the closed position if released from rest where θ is zero.
*Ans.  ω = 1.687 rad./sec.*

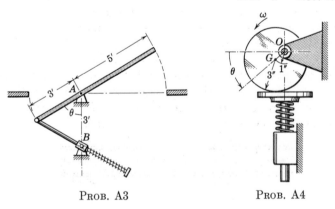

PROB. A3          PROB. A4

**A4.** The circular cam revolves counterclockwise at a constant speed of 300 rev./min. and controls the vertical motion of the 3 lb. plunger. The spring which supports the plunger has a modulus of 10 lb./in. and is compressed a total distance of 3 in. when θ = π/2. Determine the normal force *N* between the smooth surfaces of the cam and follower plate in terms of θ.
*Ans.  N = 17 + 2.34 sin θ lb.*

**A5.** A railway work car with a total weight of 1000 lb. is driven by means of an electric motor. Gear $A$ is attached to the motor shaft and in turn drives gears $B$ and $C$ which are integral with the wheels. If the car has a velocity of 30 mi./hr. and the motor is using energy at the rate of 5 k.w., determine the acceleration $a$ of the car on level track. The total rotational energy of the system is 30 per cent of the total translational energy, and the combined electrical and mechanical efficiency of the propulsion machinery is 80 per cent.

*Ans.* $a = 1.661$ ft./sec.$^2$

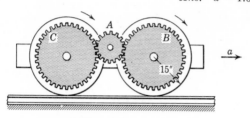

PROB. A5

**A6.** Each of the two large pulleys has a weight of 50 lb. and a radius of gyration of 10 in. The pulleys and 100 lb. load are held in equilibrium by a force $P$ applied through the center of the small sheave which has negligible weight. If $P$ is suddenly increased by 20 per cent, determine the upward acceleration $a$ of the 100 lb. weight.

*Ans.* $a = 4.78$ ft./sec.$^2$

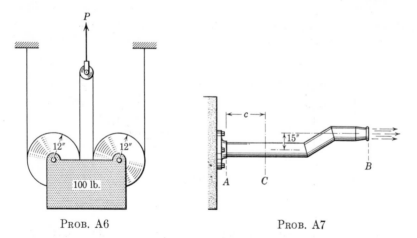

PROB. A6                     PROB. A7

**A7.** Fresh water under a pressure of 50 lb./in.$^2$ gage flows from the fixed tank through the offset pipe at the rate of 11.3 ft.$^3$/sec. and is discharged into the atmosphere. If the inside diameters of the pipe at $A$ and $B$ are 12 in. and $6\frac{3}{4}$ in., respectively, compute the tension $T$ and bending moment $M$ in the pipe at section $C$.

*Ans.* $T = 4980$ lb., $M = 1245$ lb. ft.

**A8.** The wheel rolls to the right without slipping, and its center has an acceleration $a$. A point $P$ on the wheel is at a fixed distance $r$ from the center.

Determine the value of $\theta$ and the corresponding velocity $v$ of the center in order that the acceleration of $P$ be equal to zero.

$$Ans. \quad \theta = \sin^{-1} \frac{r}{R}, \quad v = \sqrt{\frac{aR}{r}} \sqrt{R^2 - r^2}$$

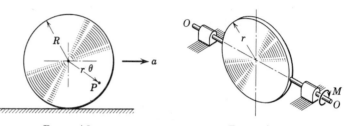

PROB. A8                               PROB. A9

**A9.** The circular disk of weight $W$ is mounted in bearings about a diametral axis $O$–$O$ and subjected to a torque $M$ starting from rest at time $t = 0$. Determine the angular velocity $\omega$ of the disk in terms of the time $t$ and also in terms of the number of revolutions $N$ through which the disk has turned from rest. Also write an expression for the kinetic energy $T$ in terms of $N$.

$$Ans. \quad \omega = \frac{4Mgt}{Wr^2}, \quad \omega = \frac{4}{r}\sqrt{\frac{Mg\pi N}{W}}, \quad T = 2\pi NM$$

**A10.** A 2 oz. bullet is fired with a velocity of 1000 ft./sec. at the 10 lb. block mounted on a stiff but light cantilever beam. The bullet is embedded in the block which is then observed to vibrate with a frequency of 4 cycles/sec. Compute the amplitude $A$ of the vibration.      $Ans.$    $A = 0.491$ ft.

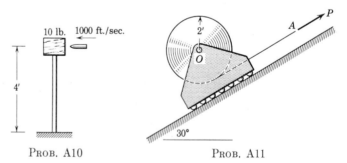

PROB. A10                               PROB. A11

**A11.** The cradle for the cable drum weighs 32.2 lb. and rolls on small rollers with negligible friction. The 4 ft. diameter drum weighs 64.4 lb. and has a radius of gyration of 1.5 ft. A constant force $P = 60$ lb. is applied to the cable beginning at the instant when the cradle has a velocity of 4 ft./sec. down the incline with the end $A$ of the cable motionless. Determine $(a)$ the velocity $v$ of the cradle and $(b)$ the angular velocity $\omega$ of the drum after $P$ has been applied for 2 sec. Find $(c)$ the component $R_t$ of the bearing reaction at $O$ in the direction tangent to the incline during this interval. Neglect the weight of the cable.     *Ans.*  $v = 3.8$ ft./sec., $\omega = 55.3$ rad./sec., $R_t = 20$ lb.

**A12.** The upper disk has a weight $W_1$ and a centroidal radius of gyration $k$ and rolls without slipping on the large disk $C$ which is rigidly fixed and cannot rotate. The connecting link has a weight $W_2$ and may be treated as a slender rod. Determine the angular acceleration $\alpha$ of $BO$ in the position shown due to the torque $M$ applied to the link at $O$.

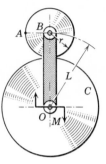

$$Ans. \quad \alpha = \dfrac{Mg/L^2}{\dfrac{W_2}{3} + \left(1 + \dfrac{k^2}{r^2}\right)W_1}$$

**A13.** For the mechanism described in Prob. A12 if $L = 9$ in. and $r = 3$ in. and if $BO$ has a clockwise angular acceleration of 4 rad./sec.$^2$ and a counterclockwise angular velocity of 2 rad./sec. in the position shown, determine the acceleration of point $A$.

*Ans.*  $a_A = 144$ in./sec.$^2$

PROB. A12

**A14.** The slotted link weighs 24 lb. with center of gravity 8 in. from $O$ and has a radius of gyration about its pivot $O$ of 10 in. The solid circular disk weighs 16 lb. and is guided by its central pin in the smooth slot. If the link is released from rest with $\theta$ essentially zero, determine the velocity $v$ of the center of the disk when $\theta = 60$ deg. Assume that the disk rolls without slipping.

*Ans.*  $v = 4.28$ ft./sec.

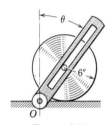

PROB. A14

**A15.** For the four-bar linkage shown prove that the ratio of the angular velocities of the two fixed-ended links is given by $\omega_a/\omega_b = n/m$.

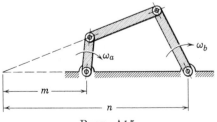

PROB. A15

**A16.** Point $A$ is given a constant acceleration $a$ to the left starting from rest with $x$ essentially zero. Determine the angular velocity $\omega$ and angular acceleration $\alpha$ of link $AB$ in terms of $x$.

$$Ans.\quad \omega = \sqrt{\frac{2ax}{4l^2 - x^2}},\ \alpha = \frac{4l^2 + x^2}{(4l^2 - x^2)^{3/2}}\,a,\ \text{both counterclockwise}$$

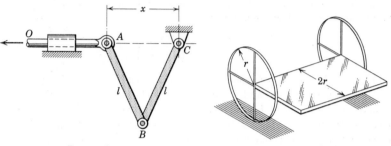

PROB. A16                                   PROB. A17

**A17.** The uniform rectangular plate has a weight $W$ and a width equal to the diameter of the light hoops to which it is welded. If the plate and hoops are released from rest with the plate in the horizontal position, determine the initial angular acceleration $\alpha$ of the plate an instant after release and find the friction force $F$ acting under each hoop. Assume that the coefficient of friction $f$ is large enough to prevent slipping.

$$Ans.\quad \alpha = \frac{3g}{7r},\ F = \tfrac{3}{14}W$$

**A18.** Work Prob. A17 for the case where the coefficient of friction $f$ is less than that required to prevent slipping.

$$Ans.\quad \alpha = \frac{3g}{r}\frac{1-f}{4-3f},\ F = \frac{fW}{2(4-3f)}$$

**A19.** A rocket with an initial total weight of 20 lb. is fired with a horizontal velocity of 800 ft./sec. from a tower which is 64.4 ft. above the ground. If the 10 lb. horizontal thrust is constant and remains horizontal, determine the horizontal distance $s$ from the foot of the tower to the point of impact with the ground. Neglect air friction. Mass is expelled at the constant rate of 5 lb./sec.

$$Ans.\quad s = 1640\ \text{ft.}$$

**A20.** Derive an expression for the net energy $\Delta E$ which is required to put an artificial satellite of mass $m$ in a circular orbit around the earth at an altitude $h$ above the earth. The satellite is to be launched from rest at the equator where it has an initial velocity equal to the equatorial surface velocity of the earth with respect to the center of the earth considered as fixed. The radius of the earth is $R$, its angular velocity is $\omega$, and the absolute acceleration of gravity at the surface of the earth is $g$.

$$Ans.\quad \Delta E = \frac{mgR}{R+h}\left(\frac{R}{2}+h\right) - \frac{mR^2\omega^2}{2}$$

**A21.** If the center $O$ of the gear has a velocity of 2 ft./sec. to the right and an acceleration of 4 ft./sec.² to the left when in the position shown, determine the instantaneous values of the velocity and acceleration of the piston $A$. Also determine the corresponding angular velocity and angular acceleration of $AB$.

$Ans.$  $v_A = 1.63$ ft./sec., $a_A = 1.01$ ft./sec.$^2$,
$\omega_{AB} = 2.51$ rad./sec., $\alpha_{AB} = 8.07$ rad./sec.$^2$

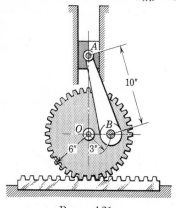

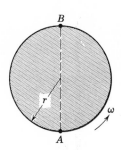

PROB. A21                    PROB. A22

**A22.** Two boys $A$ and $B$ are riding on a horizontal turntable which revolves with a constant angular velocity $\omega$. Boy $A$ throws a ball to $B$ by giving it a velocity $u$ relative to the turntable in the direction $A$ to $B$. Neglect the vertical drop of the ball, and describe its path as seen from $A$'s rotating position.

$Ans.$  Facing $B$ the ball moves to the right of $B$

**A23.** A bullet of mass $m$ is fired horizontally in the $x$-direction with a muzzle velocity $u$. Resistance to motion in the $x$-direction is proportional to the square of its velocity, $R = kv_x{}^2$. The bullet encounters a strong cross wind in the $y$-direction which causes a horizontal deflection $\delta$ from the line of sight to the target at a range $s$. Write an expression for the constant force $F_y$ exerted by the cross wind on the bullet. Assume the motion is entirely in the horizontal $x$-$y$ plane.

$$Ans. \quad F_y = \frac{2\delta}{m}\left(\frac{ku}{e^{ks/m} - 1}\right)^2$$

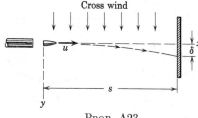

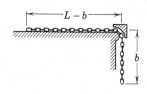

PROB. A23                    PROB. A24

**A24.** The chain is released from rest in the position shown and slides on the smooth surface through the opening and over the edge. Write the differential equation of motion of the chain, and solve for the displacement $x$ measured from the rest position in terms of the time $t$.

$$Ans. \quad x = b\left(\cosh\sqrt{\frac{g}{L}}\,t - 1\right)$$

**A25.** One end of a rope of total length $L$ is released from rest with $x = 0$. Determine the velocity $v$ of the falling end of the rope in terms of $x$. Assume that the rope is perfectly flexible in bending but inextensible. Discuss the result for the case where $x = L$ by considering the energy-conservation principle.

$$Ans. \quad v = \sqrt{\frac{gx(2L - x)}{L - x}}$$

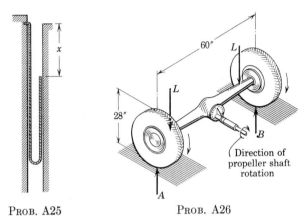

Prob. A25              Prob. A26

**A26.** The rear axle of an automobile is shown in the sketch. The gear ratio in the differential is 3.7:1 (propeller-shaft speed is 3.7 times the rear-wheel speed). The car has a total weight of 3600 lb. with center of gravity midway between the front and rear axles and 2 ft. above the road. The wheelbase is 120 in. During acceleration on a level road the engine delivers 100 h.p. to the rear wheels at a speed of 50 mi./hr. Determine the normal forces $A$ and $B$ under the rear wheels at this speed and corresponding acceleration. Assume that the rear wheels do not slip and that there are no other vertical forces on the rear-wheel assembly other than those indicated. Neglect the mass of the wheels compared with the total mass of the car.

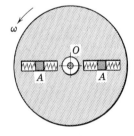

$Ans.$    $A = 928$ lb., $B = 1022$ lb.

**A27.** Each of the two slider blocks $A$ has a weight $w$ and is constrained to move in the smooth radial slots of the flywheel. Each of the four springs has a stiffness of $k/2$ and is in compression at all times. The blocks are both at a distance $r_0$ from $O$ when

Prob. A27

the wheel is at rest. Determine the frequency $f$ of vibration of the blocks for a constant speed $\omega$ of the flywheel. What is the significance of the condition when $\omega^2 \geq k/m$?

$$Ans. \quad f = \frac{1}{2\pi} \sqrt{\frac{kg}{w} - \omega^2}$$

# VECTOR METHODS

**B1. Introduction.** Mechanics is inherently a subject which depends on vector quantities. The basic concepts of a vector are set forth in Art. 3 of Chapter 1, Part I, and are not repeated here. Force, moment, displacement, velocity, acceleration, momentum, and impulse are the common vector quantities found in mechanics. Statics involves, primarily, the first three of these vectors. In the preceding chapters the addition and subtraction of vectors is denoted by the respective symbols $\leftrightarrow$ and $\rightarrow$ to call attention to the distinction between vector and scalar operations. Where the multiplication of vector quantities occurs, such as in the calculation of a moment, the magnitude of the product is specified with its scalar value, and the direction of the product, if a vector, is indicated or described separately.

An alternate system of notation may be used which incorporates the magnitude and directional aspects of a vector in a single symbol. This system, which permits the use of ordinary plus and minus signs, which distinguishes between the vector or scalar aspects of the multiplication of vectors, and which permits the representation of vector operations in three dimensions with a simplicity comparable to that in two dimensions, is contained in the dot- and cross-product notation invented by Josiah Willard Gibbs (1839–1903). This notation is widely used by physicists, mathematicians, and some engineers and is often referred to as *Gibbs' Notation*. In mechanics this vector notation finds its most important use in three-dimensional problems of dynamics where time derivatives of space vectors are encountered. It should be emphasized that the vector notation is of assistance in formulating certain general relations, primarily three dimensional, but in the end must give way to scalar computation when engineering results in the form of numerical answers are required.

It is the purpose of the following treatment to provide an introduction to the vector notation as it applies to mechanics. This notation may be used where applicable as an alternative to the scalar symbols employed in the preceding chapters. A full development of vector algebra and vector calculus may be found in numerous references devoted to this subject and is not the purpose of the following abbreviated treatment.

**B2. Notation.** In the notation of vector algebra it is necessary to distinguish between scalars and vectors by the appearance of the symbol used. The most common designation is the use of boldface type for vectors and lightface type for scalars. This designation is used hereafter in Appendix B. Thus $V$ represents some vector quantity with the scalar magnitude $V = |V|$. The vector equation $P = Q$ signifies the equality of two vectors and means not only equality of magnitudes $|P| = |Q|$, but also that the direction and sense of the two vectors are the same. A vector $V$ when multiplied by a scalar $a$ is the vector $aV$ or $Va$ which has the magnitude $aV$ and the direction of $V$.

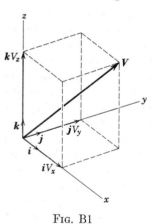

A vector $V$ may be resolved into three mutually perpendicular components in, say, the $x$-, $y$-, and $z$-directions, Fig. B1. These components are actually vectors with magnitudes equal to $V_x$, $V_y$, and $V_z$, respectively. To represent these components as vectors it is necessary to introduce the vectors $i, j, k$ of unit magnitude and directed along the $x$-, $y$-, and $z$-axes, respectively. Thus the component vectors of $V$ are $iV_x$, $jV_y$, and $kV_z$, and their vector sum is

Fig. B1

$$V = iV_x + jV_y + kV_z \qquad (B1)$$

where the plus signs denote vector addition. The quantities $V_x$, $V_y$, and $V_z$ are known as the scalar components of $V$, and they must satisfy the relation

$$V = \sqrt{V_x{}^2 + V_y{}^2 + V_z{}^2}. \qquad (B2)$$

**B3. Addition.** From the basic concept of vector addition it follows that the sum of two vectors $P$ and $Q$ may be written in terms of the sums of their components,

$$P + Q = i(P_x + Q_x) + j(P_y + Q_y) + k(P_z + Q_z).$$

This expression may be extended to cover the sum $R$ of any number of vectors $F$. Thus

$$R = \Sigma F = i\Sigma F_x + j\Sigma F_y + k\Sigma F_z,$$

and $\qquad R_x = \Sigma F_x, \qquad R_y = \Sigma F_y, \qquad R_z = \Sigma F_z.$

If the vectors represented by $\Sigma F$ constitute a system of forces, then $R$ is merely the resultant of the system, and $R_x$, $R_y$, and $R_z$ are the scalar components of the resultant. For a system of forces in equilibrium the resultant is zero, and $\Sigma F = 0$ gives $\Sigma F_x = 0$, $\Sigma F_y = 0$, $\Sigma F_z = 0$ which are the familiar force equations of equilibrium.

It has already been established that the sum of two vectors is independent of the order in which they are added. Thus

$$P + Q = Q + P$$

which is the commutative law for vector addition. Further, it is clear from the elementary concepts of vector addition that the associative law

$$P + (Q + R) = (P + Q) + R$$

also holds.

The subtraction of vectors may be considered as a special case of addition by using the fact that the negative of a vector $Q$ is a vector $-Q$ of the same magnitude but opposite in direction. Thus $P - Q = P + (-Q)$.

**B4. Dot or Scalar Product.** One type of product involving two vectors is formed by multiplying the product of their magnitudes by the cosine of the angle between them. Thus, for the vectors in Fig. B2, this product is defined as

$$P \cdot Q = PQ \cos \theta \qquad \text{(B3)}$$

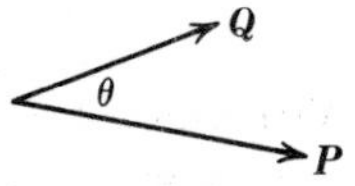

and is known as the *dot* or *scalar product*. This product may be viewed as the magnitude of $P$ multiplied by the component of $Q$ in the direction of $P$ or as the magnitude of $Q$ multiplied by the component of $P$ in the direction of $Q$. The scalar result does not depend upon the order of the multiplication. Thus

$$P \cdot Q = Q \cdot P$$

which means that the commutative law holds for scalar products.

Fig. B2

The most common example of the dot product in mechanics is the expression for work. It is seen that the foregoing definition of the dot product is identical to the definition of the work of a force $F$ whose point of application moves through a vector displacement $s$. The

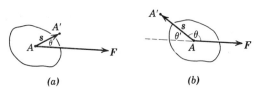

(a)                       (b)

FIG. B3

work done by the force $F$ in Fig. B3a during a displacement $s$ of its point of application from $A$ to $A'$ is

$$U = F \cdot s = Fs \cos \theta$$

and is positive if $\theta$ is less than 90 deg. For $\theta$ greater than 90 deg., Fig. B3b, the work done by $F$ is $U = Fs \cos \theta = Fs \cos (\pi - \theta') = -Fs \cos \theta'$ which shows that the work is negative.

For an infinitesimal virtual displacement $\delta s$ the virtual work done by $F$ is $U = F \cdot \delta s$. The principle of virtual work, $\delta U = 0$, is, then, equivalent to forming the sum of the dot products of each active force with the corresponding virtual displacement of its point of application and setting the sum equal to zero.

With the definition of the dot product of two vectors it is at once apparent that the following relations hold for unit vectors:

$$i \cdot i = j \cdot j = k \cdot k = 1,$$

$$i \cdot j = j \cdot i = i \cdot k = k \cdot i = j \cdot k = k \cdot j = 0.$$

With the aid of these identities the dot product of $P$ and $Q$ may be written in component form as

$$P \cdot Q = (iP_x + jP_y + kP_z) \cdot (iQ_x + jQ_y + kQ_z)$$

$$= P_x Q_x + P_y Q_y + P_z Q_z.$$

The dot product of a vector by itself becomes

$$P \cdot P = P_x{}^2 + P_y{}^2 + P_z{}^2 = P^2.$$

The distributive law holds for the dot product as may be seen by re-grouping the terms. Thus

$$P \cdot (Q + R) = P_x(Q_x + R_x) + P_y(Q_y + R_y) + P_z(Q_z + R_z)$$
$$= P \cdot Q + P \cdot R.$$

**B5. Cross or Vector Product.** A second product involving two vectors is known as the *cross product* or *vector product*. The cross product of the vectors $P$ and $Q$ in Fig. B4$a$ is defined as the vector $R$ whose magnitude equals the product of the magnitudes of $P$ and $Q$ multiplied by the sine of the angle (less than 180 deg.) between $P$ and

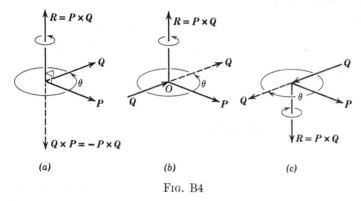

(a)          (b)          (c)

Fɪɢ. B4

$Q$. Further, the direction of $R$ is the direction of advancement of a right-hand screw when revolved from $P$ to $Q$ through an angle $\theta$ less than 180 deg. This cross product is written as

$$R = P \times Q \qquad \text{where } R = PQ \sin \theta. \qquad (\text{B4})$$

By using the right-hand rule it is seen that $P \times Q = -Q \times P$, and, hence, the commutative law does not hold for the cross product. The cross product $Q \times P$ is a vector in the opposite direction to $P \times Q$ as shown in Fig. B4$a$. The validity of the distributive law for the cross product may be shown by a relatively simple geometrical proof. It is stated here without proof and is

$$P \times (Q + R) = P \times Q + P \times R.$$

In forming the vector product it is well to consider the vectors according to the definition given. Thus in Fig. B4$b$ the product $P \times Q$ is correctly formed by moving $Q$ so that both $Q$ and $P$ stem from $O$. For the configuration of Fig. B4$c$ the angle $\theta$ (less than 180 deg.) between $P$ and $Q$ extended must be used. Advancement from

$P$ to $Q$ by the right-hand rule through the angle $\theta$ requires that the cross product be down.

With the definition of the cross product the following relations between the unit vectors are apparent:

$$i \times j = k \qquad j \times k = i \qquad k \times i = j$$

$$j \times i = -k \qquad k \times j = -i \qquad i \times k = -j$$

$$i \times i = j \times j = k \times k = 0.$$

With the aid of these identities and the distributive law the vector product may be written

$$P \times Q = (iP_x + jP_y + kP_z) \times (iQ_x + jQ_y + kQ_z)$$

$$= i(P_yQ_z - P_zQ_y) + j(P_zQ_x - P_xQ_z) + k(P_xQ_y - P_yQ_x)$$

upon rearrangement of terms. This expression may be written compactly as the determinant

$$P \times Q = \begin{vmatrix} i & j & k \\ P_x & P_y & P_z \\ Q_x & Q_y & Q_z \end{vmatrix}.$$

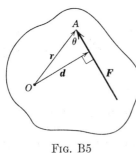

It is readily seen that the cross product as defined fits the requirement for the description of the moment of a force. In Fig. B5 consider the moment $M$ produced by the force $F$ about an axis through $O$ normal to the plane of the figure. The force acts at a point $A$ whose vector position with respect to $O$ as origin is $r = ix + jy + kz$. The moment has a magnitude of $Fd = Fr \sin \theta$. The direction of $M$ is out from the paper which is the direction of the advancement of a right-hand screw when rotated from $r$ to

Fig. B5

$F$ through the smaller of the two angles $\theta$ between them. Thus

$$M = r \times F. \tag{B5}$$

It is important to observe that $M \neq F \times r$ which expression would be a vector in the opposite sense to the moment.

In component form Eq. B5 may be written as

$$M = (ix + jy + kz) \times (iF_x + jF_y + kF_z)$$

$$= i(yF_z - zF_y) + j(zF_x - xF_z) + k(xF_y - yF_x),$$

so that the scalar components of $M$ become $M_x = yF_z - zF_y$, $M_y = zF_x - xF_z$, $M_z = xF_y - yF_x$.

In Fig. B6 two parallel forces $F_1$ and $F_2$ with equal magnitude $F$ are acting at points whose position vectors from some origin $O$ are $r_1$ and $r_2$. The sum of the moments about $O$ is $M = r_1 \times F_1 + r_2 \times F_2$. Substitution of $F_2 = -F_1$ gives $M = r_1 \times F_1 - r_2 \times F_1$, and the

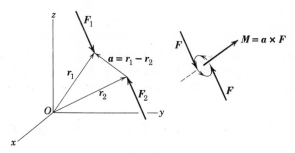

FIG. B6

distributive law permits writing $M = (r_1 - r_2) \times F_1$. Substitution of $a = r_1 - r_2$, permits the moment to be written as

$$M = a \times F \qquad (B6)$$

which is independent of any reference to the point $O$. Thus the moment of two equal and opposite forces which are parallel but not collinear is the same for all moment centers. This moment is called a *couple*, and its sense is always specified by the right-hand rule for the rotation which the two forces tend to produce as shown in the sketch at the right side of Fig. B6. The magnitude of $a \times F$ equals the product of $F$ and the perpendicular distance between the forces.

**B6. Additional Relations.** Two additional relations of vector algebra will be stated without proof, although their validity is not difficult to show geometrically.

The *triple scalar product* is the dot product of two vectors where one of them is specified as a cross product of two additional vectors. This product is a scalar and is given by any one of the equivalent expressions

$$(P \times Q) \cdot R = R \cdot (P \times Q) = -R \cdot (Q \times P).$$

Actually the parentheses are not needed since it would be meaningless to write $P \times (Q \cdot R)$. It may be shown that

$$P \times Q \cdot R = P \cdot Q \times R \qquad (B7)$$

which establishes the rule that the dot and the cross may be interchanged without changing the value of the triple scalar product. Further it may be seen upon expansion that

$$P \times Q \cdot R = \begin{vmatrix} P_x & P_y & P_z \\ Q_x & Q_y & Q_z \\ R_x & R_y & R_z \end{vmatrix} . \tag{B8}$$

The *triple vector product* is the cross product of two vectors where one of them is specified as a cross product of two additional vectors. This product is a vector and is given by any one of the equivalent expressions

$$(P \times Q) \times R = -R \times (P \times Q) = R \times (Q \times P).$$

Here the parentheses must be used since an expression $P \times Q \times R$ would be ambiguous because it would not identify the vector to be crossed. It may be shown that the triple vector product is equivalent to

$$(P \times Q) \times R = R \cdot PQ - R \cdot QP$$

or $\qquad P \times (Q \times R) = P \cdot RQ - P \cdot QR.$ (B9)

The first term in the first expression, for example, is the dot product $R \cdot P$, a scalar, multiplied by the vector $Q$. The validity of Eqs. B7 and B9 may be checked easily by carrying out the indicated operations with three arbitrary vectors with numerical coefficients.

### SAMPLE PROBLEMS

**B1.** A constant force $F = 3i + 4j + 5k$ lb. acts on a body at a point which has a displacement $s = 2i - 3j - 4k$ ft. Calculate the work done.

*Solution.* The dot product $U = F \cdot s$ represents the work done, so

$$U = F_x s_x + F_y s_y + F_z s_z$$

$$= (3)(2) + (4)(-3) + (5)(-4) = -26 \text{ ft. lb.} \qquad Ans.$$

**B2.** A force $F = 3i + 4j + 5k$ lb. acts on a body at point $A$ located as shown. Determine the moment $M$ of $F$ about the $N$-axis through $O$ as indicated in the figure.

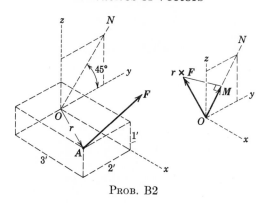

*Solution.* Point $A$ has the position vector $r = 3i - 2j + k$ ft. The moment of $F$ about an axis through $O$ normal to the plane of $F$ and $r$ is given by $M_1 = r \times F$. The component of $M_1$ along the $N$-axis has the magnitude $M_1 \cdot n$ where $n$ is a unit vector along the $N$-axis. Thus the magnitude of the required moment is

$$M = r \times F \cdot n$$

which is a triple scalar product. This product may be evaluated directly from Eq. B8. The unit vector $n$ must first be expressed as $n = j/\sqrt{2} + k/\sqrt{2}$. The determinant gives

$$M = \begin{vmatrix} 3 & -2 & 1 \\ 3 & 4 & 5 \\ 0 & \dfrac{1}{\sqrt{2}} & \dfrac{1}{\sqrt{2}} \end{vmatrix} = 3\sqrt{2} \text{ lb. ft.}$$

In vector form $M = 3j + 3k$ lb. ft.     *Ans.*

**B7. Derivatives of Vectors.** Consider the motion of a point $P$ in space as indicated by the path in Fig. B7. At time $t$ the position of $P$ is specified by $r$, and at time $t + \Delta t$ by the vector $r + \Delta r$. The instantaneous time rate of change of the position vector $r$ is defined as

$$\lim_{\Delta t \to 0} \frac{\Delta r}{\Delta t} = \frac{dr}{dt} = \dot{r} \qquad (B10)$$

and is seen to be a vector directed along the path. The dot above the $r$ signifies the first derivative with respect to time and will be used in the remainder of this article. Two dots will signify the second time

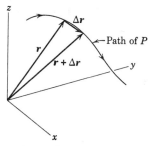

FIG. B7

derivative. Since $\Delta r = i\,\Delta x + j\,\Delta y + k\,\Delta z$, it is seen that $\dot{r} = i\dot{x} + j\dot{y} + k\dot{z}$ and $\ddot{r} = i\ddot{x} + j\ddot{y} + k\ddot{z}$ which give, respectively, the velocity and acceleration of $P$. The derivative of a vector depends both on the change in magnitude and the change in direction of the vector. It should be noted that $|\dot{r}| \neq \dot{r}$, which expresses the fact that the magnitude of the derivative is not the same as the derivative of the magnitude for vectors. One familiar example of this fact may be cited for the case of the motion of a point in the arc of a circle of radius $r$. With the center of the circle as origin of coordinates the position of the point may be described by the vector $r$. The magnitude of the derivative of $r$, which is $|\dot{r}|$, gives the magnitude of the tangential velocity $v$, whereas the derivative of the magnitude of $r$, which is $\dot{r}$, is zero since $r$ is of constant length.

It is easily shown by expansion that the derivatives of the dot and cross products of two vectors obey the ordinary rules for differentiation of scalar products. Thus

$$\frac{d}{dt}(P\cdot Q) = P\cdot\dot{Q} + \dot{P}\cdot Q \quad \text{and} \quad \frac{d}{dt}(P \times Q) = P \times \dot{Q} + \dot{P} \times Q.$$
$$(B11)$$

**B8. Integration of Vectors.** Integration of vectors poses no special problem. If $V$ is a function of $x$, $y$, and $z$ and an element of volume is $d\tau = dx\,dy\,dz$, the integral of $V$ over the volume may be written as the vector sum of the three integrals of its components. Thus

$$\int V\,d\tau = i\int V_x\,d\tau + j\int V_y\,d\tau + k\int V_z\,d\tau. \qquad (B12)$$

**B9. Basic Kinematical Relations.** Consider a point $P$ moving in a circular path about the vertical axis, Fig. B8a. The radius of the path is $r'$, and the angular velocity of the radius vector $r'$ is $\omega$. Let the origin of coordinates be any convenient fixed point $O$ on the axis. The velocity $v$ of point $P$ is given by the vector product

$$v = \omega \times r'$$

in both magnitude, direction, and sense. Since $r' = r - c$, and since $\omega \times c = 0$, it is seen by substitution that

$$v = \omega \times r. \qquad (B13)$$

This cross product is the general expression for linear velocity due to rotation about an axis. It should be carefully observed that the sequence $\boldsymbol{\omega} \times \boldsymbol{r}$ must be used and not $\boldsymbol{r} \times \boldsymbol{\omega}$ in order to preserve the correct sense of $\boldsymbol{v}$.

The acceleration of $P$ is the time derivative of $\boldsymbol{v}$. Thus $\boldsymbol{a} = \boldsymbol{\omega} \times \dot{\boldsymbol{r}} + \dot{\boldsymbol{\omega}} \times \boldsymbol{r}$. Substitution of $\boldsymbol{v} = \dot{\boldsymbol{r}} = \boldsymbol{\omega} \times \boldsymbol{r}$ permits the vector expression for acceleration to be written as

$$\boldsymbol{a} = \boldsymbol{\omega} \times \boldsymbol{v} + \dot{\boldsymbol{\omega}} \times \boldsymbol{r} \qquad \text{or} \qquad \boldsymbol{a} = \boldsymbol{\omega} \times (\boldsymbol{\omega} \times \boldsymbol{r}) + \dot{\boldsymbol{\omega}} \times \boldsymbol{r}. \qquad (B14)$$

Each term is shown in Fig. B8$b$. The magnitude of the first term is the normal acceleration $a_n = r'\omega^2 = v\omega = v^2/r'$, and the magnitude of the second term is $a_t = r'\dot{\omega}$ since $\dot{\boldsymbol{\omega}} \times \boldsymbol{r} = \dot{\boldsymbol{\omega}} \times \boldsymbol{r}'$.

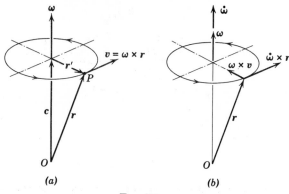

(a)             (b)

Fɪɢ. B8

When $n$- and $t$-coordinates are used for motion along a plane curve, it is convenient to introduce unit vectors $\boldsymbol{n}_1$ and $\boldsymbol{t}_1$ in the $n$- and $t$-directions, respectively. With this notation the velocity $\boldsymbol{v}$ and acceleration $\boldsymbol{a}$ may be written as

$$\boldsymbol{v} = \boldsymbol{t}_1 v \qquad \text{and} \qquad \boldsymbol{a} = \boldsymbol{n}_1 \rho \omega^2 + \boldsymbol{t}_1 \dot{v}$$

where $\rho$ is the radius of curvature of the path and $\omega$ is the angular velocity $v/\rho$. Likewise, when $r$- and $\theta$-coordinates are used for motion along a plane curve, it is convenient to introduce unit vectors $\boldsymbol{r}_1$ and $\boldsymbol{\theta}_1$ in the $r$- and $\theta$-directions, respectively. With this notation the velocity and acceleration may be written as

$$\boldsymbol{v} = \boldsymbol{r}_1 \dot{r} + \boldsymbol{\theta}_1 r\dot{\theta} \qquad \text{and} \qquad \boldsymbol{a} = \boldsymbol{r}_1(\ddot{r} - r\dot{\theta}^2) + \boldsymbol{\theta}_1(r\ddot{\theta} + 2\dot{r}\dot{\theta}).$$

**B10. Rotating Axes.** It is often convenient to describe motion by making measurements from moving axes. In Fig. B9 the motion of a point $P$ in the plane of the figure will be described from measurements made relative to the system $x$–$y$. This system has an angular velocity $\omega$ whose vector is out from the paper in the positive $z$-direction. The system also has a translation defined by the motion of $O$ in the fixed $x_0$–$y_0$ axes. Differentiation of the vector position equation $r = R + \rho$ gives for the absolute velocity of $P$

$$v = \dot{r} = \dot{R} + \dot{\rho} = \dot{R} + \frac{d}{dt}(ix + jy) = R + (\dot{i}x + \dot{j}y) + (i\dot{x} + j\dot{y}).$$

It is clear that the unit vectors $i$ and $j$ in the $x$–$y$ system have time derivatives since their direction changes with their rotation. The

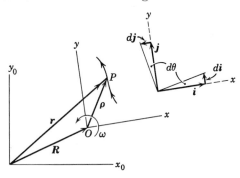

FIG. B9

change in $i$ due to a rotation $d\theta$ in time $dt$ is shown in the upper right-hand part of Fig. B9 and is $di = j\,d\theta$. Therefore $\dot{i} = j\omega$. Likewise $\dot{j} = -i\omega$. These relations may also be written as

$$\dot{i} = \omega \times i \quad \text{and} \quad \dot{j} = \omega \times j.$$

The velocity of $P$ may now be written as

$$v = \dot{R} + (\omega \times ix + \omega \times jy) + (i\dot{x} + j\dot{y}).$$

The first term is the velocity $v_O$ of point $O$. The second term is the same as $\omega \times \rho$ since $\rho = ix + jy$. The third term is the velocity which would be measured relative to the rotating position and is written as $\dot{\rho}_r = i\dot{x} + j\dot{y}$. It must be noted that $\dot{\rho}_r \neq \dot{\rho}$ because of the fact that the change in direction of the unit vectors accounts for a part of $\dot{\rho}$. Thus

$$v = v_O + \omega \times \rho + \dot{\rho}_r. \tag{B15}$$

The absolute acceleration of $P$ is obtained by differentiation of Eq. B15 which gives

$$a = \dot{v}_O + \omega \times \dot{\rho} + \dot{\omega} \times \rho + \frac{d}{dt}(i\dot{x} + j\dot{y}).$$

The first term is the acceleration $a_O$ of the origin $O$. With the aid of the derivation for $v$ the second term becomes $\boldsymbol{\omega} \times (\boldsymbol{\omega} \times \boldsymbol{\rho} + \dot{\boldsymbol{\rho}}_r)$. The last term is $(\boldsymbol{\omega} \times i\dot{x} + \boldsymbol{\omega} \times j\dot{y}) + (i\ddot{x} + j\ddot{y}) = \boldsymbol{\omega} \times \dot{\boldsymbol{\rho}}_r + \ddot{\boldsymbol{\rho}}_r$ where $\ddot{\boldsymbol{\rho}}_r = i\ddot{x} + j\ddot{y}$ is the acceleration that would be measured relative to the rotating $x$–$y$ axes. Upon combining terms the complete expression for acceleration becomes

$$a = a_O + \boldsymbol{\omega} \times (\boldsymbol{\omega} \times \boldsymbol{\rho}) + \dot{\boldsymbol{\omega}} \times \boldsymbol{\rho} + 2\boldsymbol{\omega} \times \dot{\boldsymbol{\rho}}_r + \ddot{\boldsymbol{\rho}}_r. \quad \text{(B16)}$$

The terms $\boldsymbol{\omega} \times (\boldsymbol{\omega} \times \boldsymbol{\rho}) + \dot{\boldsymbol{\omega}} \times \boldsymbol{\rho}$ together represent the normal and tangential components of the acceleration relative to $O$ of a point fixed to the $x$–$y$ system and coincident with the moving point $P$ at the instant considered. These two terms mean the same as the term $a_m$ in the derivation of Eq. 26 in Chapter 2. The term $2\boldsymbol{\omega} \times \dot{\boldsymbol{\rho}}_r$ is the Coriolis acceleration. The term $\ddot{\boldsymbol{\rho}}_r$ is the same as the term $a_p$ in Eq. 26 and is the acceleration which would be measured for $P$ relative to the rotating axes.

Although the derivation of Eq. B16 is given here for plane motion, it holds equally well for three-dimensional motion. The derivation may easily be expanded to cover the third dimension.

### SAMPLE PROBLEM

**B3.** The arm $OA$ is revolving about $O$ with an angular acceleration $\dot{\boldsymbol{\omega}} = 3$ rad./sec.$^2$ At the instant represented $\boldsymbol{\omega} = 6$ rad./sec. At the same time the

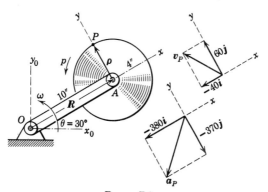

PROB. B3

disk turns counterclockwise about its bearing $A$ with an angular acceleration *relative* to $OA$ of $\dot{p} = 2$ rad./sec.$^2$, and at the instant represented the angular velocity *relative* to the arm $OA$ is $p = 4$ rad./sec. Determine the velocity $v$ and acceleration $a$ of point $P$ on the rim of the disk at this instant.

*Solution.* Point $A$ will be taken as the origin of the rotating coordinate system with the $x$-axis attached to the line $OA$. The $z$-axis is out from the paper to form a right-handed set $x$, $y$, $z$. The following terms appear in the velocity and acceleration relations:

$$R = 10i, \quad \rho = 4j, \quad \omega = 6k, \quad \dot\omega = 3k$$

$$\dot R = v_A = \omega \times R = 6k \times 10i = 60j$$

$$\omega \times \rho = 6k \times 4j = -24i$$

$$\dot\rho_r = i\dot x + j\dot y = -\rho p i = -16i$$

$$\ddot R = a_A = \dot\omega \times R + \omega \times \dot R = (3k \times 10i) + (6k \times 60j) = 30j - 360i$$

$$\omega \times (\omega \times \rho) = 6k \times (-24i) = -144j$$

$$\dot\omega \times \rho = 3k \times 4j = -12i$$

$$2\omega \times \dot\rho_r = 12k \times (-16i) = -192j$$

$$\ddot\rho_r = i\ddot x + j\ddot y = -\rho\dot p i - \rho p^2 j = -8i - 64j$$

Special attention is called to the fact, covered in the derivation in Art. B10, that $\dot\rho_r$ and $\ddot\rho_r$ represent the velocity and acceleration measured relative to the rotating axes so do not involve the time derivatives of the unit vectors which are attached to these axes.

The velocity of $P$ at the instant considered is, from Eq. B15,

$$v_B = v_A + \omega \times \rho + \dot\rho_r$$
$$= 60j - 24i - 16i = -40i + 60j \text{ in./sec.} \qquad Ans.$$

The magnitude is $v_B = \sqrt{(40)^2 + (60)^2} = 72.1$ in./sec.

Likewise the acceleration of $P$ at this instant is, from Eq. B16,

$$a_B = a_A + \omega \times (\omega \times \rho) + \dot\omega \times \rho + 2\omega \times \dot\rho_r + \ddot\rho_r$$
$$= (30j - 360i) - 144j - 12i - 192j + (-8i - 64j)$$
$$= -380i - 370j \text{ in./sec.}^2 \qquad Ans.$$

The magnitude is $a_B = \sqrt{(380)^2 + (370)^2} = 531$ in./sec.$^2$

Both $v_B$ and $a_B$ are shown in the figure.

# MOMENTS OF INERTIA

## I. MOMENTS OF INERTIA OF AREAS

**C1. Definitions.** There are many problems in engineering which involve the evaluation of an integral of the form $\int y^2 \, dA$ where $y$ is the distance from an element of area $dA$ to an axis which is either in or normal to the plane of the area. Integrals of this form appear so frequently that it is of great advantage to develop them for some of the more common areas and to tabulate the results for easy reference.

Figure C1 illustrates the physical origin of these integrals. In the $a$-part of the figure the surface area $ABCD$ is subjected to a distributed pressure $p$ whose intensity is proportional to the distance $y$ from the axis $AB$. This situation was covered in Art. 43 of Part I, "Pressure on Submerged Surfaces," and describes the action of liquid pressure on a plane surface. The moment about $AB$ that is due to the pressure on the element of area $dA$ is $py \, dA = ky^2 \, dA$. Thus the integral in question appears when the total moment $M = k \int y^2 \, dA$ is evaluated.

In the $b$-part of Fig. C1 is shown the distribution of stress acting on a transverse section of a simple elastic beam bent by equal and opposite couples applied to its ends. At any section of the beam a linear distribution of force intensity or stress, given by $\sigma = ky$, is present. The elemental moment about the axis $O\text{--}O$ is $dM = \sigma y \, dA = ky^2 \, dA$. Thus the same integral appears when the total moment $M = k \int y^2 \, dA$ is evaluated. A third example is given in the $c$-part of Fig. C1 which shows a circular shaft subjected to a twist or torsional moment. Within the elastic limits of the material this moment is resisted at each cross section of the shaft by a distribution of tangential or shear stress $\tau$ which is proportional to the radial distance $r$ from the center. Thus $\tau = kr$, and the total moment about the central axis is $M = \int \tau r \, dA$ $= k \int r^2 \, dA$. Here the integral differs from the preceding two examples in that the area is normal instead of parallel to the moment axis and that $r$ is a radial coordinate instead of a rectangular one.

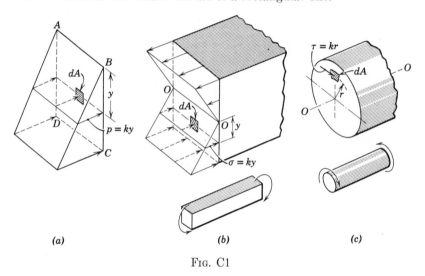

(a)                    (b)                    (c)

FIG. C1

The integral just illustrated is generally called the *moment of inertia* of the area about the axis in question. A more fitting term is the *second moment of area* since the first moment $y \, dA$ is multiplied again by the moment arm $y$ to obtain the result for the element $dA$. The word *inertia* appears in the terminology by reason of the similarity between the mathematical form of the integrals for second moments of areas and those for the resultant moments of the so-called inertia forces in the case of rotating bodies. The moment of inertia of an area is a purely mathematical property of the area and in itself has no physical significance.

Consider the area $A$ in the $x$–$y$ plane, Fig. C2. The moments of inertia of the element $dA$ about the $x$- and $y$-axes are, by definition, $dI_x = y^2 \, dA$ and $dI_y = x^2 \, dA$, respectively. Therefore the moments of inertia of $A$ about the same axes are

$$I_x = \int y^2 \, dA,$$

$$(C1)$$

$$I_y = \int x^2 \, dA,$$

where the integration covers the entire area. The moment of inertia of $dA$ about the pole $O$ ($z$-axis) is, by similar definition, $dJ_z = r^2 \, dA$, and the moment of inertia of the entire area about $O$ is

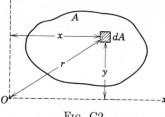

$$J_z = \int r^2 \, dA. \qquad (C2)$$

The expressions defined by Eqs. C1 are known as *rectangular* moments of inertia, whereas the expression of Eq. C2

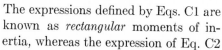

Fig. C2

is known as the *polar* moment of inertia. Since $x^2 + y^2 = r^2$, it is clear that

$$J_z = I_x + I_y. \qquad (C3)$$

A polar moment of inertia for an area whose boundaries are more simply described in rectangular coordinates than in polar coordinates is easily calculated with the aid of Eq. C3.

It should be noted that the moment of inertia of an element involves the square of the distance from the inertia axis to the element. An element whose coordinate is negative contributes as much to the moment of inertia as does an element with a positive coordinate of the same magnitude. Consequently the moment of inertia of an area about any axis is always a positive quantity. In contrast, the first moment of the area, which was involved in the computations of centroids, could be either positive or negative.

The dimensions of moments of inertia of areas are clearly $L^4$, where $L$ stands for the dimension of length. Thus the units for area moments of inertia are expressed as quartic inches (in.$^4$) or quartic feet (ft.$^4$).

The choice of the coordinates to use for the calculation of moments of inertia is important. Rectangular coordinates should be used for shapes whose boundaries are most easily expressed in these coordinates. Polar coordinates will usually simplify problems involving boundaries which are easily described in $r$ and $\theta$. The choice of an element of area which simplifies the integration as much as possible is also important. These considerations are quite analogous to those discussed in Chapter 5 of Part 1 in the calculation of centroids.

**C2. Radius of Gyration.** The moment of inertia of an area is a measure of the distribution of the area from the axis in question. Assume all the area $A$, Fig. C3, to be concentrated into a strip of negligible thickness at a distance $k_x$ from the $x$-axis so that the product $k_x{}^2 A$ equals the moment of inertia about the axis. The distance $k_x$,

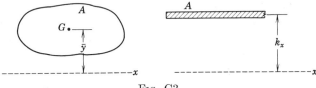

Fig. C3

called the *radius of gyration*, is then a measure of the distribution of area from the inertia axis. By definition, then, for any axis

$$I = k^2 A \qquad \text{or} \qquad k = \sqrt{\frac{I}{A}}. \tag{C4}$$

When this definition is substituted in each of the three terms in Eq. C3, there results

$$k_z{}^2 = k_x{}^2 + k_y{}^2. \tag{C5}$$

Thus the square of the radius of gyration about a polar axis equals the sum of the squares of the radii of gyration about the two corresponding rectangular axes.

It is imperative that there be no confusion between the coordinate $\bar{y}$ to the centroid of the area and the radius of gyration $k$. The square of the centroidal distance, Fig. C3, is $\bar{y}^2$ and is the square of the mean value of the distances $y$ from the elements $dA$ to the axis. The quantity $k_x{}^2$, on the other hand, is the mean of the squares of these distances. The moment of inertia is *not* equal to $A\bar{y}^2$ since the square of the mean is not equal to the mean of the squares.

**C3. Transfer of Axes.** The moment of inertia of an area about a noncentroidal axis may be easily expressed in terms of the moment of inertia about a parallel centroidal axis. In Fig. C4 the $x_o$–$y_o$ axes pass through the centroid $G$ of the area. Let it be desired to determine the moments of inertia of the area about the parallel $x$–$y$ axes.

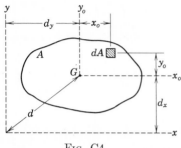

FIG. C4

By definition the moment of inertia of the element $dA$ about the $x$-axis is

$$dI_x = (y_o + d_x)^2 \, dA.$$

Expanding and integrating give

$$I_x = \int y_o{}^2 \, dA + 2d_x \int y_o \, dA + d_x{}^2 \int dA.$$

The first integral is the moment of inertia $\bar{I}_x$ about the centroidal $x_o$-axis. The second integral is zero since $A\bar{y}_o = \int y_o \, dA$ and $\bar{y}_o$ is automatically zero. The third integral is simply $Ad_x{}^2$. Thus the expression for $I_x$ and the similar expression for $I_y$ become

$$
\begin{aligned}
I_x &= \bar{I}_x + Ad_x{}^2, \\
I_y &= \bar{I}_y + Ad_y{}^2.
\end{aligned}
\tag{C6}
$$

By Eq. C3 the sum of these two equations gives

$$J_z = \bar{J}_z + Ad^2. \tag{C6a}$$

Equations C6 and C6a are the so-called *parallel-axis theorems*. Two points in particular should be noted. First, the axes between which the transfer is made must be parallel, and, second, one of the axes must pass through the centroid of the area.

If a transfer is desired between two parallel axes neither one of which passes through the centroid, it is first necessary to transfer from one axis to the parallel centroidal axis and then to transfer from the centroidal axis to the second axis.

The parallel-axis theorems also hold for radii of gyration. With substitution of the definition of $k$ into Eqs. C6, the transfer relation becomes

$$k^2 = \bar{k}^2 + d^2, \tag{C6b}$$

where $\bar{k}$ is the radius of gyration about a centroidal axis parallel to the axis about which $k$ applies and $d$ is the distance between the two axes. The axes may be either in the plane or normal to the plane of the area.

A summary of the moment of inertia relations for some of the common plane figures is given in Table D5, Appendix D.

### SAMPLE PROBLEMS

**C1.** Determine the moments of inertia of the rectangular area about the centroidal $x_o$–$y_o$ axes, the centroidal polar axis $G$, the $x$-axis, and the polar axis $O$.

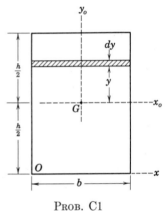

PROB. C1

*Solution.* For the calculation of the moment of inertia $\bar{I}_x$ about the $x_o$-axis a horizontal strip of area $b\,dy$ is chosen so that all elements of the strip have the same $y$-coordinate. Thus

$$[I_x = \int y^2\,dA] \qquad \bar{I}_x = \int_{-h/2}^{h/2} y^2 b\,dy = \tfrac{1}{12}bh^3. \qquad Ans.$$

By interchanging symbols the moment of inertia about the centroidal $y_o$-axis is

$$\bar{I}_y = \tfrac{1}{12}hb^3. \qquad Ans.$$

The centroidal polar moment of inertia is

$$[J_z = I_x + I_y] \qquad \bar{J}_z = \tfrac{1}{12}(bh^3 + hb^3) = \tfrac{1}{12}A(b^2+h^2). \qquad Ans.$$

By the parallel-axis theorem the moment of inertia about the $x$-axis is

$$[I_x = \bar{I}_x + Ad_x^2] \qquad I_x = \tfrac{1}{12}bh^3 + bh\left(\frac{h}{2}\right)^2 = \tfrac{1}{3}bh^3 = \tfrac{1}{3}Ah^2. \qquad Ans.$$

The polar moment of inertia about $O$ may also be obtained by the parallel-axis theorem. Thus

$$[J_z = \bar{J}_z + Ad^2] \qquad J_z = \tfrac{1}{12}A(b^2 + h^2) + A\left[\left(\frac{b}{2}\right)^2 + \left(\frac{h}{2}\right)^2\right],$$

$$J_z = \tfrac{1}{3}A(b^2 + h^2). \qquad\qquad Ans.$$

**C2.** Calculate the moments of inertia of the area of the circle about a diametral axis and about the polar axis through the center. Specify the radii of gyration.

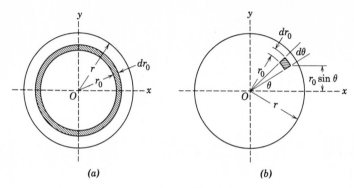

PROB. C2

*Solution.* An element of area in the form of a circular ring, shown in the $a$-part of the figure, may be used for the calculation of the moment of inertia about the polar $z$-axis through $O$ since all elements of the ring are equidistant from $O$. The elemental area is $dA = 2\pi r_o\, dr_o$, and thus

$$[J_z = \int r^2\, dA] \qquad J_z = \int_0^r r_o{}^2(2\pi r_o\, dr_o) = \frac{\pi r^4}{2} = \tfrac{1}{2}Ar^2. \qquad Ans.$$

The polar radius of gyration is

$$\left[k = \sqrt{\frac{J}{A}}\right] \qquad\qquad k_z = \frac{r}{\sqrt{2}}. \qquad\qquad Ans.$$

By symmetry $I_x = I_y$, so that from Eq. C3

$$[J_z = I_x + I_y] \qquad\qquad I_x = \tfrac{1}{2}J_z = \frac{\pi r^4}{4} = \tfrac{1}{4}Ar^2. \qquad Ans.$$

The radius of gyration about the diametral axis is

$$\left[k = \sqrt{\frac{I}{A}}\right] \qquad\qquad k_x = \frac{r}{2}. \qquad\qquad Ans.$$

The foregoing determination of $I_x$ is the simplest possible. The result may also be obtained by direct integration, using the element of area $dA = r_o\, dr_o\, d\theta$

shown in the $b$-part of the figure. By definition

$$[I_x = \int y^2\, dA] \qquad I_x = \int_0^{2\pi}\int_0^r (r_o \sin\theta)^2 r_o\, dr_o\, d\theta,$$

$$= \int_0^{2\pi} \frac{r^4 \sin^2\theta}{4}\, d\theta = \frac{r^4}{4}\frac{1}{2}\left[\theta - \frac{\sin 2\theta}{2}\right]_0^{2\pi} = \frac{\pi r^4}{4}. \quad Ans.$$

**C3.** Determine the moments of inertia of the triangular area about its base and about parallel axes through its centroid and vertex.

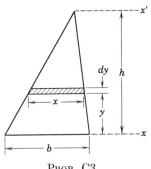

PROB. C3

*Solution.* A strip of area parallel to the base is selected as shown in the figure and it has the area $dA = x\, dy = [(h-y)b/h]\, dy$. By definition

$$[I_x = \int y^2\, dA] \qquad I_x = \int_0^h y^2 \frac{h-y}{h} b\, dy = b\left[\frac{y^3}{3} - \frac{y^4}{4h}\right]_0^h = \frac{bh^3}{12}. \quad Ans.$$

By the parallel-axis theorem the moment of inertia $\bar{I}$ about an axis through the centroid, a distance $h/3$ above the $x$-axis, is

$$[\bar{I} = I - Ad^2] \qquad \bar{I} = \frac{bh^3}{12} - \left(\frac{bh}{2}\right)\left(\frac{h}{3}\right)^2 = \frac{bh^3}{36}. \qquad Ans.$$

A transfer from the centroidal axis to the $x'$-axis through the vertex gives

$$[I = \bar{I} + Ad^2] \qquad I_{x'} = \frac{bh^3}{36} + \left(\frac{bh}{2}\right)\left(\frac{2h}{3}\right)^2 = \frac{bh^3}{4}. \qquad Ans.$$

**C4.** Determine the moment of inertia about the $x$-axis of the semicircular area shown.

*Solution.* The moment of inertia of the semicircular area about the $x'$-axis is one half of that for a complete circle about the same axis. Thus from the results of Prob. C2

$$I_{x'} = \frac{1}{2}\frac{\pi r^4}{4} = \frac{2^4\pi}{8} = 2\pi \text{ in.}^4$$

The moment of inertia $\bar{I}$ about the parallel centroidal axis $x_o$ is obtained next.

Transfer is made through the distance $\bar{r} = 4r/3\pi = (4 \times 2)/3\pi = 8/3\pi$ in. by the parallel-axis theorem. Hence

$$[\bar{I} = I - Ad^2] \qquad \bar{I} = 2\pi - \left(\frac{2^2\pi}{2}\right)\left(\frac{8}{3\pi}\right)^2 = 1.755 \text{ in.}^4$$

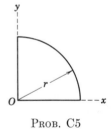

PROB. C4

Finally, tiansfer is made from the centroidal $x_o$-axis to the $x$-axis, which gives

$$[I = \bar{I} + Ad^2] \qquad I_x = 1.755 + \left(\frac{2^2\pi}{2}\right)\left(3 + \frac{8}{3\pi}\right)^2,$$

$$= 1.755 + 93.1 = 94.9 \text{ in.}^4 \qquad Ans.$$

## PROBLEMS

**C5.** Find the moments of inertia of the area of the quarter circle shown about the diametral $x$-axis and the polar axis through $O$.    *Ans.* $I_x = \dfrac{\pi r^4}{16}, J_z = \dfrac{\pi r^4}{8}$

PROB. C5      PROB. C6

**C6.** Find the moments of inertia of the area of the parallelogram about the base ($x$-axis) and about a parallel centroidal axis. (Compare with Sample Prob. C1.)

**C7.** Approximate the result for the moment of inertia of a circular area about a diameter by dividing the circle into strips parallel to the inertia axis and of width $r/5$. Treat the moment of inertia of each strip as its area times the square of the distance from its center to the axis.

**C8.** Find the radius of gyration $k$ of a square of side $b$ about one diagonal.

$$Ans. \quad k = \frac{b}{2\sqrt{3}}$$

**C9.** Find the moment of inertia of the shaded area about the $x$-axis by taking a horizontal strip of area $dA$.     $Ans. \quad I_x = \frac{4}{15}ab^3$

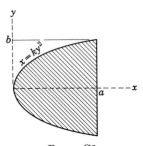

PROB. C9

**C10.** Solve Prob. C9 by choosing a vertical strip of area $dA$ and applying the results of Sample Prob. C1 to this element.

**C11.** Find the moment of inertia of the figure in Prob. C9 about the $y$-axis.

$$Ans. \quad I_y = \frac{4}{7}a^3b$$

**C12.** Calculate the moments of inertia of the elliptical area about the major axes and the central polar axis.

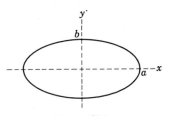

PROB. C12

**C13.** The $x$- and $x'$-axes are located from the centroid $G$ of the irregular area as shown. If the moments of inertia about these axes are $I_x = 1800$ in.$^4$ and $I_{x'} = 2200$ in.$^4$, determine the area $A$ of the figure.     $Ans. \quad A = 20$ in.$^2$

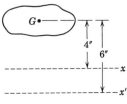

PROB. C13

**C14.** Use the results of Probs. C9 and C11 to find the polar moment of inertia $J$ of the figure in Prob. C9 about the point $(a, 0)$. (The centroid is a distance $3a/5$ from the origin, and the area of the figure is $4ab/3$.)

**C15.** Determine the moments of inertia of the area of the circular sector about the $x$- and $y$-axes.

$$Ans. \quad I_x = \frac{r^4}{4}\left(\alpha - \frac{\sin 2\alpha}{2}\right), \quad I_y = \frac{r^4}{4}\left(\alpha + \frac{\sin 2\alpha}{2}\right)$$

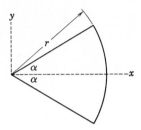

PROB. C15

**C16.** The area of a circular ring of inside radius $r$ and outside radius $r + \Delta r$ is approximately equal to the circumference at the mean radius times the thickness $\Delta r$. The polar moment of inertia of the ring may be approximated by multiplying this area by the square of the mean radius. What per cent error is involved if $\Delta r = r/10$?      *Ans.* Error $= 0.226\%$

**C4. Composite Areas.** The moment of inertia of a composite area about a particular axis is the algebraic sum of the moments of inertia of the various parts about the same axis. The results of the problems in Art. C3 and the tabulation of results in Table D5, Appendix D, may be used to determine the moments of inertia for component parts of the shapes given. It is often convenient to regard a composite area as composed of positive and negative parts. The moment of inertia of a negative area is a minus quantity.

When the section is composed of a large number of parts, it is convenient to tabulate the results for the parts in terms of the area $A$, centroidal moment of inertia $\bar{I}$, distance $d$ from the centroidal axis to the axis about which the moment of inertia of the entire section is being computed, and the product $Ad^2$. For any one of the parts the desired moment of inertia is $\bar{I} + Ad^2$, and thus for the entire section the desired moment of inertia may be expressed as $I = \Sigma \bar{I} + \Sigma Ad^2$.

**C17.** Compute the moment of inertia and radius of gyration about the $x$-axis for the cross section shown.

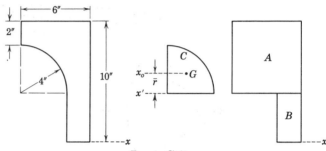

PROB. C17

*Solution.* The composite area may be considered as composed of the two rectangles $A$ and $B$ and the negative quarter circular area $C$. For the rectangle $A$ the moment of inertia about the $x$-axis is

$$[I = \bar{I} + Ad^2] \qquad I_x = \tfrac{1}{12} \times 6 \times 6^3 + 6^2 \times 7^2 = 1872 \text{ in.}^4$$

The moment of inertia of $B$ about the $x$-axis is

$$I_x = \tfrac{1}{3} \times 2 \times 4^3 = 42.67 \text{ in.}^4$$

The moment of inertia of the negative quarter circle $C$ about its horizontal diameter is

$$I_{x'} = -\tfrac{1}{4} \times \tfrac{1}{4}\pi \times 4^4 = -50.27 \text{ in.}^4$$

Transfer of this result through the distance $\bar{r} = 4r/3\pi = (4 \times 4)/3\pi = 1.697$ in. gives for the centroidal moment of inertia of $C$

$$[\bar{I} = I - Ad^2] \qquad I = -50.27 - \left(-\frac{\pi}{4} \times 4^2\right)(1.697)^2 = -14.07 \text{ in.}^4$$

The moment of inertia of $C$ may now be found with respect to the $x$-axis, and the transfer from the centroidal axis gives

$$[I = \bar{I} + Ad^2] \qquad I_x = -14.07 + \left(-\frac{\pi}{4} \times 4^2\right)(4 + 1.697)^2 = -422 \text{ in.}^4$$

The moment of inertia of the net section about the $x$-axis is the sum of moments of inertia of its component parts. Thus

$$I_x = 1872 + 42.7 - 422 = 1493 \text{ in.}^4, \qquad\qquad Ans.$$

and

$$k_x = \sqrt{\frac{I_x}{A}} = \sqrt{\frac{1493}{31.43}} = 6.89 \text{ in.} \qquad\qquad Ans.$$

## PROBLEMS

**C18.** Determine the polar moment of inertia $J$ for the section about point $O$.
$$Ans. \quad J = 138.9 \text{ in.}^4$$

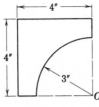

PROB. C18

**C19.** Find the polar moment of inertia $J$ about point $O$ for the cross section bounded by the two squares.

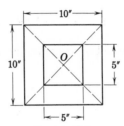

PROB. C19

**C20.** Find the polar moment of inertia of the net area about $O$.

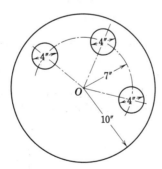

PROB. C20

**C21.** Determine the moment of inertia of the area of a rectangle of sides $a$ and $b$ about a diagonal.
$$Ans. \quad I = \frac{a^3 b^3}{6(a^2 + b^2)}$$

**C22.** Find the moment of inertia about the $x$-axis of the area between the curves $x = y^2$ and $x = y$ from $x = 0$ to $x = 1$, where $x$ and $y$ are in inches.

**C23.** Determine the moments of inertia of the $Z$-section about the centroidal $x_o$- and $y_o$-axes.

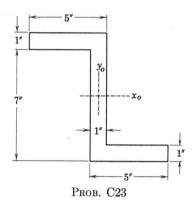
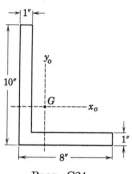

PROB. C23                 PROB. C24

**C24.** Determine the moment of inertia of the angle section about its horizontal centroidal axis $x_o$.          *Ans.* $\bar{I}_x = 167.3$ in.$^4$

**C25.** Determine the moment of inertia of the area of the hexagon of side $b$ about the $x$-axis.

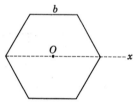

PROB. C25

**C26.** Determine the polar moment of inertia $J$ of the hexagonal area of Prob. C25 about $O$.

$$Ans. \quad J = \frac{5\sqrt{3}}{8} b^4$$

**C27.** Determine the radius of gyration of the section about the 45 deg. axis of symmetry. (*Hint:* Use the results of Prob. C15.)

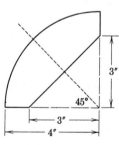

PROB. C27

**C28.** In the calculation of the stability of a ship's hull it is necessary to know the moment of inertia about the longitudinal center line of the area of the horizontal cross section of the hull at the waterline. Estimate this moment of inertia for the waterline shape reproduced here by dividing the area into a number of approximating strips.  *Ans.* $I \cong 53,000$ ft.$^4$

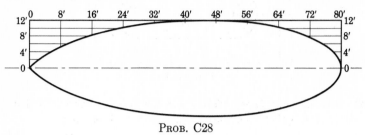

PROB. C28

**C29.** Determine the moment of inertia of the built-up structural section about its centroidal $x_o$-axis.

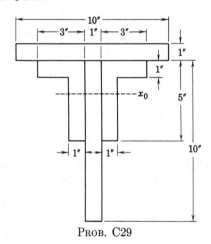

PROB. C29

**C30.** Calculate the moment of inertia of the standard $12 \times 4$ in. channel section about the centroidal $x_o$-axis. Neglect the fillets and radii and compare with the handbook value of $\bar{I}_x = 16.0$ in.$^4$

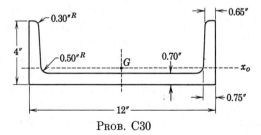

PROB. C30

**C31.** Determine the moment of inertia about the $x$-axis of the cross section shown.      *Ans.*   $I_x = 1611$ in.$^4$

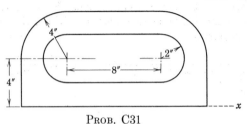

PROB. C31

**C32.** Determine the flange width $b$ for the H-beam section so that the moments of inertia about the central $x$- and $y$-axes will be equal.

                                 *Ans.*   $b = 16.1$ in.

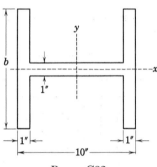

PROB. C32

## C5. Product of Inertia.

In certain problems involving unsymmetrical cross sections an expression occurs which has the form

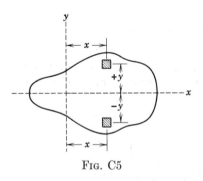

FIG. C5

$$dP_{xy} = xy\, dA,$$

$$P_{xy} = \int xy\, dA,$$

(C7)

where $x$ and $y$ are the coordinates of the element of area $dA$. The quantity $P_{xy}$ is called the *product of inertia* of the area $A$ about the $x$-$y$ axes. Unlike moments of inertia, the product of inertia can be positive or negative.

By reference to Fig. C5 it can be seen for an axis of symmetry, such as the $x$-axis, that the sum of the terms $x(-y)\, dA$ and $x(+y)\, dA$ due to symmetrically placed elements vanishes. Since the entire area may be considered as composed of pairs of such elements, it follows that the product of inertia vanishes.

A transfer-of-axis theorem exists for products of inertia which is similar to that for moments of inertia. By definition the product of inertia of the area $A$ in Fig. C4 about the $x$- and $y$-axes in terms of the coordinates $x_o$, $y_o$ to the centroidal axes is

$$P_{xy} = \int (x_o + d_y)(y_o + d_x)\, dA,$$

$$= \int x_o y_o\, dA + d_x \int x_o\, dA + d_y \int y_o\, dA + d_x d_y \int dA,$$

$$P_{xy} = \bar{P}_{xy} + d_x d_y A, \tag{C8}$$

where $\bar{P}_{xy}$ is the product of inertia with respect to the centroidal $x_o$-$y_o$ axes which are parallel to the $x$-$y$ axes.

**C6. Inclined Axes.** It is often necessary to calculate the moment of inertia of an area about inclined axes. This consideration leads directly to the important problem of determining the axes about which the moment of inertia is a maximum and a minimum.

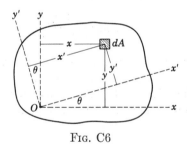

FIG. C6

In Fig. C6 the moments of inertia of the area about the $x'$- and $y'$-axes are

$$I_{x'} = \int y'^2\, dA = \int (y \cos \theta - x \sin \theta)^2\, dA,$$

$$I_{y'} = \int x'^2\, dA = \int (y \sin \theta + x \cos \theta)^2\, dA.$$

Expanding and substituting the trigonometric identities,

$$\sin^2 \theta = \frac{1 - \cos 2\theta}{2}, \qquad \cos^2 \theta = \frac{1 + \cos 2\theta}{2},$$

and the defining relations for $I_x$, $I_y$, $P_{xy}$ give

$$I_{x'} = \frac{I_x + I_y}{2} + \frac{I_x - I_y}{2} \cos 2\theta - P_{xy} \sin 2\theta,$$

$$I_{y'} = \frac{I_x + I_y}{2} - \frac{I_x - I_y}{2} \cos 2\theta + P_{xy} \sin 2\theta.$$

(C9)

In a similar manner

$$P_{x'y'} = \int x'y' \, dA = \frac{I_x - I_y}{2} \sin 2\theta + P_{xy} \cos 2\theta. \qquad (C9a)$$

Adding Eqs. C9 gives $I_{x'} + I_{y'} = I_x + I_y = J_z$, the polar moment of inertia about $O$, which checks the result of Eq. C3.

The angle which makes $I_{x'}$ and $I_{y'}$ a maximum or a minimum may be determined by setting the derivative of either $I_{x'}$ or $I_{y'}$ with respect to $\theta$ equal to zero. Thus

$$\frac{dI_{x'}}{d\theta} = (I_y - I_x) \sin 2\theta - 2P_{xy} \cos 2\theta = 0.$$

Denoting this critical angle by $\alpha$ gives

$$\tan 2\alpha = \frac{2P_{xy}}{I_y - I_x}. \qquad (C10)$$

Equation C10 gives two values for $2\alpha$ which differ by $\pi$ since $\tan 2\alpha = \tan (2\alpha + \pi)$. Consequently the two solutions for $\alpha$ will differ by $\pi/2$. One value defines the axis of maximum moment of inertia, and the other value defines the axis of minimum moment of inertia.

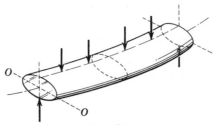

Fɪɢ. C7

These two rectangular axes are known as the *principal axes of inertia*. Substitution of Eq. C10 in Eq. C9a shows that the product of inertia is zero for principal axes of inertia. A beam of oval cross section loaded transversely, Fig. C7, if free to rotate about its longitudinal axis, will turn until the horizontal axis of its cross section is the minimum axis of inertia *O–O*.

The relations in Eqs. C9, C9a, and C10 may be represented graphically by a diagram known as Mohr's circle. For given values of $I_x$, $I_y$, and $P_{xy}$ the corresponding values of $I_{x'}$, $I_{y'}$, and $P_{x'y'}$ may be determined from the diagram for any desired angle $\theta$. A horizontal axis for the measurement of moments of inertia and a vertical axis for the measurement of products of inertia are first selected, Fig. C8. Next,

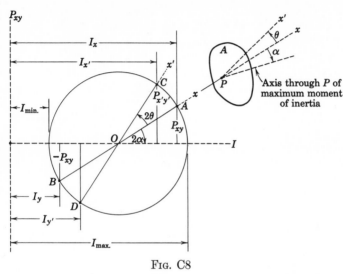

FIG. C8

point *A*, which has the coordinates $(I_x, P_{xy})$, and point *B*, which has the coordinates $(I_y, -P_{xy})$, are located. A circle is drawn with these two points as the extremities of a diameter. The angle from the radius *OA* to the horizontal axis is $2\alpha$ or twice the angle from the *x*-axis of the area in question to the axis of maximum moment of inertia. Both the angle on the diagram and the angle on the area are measured in the same sense as shown. The coordinates of any point *C* are $(I_{x'}, P_{x'y'})$, and those of the corresponding point *D* are $(I_{y'}, -P_{x'y'})$. Also the angle between *OA* and *OC* is $2\theta$ or twice the angle from the *x*-axis to the *x'*-axis. Again both angles are measured in the same sense as shown. It may be verified from the trigonometry of the circle that Eqs. C9, C9a, and C10 agree with the statements made.

## SAMPLE PROBLEMS

**C33.** Determine the product of inertia for the area under the parabola shown.

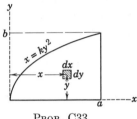

Prob. C33

*Solution.* The equation of the curve becomes $x = ay^2/b^2$. The product of inertia for the element $dA = dx\, dy$ is $dP_{xy} = xy\, dx\, dy$ and for the entire area is

$$P_{xy} = \int_0^b \int_{ay^2/b^2}^a xy\, dx\, dy = \int_0^b \frac{1}{2}\left(a^2 - \frac{a^2 y^4}{b^4}\right) y\, dy = \tfrac{1}{6}a^2 b^2. \qquad Ans.$$

**C34.** Locate the principal centroidal axes of inertia with their corresponding maximum and minimum moments of inertia for the angle section.

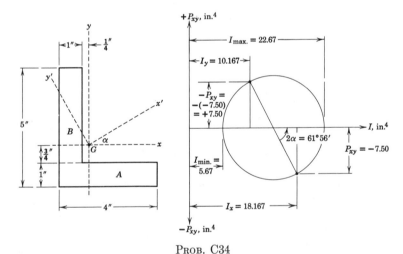

Prob. C34

*Solution.* The centroid $G$ is easily located as shown. The product of inertia for each rectangle about its own centroidal axes parallel to the $x$- and $y$-axes is zero by symmetry. Thus the product of inertia for part $A$ is

$$[P_{xy} = \bar{P}_{xy} + d_x d_y A] \qquad P_{xy} = 0 + (-\tfrac{5}{4})(+\tfrac{3}{4})(4) = -3.75 \text{ in.}^4$$

Likewise for $B$,

$$[P_{xy} = \bar{P}_{xy} + d_x d_y A] \qquad P_{xy} = 0 + (\tfrac{5}{4})(-\tfrac{3}{4})(4) = -3.75 \text{ in.}^4$$

For the complete angle

$$P_{xy} = -3.75 - 3.75 = -7.50 \text{ in.}^4$$

The moments of inertia for part $A$ are

$$[I = \bar{I} + Ad^2] \qquad I_x = \tfrac{1}{12} \times 4 \times 1^3 + (\tfrac{5}{4})^2 \times 4 = 6.583 \text{ in.}^4,$$

$$I_y = \tfrac{1}{12} \times 1 \times 4^3 + (\tfrac{3}{4})^2 \times 4 = 7.583 \text{ in.}^4$$

In similar manner the moments of inertia for part $B$ are $I_x = 11.583$ in.$^4$, $I_y = 2.583$ in.$^4$ Thus for the entire section

$$I_x = 6.583 + 11.583 = 18.167 \text{ in.}^4,$$

$$I_y = 7.583 + 2.583 = 10.167 \text{ in.}^4$$

The inclination of the principal axes of inertia is given by Eq. C10. Therefore

$$\left[ \tan 2\alpha = \frac{2P_{xy}}{I_y - I_x} \right] \qquad \tan 2\alpha = \frac{-2 \times 7.50}{10.167 - 18.167} = 1.875,$$

$$2\alpha = 61° \, 56', \qquad \alpha = 30° \, 58'. \qquad\qquad Ans.$$

From Eqs. C9 the principal moments of inertia are

$$I_{max.} = I_{x'} = \frac{18.167 + 10.167}{2} + \frac{18.167 - 10.167}{2} \times 0.4705 + 7.50 \times 0.8824$$

$$= 22.67 \text{ in.}^4; \qquad\qquad Ans.$$

$$I_{min.} = I_{y'} = \frac{18.167 + 10.167}{2} - \frac{18.167 - 10.167}{2} \times 0.4705 - 7.50 \times 0.8824$$

$$= 5.67 \text{ in.}^4 \qquad\qquad Ans.$$

These results may also be obtained graphically by construction of the Mohr circle as shown to the right of the angle in the figure.

## PROBLEMS

**C35.** Determine the product of inertia $P_{xy}$ of the area of a rectangle about $x$- and $y$-axes coinciding with two adjacent sides of lengths $a$ and $b$. The rectangle lies in the first quadrant.

**C36.** Obtain the product of inertia for the area of the quarter circle shown with Prob. C5 about the $x$- and $y$-axes by direct integration. $\quad Ans. \quad P_{xy} = \dfrac{r^4}{8}$

**C37.** Solve Prob. C21 for the moment of inertia about a diagonal of the rectangle of sides $a$ and $b$ by the method of this article.

**C38.** The moments of inertia of an area with respect to the principal axes of inertia $x$, $y$ through a point $P$ are $I_x = 32.0$ in.$^4$ and $I_y = 12.0$ in.$^4$ With the aid of Mohr's circle determine the moment of inertia $I_{x'}$ and the product of inertia $P_{x'y'}$ for the area about axes $x'$, $y'$ through $P$ and rotated 15 deg. clockwise from the axes $x$, $y$.                    *Ans.*    $I_{x'} = 30.66$ in.$^4$, $P_{x'y'} = -5$ in.$^4$

**C39.** The moments of inertia of an area about axes $x$, $y$ through a point $P$ are $I_x = 62.8$ in.$^4$ and $I_y = 148.2$ in.$^4$ The product of inertia $P_{xy}$ is negative, and the minimum moment of inertia about the axis through $P$ is 42.8 in.$^4$ Determine with the aid of Mohr's circle the maximum moment of inertia and the angle $\alpha$ measured positive counterclockwise from the $x$-axis to the axis of maximum moment of inertia.

**C40.** Determine the maximum and minimum moments of inertia about centroidal axes for the $Z$-section of Prob. C23 and indicate the counterclockwise angle $\alpha$ made by the axis of maximum moment of inertia with the $x_o$-axis.

*Ans.*    $\bar{I}_{max.} = 181.9$ in.$^4$, $\bar{I}_{min.} = 20.7$ in.$^4$, $\alpha = 30° \, 8'$

**C41.** Determine the maximum and minimum moments of inertia about centroidal axes for the angle section of Prob. C24 and indicate the counterclockwise angle $\alpha$ made by the axis of maximum moment of inertia with the $x_o$-axis.

## II. MOMENTS OF INERTIA OF MASS

**C7. Definitions.** The mass moment of inertia of a body is a measure of the inertial resistance to rotational acceleration. In Fig. C9 the body of mass $m$ is caused to rotate about the axis $O$–$O$ with an angular acceleration $\alpha$. An element of mass $dm$ has a component of acceleration tangent to its circular path equal to $r\alpha$, and the resultant tangential force on this element equals the force $r\alpha \, dm$. The moment of this force about the axis $O$–$O$ is $r^2\alpha \, dm$. The sum of the moments of these forces for all elements is $\int r^2\alpha \, dm$. For a rigid body $\alpha$ is the same for all radial lines in the body and may be taken outside the integral sign. The remaining integral is known as the moment of inertia $I$ of the mass $m$ and is

$$I = \int r^2 \, dm. \qquad \text{(C11)}$$

Fɪɢ. C9

This integral represents an important property of a body and is involved in the force analysis of any body which has rotational acceleration. Just as the mass $m$ of a body is a measure of the resistance to translational acceleration, the moment of inertia is a measure of resistance to rotational acceleration due to the mass or inertia of the body.

If the mass density $\rho$ is constant throughout the body, the moment of inertia becomes

$$I = \rho \int r^2 \, dV,$$

where $dV$ is the element of volume. In this case the integral by itself defines a purely geometrical property of the body. When the mass density is not constant but is expressed as a function of the coordinates of the body, it must be left within the integral sign and its effect accounted for in the integration process.

If the body is a wire or slender rod of length $L$ and mass $\rho$ per unit length, the moment of inertia about an axis becomes $I = \int r^2 \rho \, dL$, where $r$ is the perpendicular distance from the element $dL$ to the axis in question. If the body is a thin flat plate of area $A$ and mass $\rho$ per unit area, the moment of inertia is $I = \int r^2 \rho \, dA$. When $\rho$ is constant over the plate, the expression becomes $I = \rho \int r^2 \, dA$. Thus the moment of inertia of the plate equals the mass per unit area times the *area* moment of inertia, described in Part I of this appendix for axes in or normal to the plane of the area.

In general the coordinates which best fit the boundaries of the body should be used in the integration. It is particularly important to make a good choice of the element of volume $dV$. An element of lowest possible order should be chosen, and the correct expression for the moment of inertia of the element about the axis involved should be used. For example, in finding the moment of inertia of a right circular cone about its central axis, a cylindrical element in the form of a circular slice of infinitesimal thickness should be used. The differential moment of inertia for this element is the correct expression for the moment of inertia of a circular cylinder of infinitesimal thickness about its central axis.

The dimensions of mass moments of inertia are (mass) $\times$ (distance)$^2$ and are usually expressed in the units *lb. ft. sec.*$^2$ Frequently the units *ft.*$^2$ *slugs* are used, where the slug is taken as the unit of mass.

**C8. Radius of Gyration.** The radius of gyration $k$ of a mass $m$ about an axis for which the moment of inertia is $I$ is

$$k = \sqrt{\frac{I}{m}} \qquad \text{or} \qquad I = k^2 m. \tag{C12}$$

Thus $k$ is a measure of the distribution of mass of a given body about the axis in question, and its definition is analogous to the definition for the radius of gyration for second moments of area. If all the mass $m$ could be concentrated at a distance $k$ from the axis, the correct moment of inertia would be $k^2 m$. The moment of inertia of a body about a particular axis is frequently indicated by specifying the radius of gyration of the body about the axis and the weight of the body. The moment of inertia is then calculated from Eq. C12.

**C9. Transfer of Axes.** If the moment of inertia of a body is known about a centroidal axis, it may be determined easily about any parallel axis. To prove this statement consider the two parallel axes in Fig.

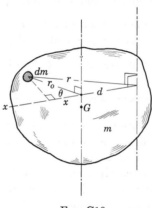

Fig. C10

C10, one of which is a centroidal axis through the center of gravity $G$. The radial distances from the two axes to any element of mass $dm$ are $r_o$ and $r$, and the separation of the axes is $d$. Substituting the law of cosines $r^2 = r_o{}^2 + d^2 + 2r_o d \cos \theta$ into the definition for the moment of inertia about the noncentroidal axis gives

$$I = \int r^2 \, dm = \int (r_o{}^2 + d^2 + 2r_o d \cos \theta) \, dm,$$

$$= \int r_o{}^2 \, dm + d^2 \int dm + 2d \int x \, dm.$$

The first integral is the moment of inertia $\bar{I}$ about the centroidal axis, the second integral is $md^2$, and the third integral equals zero since the $x$-coordinate of the center of gravity with respect to an origin at $G$ is zero. Thus the parallel-axis theorem is

$$I = \bar{I} + md^2. \tag{C13}$$

It must be remembered that the transfer cannot be made unless one axis passes through the center of gravity and unless the axes are parallel. When the expressions for the radii of gyration are substituted in Eq. C13, there results

$$k^2 = \bar{k}^2 + d^2, \qquad\qquad (C13a)$$

which is the parallel-axis theorem for obtaining the radius of gyration $k$ about an axis a distance $d$ from a parallel centroidal axis for which the radius of gyration is $\bar{k}$.

**C10. Product of Inertia.** In a few problems of advanced mechanics the integrals

$$I_{xy} = \int xy\, dm, \qquad I_{yz} = \int yz\, dm, \qquad I_{xz} = \int xz\, dm$$

are useful. These integrals are called the products of inertia of the mass $m$. They may be either positive or negative. In general, a three-dimensional body has three moments of inertia about the three mutually perpendicular coordinate axes and three products of inertia about the three coordinate planes. For an unsymmetrical body of any shape it is found that for a given origin of coordinates there is one orientation of axes for which the products of inertia vanish. These axes are called the *principal axes of inertia*. The corresponding moments of inertia about these axes are known as the *principal moments of inertia* and include the maximum possible value, the minimum possible value, and an intermediate value for any orientation of axes about the given origin.

**C11. Moment of Inertia with Respect to a Plane.** The moment of inertia of a body with respect to a plane is useful in some problems primarily as an aid to the calculation of the moment of inertia with respect to a line. The moment of inertia with respect to the $y$–$z$ plane is defined as $\int x^2\, dm$ and that with respect to the $x$–$z$ plane is $\int y^2\, dm$. Since $x^2 + y^2 = r^2$, where $r$ is the distance from $dm$ to the $z$-axis, the moment of inertia $I_z$ about the $z$-axis is

$$I_z = \int r^2\, dm = \int x^2\, dm + \int y^2\, dm.$$

Similar expressions may be written for the two other axes.

A summary of some of the more useful formulas for mass moments of inertia is given in Table D6, Appendix D.

## SAMPLE PROBLEMS

**C42.** Determine the moment of inertia and radius of gyration of a homogeneous right circular cylinder of mass $m$ and radius $r$ about its central axis $O$–$O$.

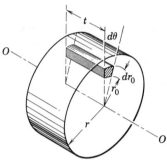

PROB. C42

*Solution.* An element of mass in cylindrical coordinates is $dm = \rho \, dV = \rho t r_o \, dr_o \, d\theta$. The moment of inertia about the axis of the cylinder is

$$I = \int r_o{}^2 \, dm = \rho t \int_0^{2\pi} \int_0^r r_o{}^3 \, dr_o \, d\theta = \rho t \frac{\pi r^4}{2} = \tfrac{1}{2} m r^2. \qquad Ans.$$

The radius of gyration is

$$k = \sqrt{\frac{I}{m}} = \frac{r}{\sqrt{2}}. \qquad Ans.$$

The result $I = \tfrac{1}{2} m r^2$ applies *only* to a solid homogeneous circular cylinder and cannot be used for any other wheel of circular periphery.

**C43.** Determine the moment of inertia and radius of gyration of a homogeneous solid sphere of mass $m$ and radius $r$ about a diameter.

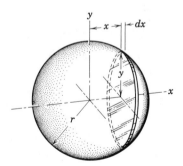

PROB. C43

*Solution.* A circular slice of radius $y$ and thickness $dx$ is chosen as the volume element. From the results of Prob. C42 the moment of inertia about the $x$-axis of the elemental cylinder is

$$dI_x = \tfrac{1}{2}(dm)y^2 = \tfrac{1}{2}(\pi\rho y^2\, dx)y^2 = \frac{\pi\rho}{2}(r^2 - x^2)^2\, dx,$$

where $\rho$ is the constant mass density of the sphere. The total moment of inertia about the $x$-axis is

$$I_x = \frac{\pi\rho}{2} \int_{-r}^{r} (r^2 - x^2)^2\, dx = \tfrac{8}{15}\pi\rho r^5 = \tfrac{2}{5}mr^2. \qquad Ans.$$

The radius of gyration is

$$k = \sqrt{\frac{I}{m}} = \sqrt{\frac{2}{5}}\, r. \qquad Ans.$$

**C44.** Determine the moments of inertia of the homogeneous rectangular parallelepiped of mass $m$ about the centroidal $x_o$- and $z$-axes and about the $x$-axis through one end.

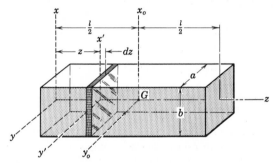

Prob. C44

*Solution.* A transverse slice of thickness $dz$ is selected as the element of volume. The moment of inertia of this slice of infinitesimal thickness equals the moment of inertia of the area of the section times the mass per unit area $\rho\, dz$. Thus the moment of inertia of the transverse slice about the $y'$-axis is

$$dI_{y'} = (\rho\, dz)(\tfrac{1}{12}ab^3),$$

and that about the $x'$-axis is

$$dI_{x'} = (\rho\, dz)(\tfrac{1}{12}a^3b).$$

As long as the element is a plate of differential thickness, the principle of Eq. C3 may be applied to give

$$dI_z = dI_{x'} + dI_{y'} = (\rho\, dz)\frac{ab}{12}(a^2 + b^2).$$

These expressions may now be integrated to obtain the desired results.

The moment of inertia about the $z$-axis is

$$I_z = \int dI_z = \frac{\rho ab}{12} (a^2 + b^2) \int_0^l dz = \tfrac{1}{12}m(a^2 + b^2), \qquad Ans.$$

where $m$ is the mass of the block. By interchanging symbols the moment of inertia about the $x_0$-axis is

$$I_{x_0} = \tfrac{1}{12}m(a^2 + l^2). \qquad Ans.$$

The moment of inertia about the $x$-axis may be found by the parallel-axis theorem, Eq. C13. Thus

$$I_x = I_{x_0} + m \left(\frac{l}{2}\right)^2 = \tfrac{1}{12}m(a^2 + 4l^2). \qquad Ans.$$

This last result may be obtained by expressing the moment of inertia of the elemental slice about the $x$-axis and integrating the expression over the length of the bar. Again by the parallel-axis theorem

$$dI_x = dI_{x'} + z^2\, dm = (\rho\, dz)(\tfrac{1}{12}a^3b) + z^2\rho ab\, dz.$$

$$= \rho ab \left(\frac{a^2}{12} + z^2\right) dz.$$

Integrating gives the result obtained previously,

$$I_x = \rho ab \int_0^l \left(\frac{a^2}{12} + z^2\right) dz = \frac{\rho abl}{3} \left(l^2 + \frac{a^2}{4}\right) = \tfrac{1}{12}m(a^2 + 4l^2).$$

The expression for $I_x$ may be simplified for a long prismatical bar or slender rod whose transverse dimensions are small compared with the length. In this case $a^2$ may be neglected compared with $4l^2$, and the moment of inertia of such a slender bar about an axis through one end normal to the bar becomes $I = \tfrac{1}{3}ml^2$. By the same approximation the moment of inertia about a centroidal axis normal to the bar is $I = \tfrac{1}{12}ml^2$.

## PROBLEMS

**C45.** A bar 10 in. long has a square cross section 1 in. on a side. Determine the percentage error $e$ in using the approximate formula $I = \tfrac{1}{3}ml^2$ for the moment of inertia about an axis normal to the bar and through the center of one end parallel to an edge. (See Prob. C44.)      *Ans.* $e = 0.249\%$

**C46.** The moment of inertia of a solid homogeneous cylinder of radius $r$ about an axis parallel to the central axis of the cylinder may be obtained approximately by multiplying the mass of the cylinder by the square of the distance $d$ between the two axes. What per cent error $e$ results if (a) $d = 10r$, (b) $d = 2r$?

**C47.** From the results of Prob. C43 state without computation the moments of inertia of the solid homogeneous hemisphere of mass $m$ about the $x$- and $z$-axes.

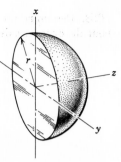

**C48.** Determine the moment of inertia of a circular ring of mass $m$ and inside and outside radii $r_1$ and $r_2$, respectively, about its central polar axis.

*Ans.* $I = \frac{1}{2}m(r_2{}^2 + r_1{}^2)$

**C49.** Calculate the moment of inertia of a homogeneous right circular cone of mass $m$ and base radius $r$ about the cone axis. *Ans.* $I = \frac{3}{10}mr^2$

PROB. C47

**C50.** Without integrating determine from the results of Probs. C43 and C49 the moments of inertia about the $z$-axis for (a) the spherical wedge and (b) the conical wedge. Each wedge has a mass $m$.

*Ans.* (a) $I_z = \frac{2}{5}ma^2$, (b) $I_z = \frac{3}{10}mr^2$

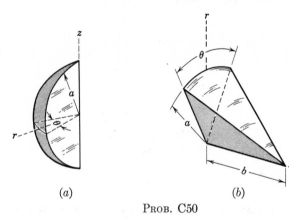

(a)                    (b)

PROB. C50

**C51.** Find the moment of inertia of the slender rod of mass $m$ about the $x$-axis.

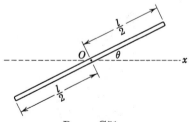

PROB. C51

**C52.** The moment of inertia of a body with respect to the $x$–$y$ plane is 0.202 lb. ft. sec.$^2$, and that with respect to the $y$–$z$ plane is 0.440 lb. ft. sec.$^2$ The radius of gyration about the $y$-axis is 1.20 ft. Find the weight $W$ of the body.

**C53.** Determine the moment of inertia of the elliptical cylinder of mass $m$ about the cylinder axis $O$-$O$.     *Ans.*   $I = \frac{1}{4}m(a^2 + b^2)$

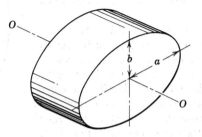

PROB. C53

**C54.** Determine the moment of inertia about the $z$-axis of the homogeneous solid paraboloid of revolution of mass $m$.

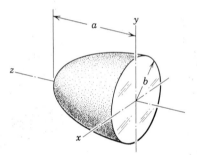

PROB. C54

**C55.** Find the moment of inertia of the tetrahedron of mass $m$ about the $z$-axis.

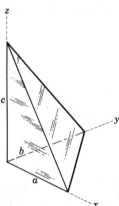

PROB. C55

**C56.** The homogeneous bar of square cross section has a mass $m$. Determine the moment of inertia of the bar about the centroidal $x$-axis shown which is a diagonal of the square section.           *Ans.* $I_x = \frac{1}{12}m(a^2 + l^2)$

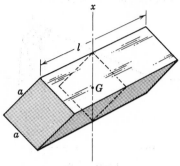

PROB. C56

**C57.** Determine the moments of inertia of the homogeneous right circular cylinder of mass $m$ about the $x_o$-, $x$-, and $y'$-axes shown.

*Ans.* $I_{x_0} = \frac{1}{12}m(3r^2 + l^2)$, $I_x = \frac{1}{12}m(3r^2 + 4l^2)$, $I_{y'} = \frac{3}{2}mr^2$

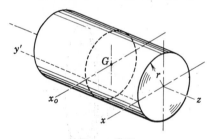

PROB. C57

**C58.** The density of a sphere of radius $r$ varies linearly with the radius from $\rho_o$ at the center to twice that value at the surface. Determine the moment of inertia of the sphere about a diameter in terms of the mass $m$ of the sphere.

**C59.** Determine the moments of inertia of the half spherical shell with re-

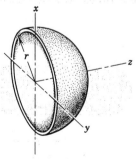

PROB. C59

spect to the $x$- and $z$-axes. The mass of the shell is $m$, and its thickness is negligible compared with the radius $r$.  $Ans.$  $I_x = I_z = \frac{2}{3}mr^2$

**C60.** Determine the moment of inertia of the conical shell of mass $m$ about the axis of rotation. Wall thickness is negligible.  $Ans.$  $I_z = \frac{1}{2}mr^2$

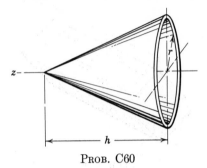

PROB. C60

**\* C61.** Determine the moment of inertia about the $z$-axis of the bell-shaped shell of uniform small thickness if the mass is $m$.  $Ans.$  $I_z = \dfrac{15\pi - 44}{6(\pi - 2)}ma^2$

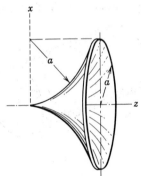

PROB. C61

**\* C62.** Determine the moment of inertia about the generating axis of a complete ring of circular section (torus) with the dimensions shown in the sectional view.  $Ans.$  $I = m(R^2 + \frac{3}{4}a^2)$

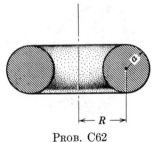

PROB. C62

**C12. Composite Bodies.** The defining integral, Eq. C11, involves the square of the distance from the axis to the element and so is always positive. Thus, as in the case of area moments of inertia, the mass moment of inertia of a composite body is the sum of the moments of inertia of the individual parts about the same axis. It is often convenient to consider a composite body as defined by positive volumes and negative volumes. The moment of inertia of a negative element, such as a hole, must be considered a minus quantity.

### PROBLEMS

**C63.** Calculate the moment of inertia about the $z$-axis of the cylinder with the hemispherical cavity if the net mass is $m$.       *Ans.* $I_z = \frac{7}{10}ma^2$

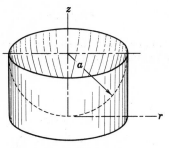

PROB. C63

**C64.** Calculate the moment of inertia about the central axis of the aluminum rotor shown in section.

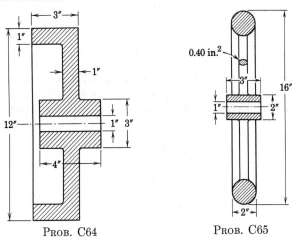

PROB. C64         PROB. C65

**C65.** Calculate the moment of inertia of the steel handwheel about its axis.

There are six spokes, each of which has a uniform cross-sectional area of 0.40 in.²                                        *Ans.  I* = 0.431 lb. ft. sec.²

**C66.** Determine the radius of gyration of the homogeneous rotor, shown in section, about its central axis.                  *Ans.  k* = 2.43 in.

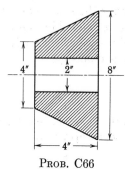

PROB. C66

**C67.** The slender rod bent into the shape shown weighs 0.52 lb./ft.  Determine the moment of inertia of the rod about the *x*-axis.

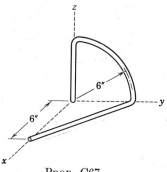

PROB. C67

**C68.** Determine the moment of inertia of the mallet with respect to the axis *O–O*.  The head is made from hardwood weighing 65 lb./ft.³, and the handle is made from steel weighing 0.283 lb./in.³      *Ans.  I_O* = 0.1896 lb. ft. sec.²

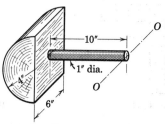

PROB. C68

**C69.** The part shown weighs 3.22 lb. Determine its moment of inertia about the axis $O–O$.

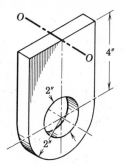

PROB. C69

\* **C70.** Determine the moments of inertia of the steel body shown about axes $A$ and $B$. *Ans.* $I_A = 0.1446$ lb. ft. sec.$^2$, $I_B = 0.302$ lb. ft. sec.$^2$

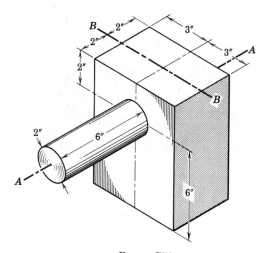

PROB. C70

* **C71.** Determine the radius of gyration of the symmetrical steel link about the axis *O–O*.                                    *Ans.*   $k = 4.36$ in.

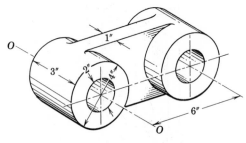

PROB. C71

* **C72.** The desired moment of inertia of the steel rocker about the *O–O* axis is 0.204 lb. ft. sec.² Determine the necessary thickness $t$.   *Ans.*   $t = 3.17$ in.

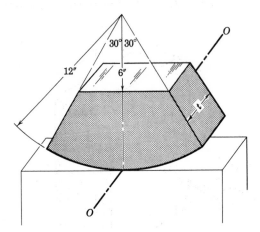

PROB. C72

# USEFUL TABLES

TABLE D1. DENSITIES, lb./ft.$^3$

| Aluminum | 168 | Mercury | 847 |
|---|---|---|---|
| Concrete (av.) | 150 | Oil (av.) | 56 |
| Copper | 556 | Steel | 489 |
| Earth (wet, av.) | 110 | Water (fresh) | 62.4 |
| (dry, av.) | 80 | (salt) | 64 |
| Ice | 56 | Wood (soft, pine) | 30 |
| Iron (cast) | 450 | (hard, oak) | 50 |
| Lead | 710 | | |

TABLE D2. COEFFICIENTS OF FRICTION

The coefficients in the following table represent typical values only. Actual coefficients for a given situation will depend on the exact nature of the contacting surfaces. A variation of the order of 25 to 100 per cent from these values could be expected in an actual problem, depending on prevailing conditions of cleanliness, roughness, pressure, lubrication, and velocity.

TABLE D2. COEFFICIENTS OF FRICTION—*Continued*

| Contacting Surfaces | Coefficient of Static Friction | Coefficient of Kinetic Friction |
|---|---|---|
| Metal on metal (dry) | 0.2 | 0.1 |
| Metal on metal (greasy) | 0.1 | 0.05 |
| Rubber or leather on wood or metal (dry) | 0.4 | 0.3 |
| Hardwood on metal (dry) | 0.6 | 0.4 |
| Hardwood on metal (greasy) | 0.2 | 0.1 |
| Hemp on metal (dry) | 0.3 | 0.2 |
| Wire rope on iron pulley (dry) | 0.2 | 0.15 |
| Rubber tires on smooth pavement (dry) | 0.9 | 0.8 |
| Asbestos brake lining on cast iron | 0.4 | 0.3 |
| Metal on ice | . . . | 0.02 |
| Steel on wet grindstone | . . . | 0.7 |
| Cast-iron brake shoes on steel railway tires | | |
| (10 m.p.h.) | . . . | 0.3 |
| (30 m.p.h.) | . . . | 0.2 |
| (60 m.p.h.) | . . . | 0.05 |

| | Coefficient of Rolling Friction, $f_r$ |
|---|---|
| Pneumatic tires on smooth pavement | 0.02 |
| Steel tires on steel rails | 0.006 |

TABLE D3. USEFUL MATHEMATICAL RELATIONS

*A. Series* (expression in bracket following series indicates range of convergence)

$$(1 \pm x)^n = 1 \pm nx + \frac{n(n-1)}{2!}x^2 \pm \frac{n(n-1)(n-2)}{3!}x^3 + \cdots \quad [x^2 < 1]$$

$$\sin x = x - \frac{x^3}{3!} + \frac{x^5}{5!} - \frac{x^7}{7!} + \cdots \quad [x^2 < \infty]$$

$$\cos x = 1 - \frac{x^2}{2!} + \frac{x^4}{4!} - \frac{x^6}{6!} + \cdots \quad [x^2 < \infty]$$

$$\sinh x = \frac{e^x - e^{-x}}{2} = x + \frac{x^3}{3!} + \frac{x^5}{5!} + \frac{x^7}{7!} + \cdots \quad [x^2 < \infty]$$

$$\cosh x = \frac{e^x + e^{-x}}{2} = 1 + \frac{x^2}{2!} + \frac{x^4}{4!} + \frac{x^6}{6!} + \cdots \quad [x^2 < \infty]$$

TABLE D3. USEFUL MATHEMATICAL RELATIONS—*Continued*

## B. *Differentials*

$$\frac{dx^n}{dx} = nx^{n-1}, \qquad \frac{d(uv)}{dx} = u\frac{dv}{dx} + v\frac{du}{dx}, \qquad \frac{d\left(\frac{u}{v}\right)}{dx} = \frac{v\frac{du}{dx} - u\frac{dv}{dx}}{v^2}$$

$$\lim_{\Delta x \to 0} \sin \Delta x = \sin dx = \tan dx = dx$$

$$\lim_{\Delta x \to 0} \cos \Delta x = \cos dx = 1$$

$$\frac{d \sin x}{dx} = \cos x, \qquad \frac{d \cos x}{dx} = -\sin x, \qquad \frac{d \tan x}{dx} = \sec^2 x$$

$$\frac{d \sinh x}{dx} = \cosh x, \qquad \frac{d \cosh x}{dx} = \sinh x, \qquad \frac{d \tanh x}{dx} = \operatorname{sech}^2 x$$

## C. *Integrals*

$$\int x^n \, dx = \frac{x^{n+1}}{n+1}$$

$$\int \frac{dx}{x} = \log x$$

$$\int \sqrt{a + bx} \, dx = \frac{2}{3b} \sqrt{(a + bx)^3}$$

$$\int \frac{dx}{\sqrt{a + bx}} = \frac{2\sqrt{a + bx}}{b}$$

$$\int \frac{x \, dx}{a + bx} = \frac{1}{b^2} [a + bx - a \log (a + bx)]$$

$$\int \frac{dx}{a + bx^2} = \frac{1}{\sqrt{ab}} \tan^{-1} \frac{x\sqrt{ab}}{a} \qquad \text{or} \qquad \frac{1}{\sqrt{-ab}} \tanh^{-1} \frac{x\sqrt{-ab}}{a}$$

$$\int \sqrt{x^2 \pm a^2} \, dx = \tfrac{1}{2}[x\sqrt{x^2 \pm a^2} \pm a^2 \log (x + \sqrt{x^2 \pm a^2})]$$

$$\int \sqrt{a^2 - x^2} \, dx = \tfrac{1}{2}\left(x\sqrt{a^2 - x^2} + a^2 \sin^{-1}\frac{x}{a}\right)$$

$$\int x\sqrt{a^2 - x^2} \, dx = -\tfrac{1}{3}\sqrt{(a^2 - x^2)^3}$$

$$\int x^2\sqrt{a^2 - x^2} \, dx = -\frac{x}{4}\sqrt{(a^2 - x^2)^3} + \frac{a^2}{8}\left(x\sqrt{a^2 - x^2} + a^2 \sin^{-1}\frac{x}{a}\right)$$

$$\int x^3\sqrt{a^2 - x^2} \, dx = -\tfrac{1}{5}(x^2 + \tfrac{2}{3}a^2)\sqrt{(a^2 - x^2)^3}$$

TABLE D3.  USEFUL MATHEMATICAL RELATIONS—*Continued*

$$\int \frac{dx}{\sqrt{x^2 \pm a^2}} = \log\left(x + \sqrt{x^2 \pm a^2}\right)$$

$$\int \frac{dx}{\sqrt{a^2 - x^2}} = \sin^{-1}\frac{x}{a}$$

$$\int x\sqrt{x^2 \pm a^2}\, dx = \tfrac{1}{3}\sqrt{(x^2 \pm a^2)^3}$$

$$\int x^2\sqrt{x^2 \pm a^2}\, dx = \frac{x}{4}\sqrt{(x^2 \pm a^2)^3} \mp \frac{a^2}{8}x\sqrt{x^2 \pm a^2} - \frac{a^4}{8}\log\left(x + \sqrt{x^2 \pm a^2}\right)$$

$$\int \frac{x\,dx}{\sqrt{x^2 - a^2}} = \sqrt{x^2 - a^2}$$

$$\int \frac{x\,dx}{\sqrt{a^2 \pm x^2}} = \pm\sqrt{a^2 \pm x^2}$$

$$\int \sin x\, dx = -\cos x$$

$$\int \cos x\, dx = \sin x$$

$$\int \sec x\, dx = \frac{1}{2}\log\frac{1 + \sin x}{1 - \sin x} \qquad \int x \sin x\, dx = \sin x - x \cos x$$

$$\int \sin^2 x\, dx = \frac{x}{2} - \frac{\sin 2x}{4} \qquad \int x \cos x\, dx = \cos x + x \sin x$$

$$\int \cos^2 x\, dx = \frac{x}{2} + \frac{\sin 2x}{4} \qquad \int \sinh x\, dx = \cosh x$$

$$\int \sin^3 x\, dx = -\frac{\cos x}{3}(2 + \sin^2 x) \qquad \int \cosh x\, dx = \sinh x$$

$$\int \cos^3 x\, dx = \frac{\sin x}{3}(2 + \cos^2 x) \qquad \int \tanh x\, dx = \log\cosh x$$

$$\int e^{ax} \sin px\, dx = \frac{e^{ax}(a \sin px - p \cos px)}{a^2 + p^2}$$

$$\int e^{ax} \cos px\, dx = \frac{e^{ax}(a \cos px + p \sin px)}{a^2 + p^2}$$

$$\int \log x\, dx = x \log x - x$$

$$\int x e^{ax}\, dx = \frac{e^{ax}}{a^2}(ax - 1)$$

TABLE D4. CENTROIDS

| | |
|---|---|
| Arc Segment $$\bar{r} = \frac{r \sin \alpha}{\alpha}$$ |  |
| Quarter and Semicircular Arcs $$\bar{y} = \frac{2r}{\pi}$$ | 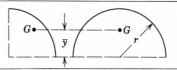 |
| Triangular Area $$\bar{y} = \frac{h}{3}$$ | 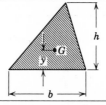 |
| Trapezoidal Area $$\bar{y} = \frac{1}{3}\frac{2a_1 + a_2}{a_1 + a_2}h$$ | 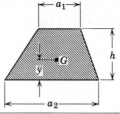 |
| Area of Circular Sector $$\bar{r} = \frac{2}{3}\frac{r \sin \alpha}{\alpha}$$ |  |
| Quarter and Semicircular Areas $$\bar{y} = \frac{4r}{3\pi}$$ | 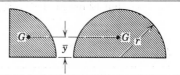 |
| Area of Elliptical Quadrant $$\bar{x} = \frac{4a}{3\pi}$$ $$\bar{y} = \frac{4b}{3\pi}$$ | 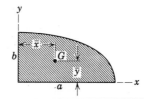 |

TABLE D4.   CENTROIDS—*Continued*

Lateral Area of Cone or Pyramid

$$\bar{y} = \frac{h}{3}$$

Area of Hemisphere, or Hemispherical Shell

$$\bar{r} = \frac{r}{2}$$

Volume of Cone or Pyramid

$$\bar{y} = \frac{h}{4}$$

Hemispherical Volume

$$\bar{r} = \frac{3r}{8}$$

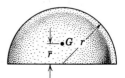

Volume of Paraboloid of Revolution

$$\bar{x} = \frac{a}{3}$$

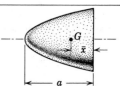

Volume of Half Ellipsoid of Revolution

$$\bar{x} = \frac{3a}{8}$$

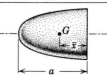

TABLE D5. MOMENTS OF INERTIA OF AREAS

Rectangle

$$\bar{I}_x = \frac{bh^3}{12}$$

$$I_x = \frac{bh^3}{3}$$

$$\bar{J} = \frac{bh}{12}(b^2 + h^2)$$

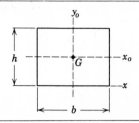

Triangle

$$\bar{I}_x = \frac{bh^3}{36}$$

$$I_x = \frac{bh^3}{12}$$

$$I_{x'} = \frac{bh^3}{4}$$

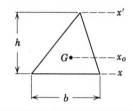

Circle

$$\bar{I}_x = \bar{I}_y = \frac{\pi r^4}{4}$$

$$\bar{J} = \frac{\pi r^4}{2}$$

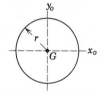

Ellipse

$$\bar{I}_x = \frac{\pi ab^3}{4}$$

$$\bar{I}_y = \frac{\pi a^3 b}{4}$$

$$\bar{J} = \frac{\pi ab}{4}(a^2 + b^2)$$

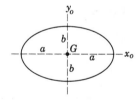

TABLE D6. MOMENTS OF INERTIA OF MASS

($m$ = mass of homogeneous solid shown)

---

Circular Cylindrical Shell

$$I_z = mr^2$$

---

Right Circular Cylinder

$$I_z = \tfrac{1}{2}mr^2$$

$$I_x = \tfrac{1}{12}m(3r^2 + 4l^2)$$

---

Sphere

$$I_z = \tfrac{2}{5}mr^2$$

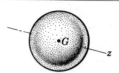

---

Semicylinder

$$I_z = \tfrac{1}{2}(\tfrac{1}{2} \times 2mr^2)$$

$$= \tfrac{1}{2}mr^2$$

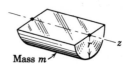

---

Hemisphere

$$I_x = I_z = \tfrac{1}{2}(\tfrac{2}{5} \times 2mr^2)$$

$$= \tfrac{2}{5}mr^2$$

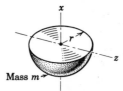

---

Rectangular Parallelepiped

$$I_z = \tfrac{1}{12}m(a^2 + b^2)$$

$$I_x = \tfrac{1}{12}m(4l^2 + a^2)$$

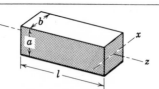

---

Uniform Slender Rod

$$I_x = \tfrac{1}{3}ml^2$$

$$I_{x_0} = \tfrac{1}{12}ml^2$$

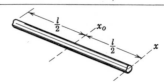

---

TABLE D6. MOMENTS OF INERTIA OF MASS—*Continued*

($m$ = mass of homogeneous solid shown)

---

Right Circular Cone

$$I_z = \tfrac{3}{10}mr^2$$

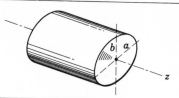

---

Elliptical Cylinder

$$I_z = \tfrac{1}{4}m(a^2 + b^2)$$

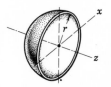

---

Hemispherical Shell

$$I_x = I_z = \tfrac{2}{3}mr^2$$

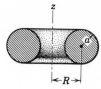

---

Torus (complete)

$$I_z = m(R^2 + \tfrac{3}{4}a^2)$$

# INDEX